Structural Models:

An Introduction to the Theory of Directed Graphs

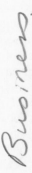

Library of Congress Catalog Card Number: 65-12710
Printed in the United States of America

Structural Model

An Introduction to the Theory of Directed

- **Frank Harary**
  The University of Michigan

- **Robert Z. Norman**
  Dartmouth College

- **Dorwin Cartwright**
  The University of Michigan

John Wiley & Sons, Inc.   New York · Lor

Preface

> I see no good reasons why the views given in this volume
> should shock the religious feelings of anyone.
>
> CHARLES DARWIN
> *On the Origin of Species by Means of Natural Selection*

The purpose of this book is to present an introduction to a body of mathematics concerned with the abstract notion of "structure." Its preparation has been motivated by the belief that knowledge of the mathematics of abstract structures will be of value to investigators interested in various kinds of empirical structures. The mathematics with which we are concerned is known as the theory of directed graphs, or more briefly as digraph theory. It deals with abstract configurations called digraphs, which consist of "points" and "directed lines." When these terms are given concrete referents, digraphs serve as mathematical models of empirical structures, and properties of digraphs reflect structural properties of the empirical world. Since the same mathematical terms can be given a variety of empirical meanings, digraph theory has applicability to many different fields of investigation.

The authors of this book, two mathematicians and a psychologist, have collaborated over a period of years in an attempt to develop a theory of digraphs that will reveal as clearly as possible its potential usefulness to the empirical investigator. In addition to organizing the known results about digraph theory, we have endeavored to fill a few of the gaps in the existing mathematical literature. In this work, we have addressed ourselves primarily to structural phenomena of interest to social scientists. We believe, however, that the material will also be of value to those working with computers, programming, information retrieval, automata, linguistics, cryptology, and electrical engineering.

One attractive feature of digraph theory for the nonmathematician is its relatively self-contained nature. The mathematical training acquired by most social scientists is sufficient for understanding the contents of this book, although some informal knowledge of logic, a facility in abstract thinking, and that mysterious quality known as "mathematical maturity" will make the task easier. In fact, high school graduates trained in "modern mathematics" should find the book not at all difficult. Use will be made of certain elementary materials from set theory and matrix algebra, but even here we have attempted to include all that the reader will need.

The book begins by examining an axiom system for digraphs. This discussion is intended not only to give a logical basis for developing digraph theory but also to show the very close association between digraphs and relations. The first chapter should also serve as an introduction for the student interested in the role of axiomatics in formal theories and in the general nature of mathematical models.

The next three chapters investigate the basic concepts of "joining" and "reaching" in structures. They also show how these may be employed to characterize types of connectedness of structures and an important set of points called a point basis for a digraph.

Chapter 5 presents a detailed discussion of the relations between digraphs and matrices. It demonstrates how matrix algebra may be used in the treatment of the more important properties of structures.

In Chapter 6 a study is made of the concept of distance within a structure. This discussion gives precise meaning to such notions as the compactness of a structure and the relative centrality of each of its parts.

The next two chapters, which are concerned with the effect on the connectedness of a digraph of removing a point or line, provide a useful basis for classifying points and lines, and give information about the vulnerability of structures.

Chapters 9 through 12 investigate four special kinds of digraphs obtained by imposing certain restrictions upon them. The first of these, called a block, has no point whose removal disconnects the digraph. Blocks have important features, and it is often useful to analyze a digraph that is not a block according to its subgraphs, which themselves are blocks. The second, called an acyclic digraph, may be used to represent a common type of empirical structure whose entities can be assigned numerical levels. The third, known as a tournament, is applicable to such diverse structures as the preference relation revealed by the method of paired comparisons on a set of objects or the dominance relation on a flock of chickens. The fourth kind of digraph is one in which restrictions are imposed upon the number of lines incident with the points.

In the final two chapters, some extensions of digraph theory are considered. We first examine how signed digraphs may be constructed by attaching either positive or negative signs to lines. Signed digraphs have extensive applicability to the analysis of balance in attitudinal or interpersonal structures. In the concluding chapter, we return to certain subjects introduced in Chapter 1 and show how the axioms of digraph theory may be relaxed so as to permit the treatment of probabilities, as in markov chains, and of empirical phenomena involving costs and flow.

The reader will find that the material presented in the first five chapters is basic to the rest of the book, whereas the remaining chapters are relatively independent of one another. However, Chapters 7 and 8 should be read as a unit.

In developing the theory, it has been found necessary to provide explicit definitions of a large number of terms. The reader will observe, especially at the beginning of the book, that there is a preponderance of definitions, but later the proportion of theorems to definitions increases noticeably. For ease of reference, a glossary of the most important concepts and a list of the major theorems are presented at the end of the book. Each chapter contains a number of exercises designed to give practice in working with the theory, and some of the exercises present small theorems not discussed in the text.

In order to indicate some of the ways in which digraph theory may be used, we have illustrated most of the material in this book by interpreting points as people and directed lines as relationships between them. In addition, we have occasionally drawn illustrations from such diverse areas as organization theory, sociometry, flows in networks, consumer behavior, scaling theory, propositional logic, and cognitive structure. It is hoped that these will suggest to the reader how digraph theory may be utilized in his own field of investigation.

In preparing this book, we have benefited from the help of many people. We want especially to thank Lowell W. Beineke, who provided valuable assistance in developing the mathematical material. We were also fortunate, at various stages of the work, in having the help of Ronald G. Ragsdale, Ian C. Ross, and Julian O. Morrissette. In our discussion of tournaments, we have relied heavily upon the work of Leo Moser. For the arduous task of typing the manuscript, we owe a large debt to the skill and patience of Mrs. Alice Phelps. Finally, we wish to acknowledge the valuable criticisms of those who read earlier drafts of the manuscript. The present version, for which we alone can be held responsible, is considerably improved owing to the thoughtful suggestions made by R. Duncan Luce and Abraham Kaplan.

This book has been long in the making, and several agencies have provided financial and other support. We hereby express our gratitude to the following benefactors: Rockefeller Foundation, Ford Foundation,

National Science Foundation, Office of Naval Research, Logistics Project in the Mathematics Department of Princeton University, The Institute for Advanced Study, Center for Advanced Study in the Behavioral Sciences, Tavistock Institute of Human Relations, Mathematics Department of University College London, Dartmouth College, and The University of Michigan.

Ann Arbor, Michigan   FRANK HARARY
Hanover, New Hampshire   ROBERT Z. NORMAN
January, 1965   DORWIN CARTWRIGHT

Contents

1 · Digraphs and Structures

It is only the very great and good who have any
living faith in the simplest axioms.

SAMUEL BUTLER, *Erewhon*

The word "structure" is found extensively in the literature of the social
sciences. "Social structure" and such related concepts as "kinship
structure," "authority structure," "communication structure," and
"sociometric structure" are commonplace.[1] Psychologists speak of such
matters as "personality structure," "cognitive structure," and "attitude
structure."[2] Linguists are interested in the "structure of a language"
or "syntactical structure."[3] And many other examples could be cited.
But despite the widespread use of structural concepts in the social
sciences, it is fair to say that the formal analysis of structure has been
relatively underdeveloped in these fields. The technical terminology
employed in describing structures is meager; few concepts are defined
rigorously. As a consequence, the social scientific description of
structural properties tends to be couched in ambiguous terminology,
and detailed studies of structure, as such, are rather rare.

In the natural sciences and engineering, problems of "structure" have
also been encountered. As a result of these and other less applied considerations, mathematicians have actively turned their attention to
certain branches of mathematics which deal with the abstract notion
of structure. One line of investigation began with the work of Euler

---

[1] See, for example, Bavelas (1950), Glanzer and Glaser (1959, 1961), Hunter (1953),
Lindzey and Borgatta (1954), Merton (1957), Nadel (1957), and Weiss (1956).
[2] For examples, see Baldwin (1942), Lewin (1951), Rosenberg et al. (1960), and Sanford
(1956).
[3] See Harris (1951) and Chomsky (1957).

(1707–1783) in the fields subsequently known as topology and graph theory. It has been significantly advanced by such men as Cayley (who was interested in certain structural problems in chemistry), Kirchhoff (whose laws of electrical network theory are famous), and more recently by numerous engineers concerned with communication systems. It has also benefited from the contributions of mathematicians and logicians who have worked on problems in the theory of relations, matrices, and combinatorics. The resulting body of mathematical knowledge contains, we believe, much that will be of value to social scientists in their investigations of various kinds of empirical structures.

Our object in this volume, then, is to present some mathematical theory about the abstract notion "structure." Specifically, we shall provide an introduction to the theory of directed graphs, or more briefly "digraphs" (a term suggested by G. Pólya). This theory is concerned with patterns of relationships among pairs of abstract elements. As such, digraph theory makes no reference to the empirical world. Nevertheless, it has potential usefulness to the empirical scientist, for it can serve as a mathematical model of the structural properties of any empirical system consisting of relationships among pairs of elements.

Consider, for example, the "communication structure" of a group of people. We may conceive of each member of the group as an "element" and the fact that a particular member can communicate directly to another as a "relationship." Then, upon coordinating these empirical entities and relationships to the abstract terms of digraph theory, we obtain a digraph which represents the communication structure of the group. The properties of this digraph, with which digraph theory is concerned, are at the same time properties of the communication structure.

In a similar way, a "sociometric structure" may be conceived as consisting of elements, which are people, and relationships among pairs of people, as indicated by interpersonal choices obtained from a questionnaire. A digraph may be constructed to represent any particular sociometric structure.

As another example, consider an individual's "preference structure" on a set of objects as revealed by the method of paired comparisons. In this case, the elements of the structure are objects, for example, pictures, and the relationships are the individual's indicated preferences of each object relative to each other. Again, the resulting structure may be represented by a digraph.

It should be apparent that there is an almost endless variety of empirical structures which may be represented by digraphs. The structure of a task may be conceived in terms of required precedence relationships on a set of operations. The authority structure of an organization may be thought of as supervisory relationships on a set of positions. Or, the causal structure of a scientific theory may be viewed as causal relationships on a set of variables.

Knowledge of digraph theory is useful to the researcher interested in the structural properties of any empirical system, for it provides concepts, theorems, and methods appropriate to the analysis of structure, *per se*. There are three principal benefits which the scientist may gain from employing digraph theory in his treatment of structural phenomena.

First, he will find that his vocabulary for describing empirical structures is enriched by useful new terms having precise meanings, for the language of digraphs contains a large number of concepts which refer to relatively complex structural properties. We shall find in the course of this volume that precise definitions can be given to such ideas as the degree of connectedness of a structure, its diameter, its vulnerability, and its stratification into levels. Although everyday language contains terms referring to such properties, these are poorly defined and have no clear conceptual relationships to one another. Even though this use of digraph theory exploits its definitions more than its theorems, the contribution is a significant one.

Second, digraph theory and associated branches of mathematics provide techniques of computation and formulas for calculating certain quantitative features of empirical structures. Matrix algebra has an especially close relation to digraph theory, and we shall examine in some detail its computational value in dealing with structures. We shall see, for example, that it is possible to ascertain the distance in a structure from one element to another and to construct measures of such things as the degree of centrality and the relative status of an element within a structure. Other indexes will be developed to measure the degree of consistency and the degree of balance of a structure as a whole. Digraph theory thus provides the researcher with useful means for quantifying certain aspects of structure.

The third, and perhaps most important, benefit of the use of digraph theory stems from its theorems. We shall find that the axioms for digraph theory to be presented in this chapter lead to an extensive body of logically derived statements. Each of these statements or theorems becomes a valid assertion about any empirical structure that satisfies the axioms of digraph theory. The theorems thereby give additional information about empirical structures. By specifying properties of digraphs that necessarily follow from given conditions, they permit us to draw conclusions about certain properties of a structure from knowledge about other properties. Since it is difficult to illustrate the place of theorems in digraph theory before its nature has been elaborated, we defer further discussion of this topic until the end of the chapter.

In order for the researcher to gain these benefits from using digraph theory, it is essential that he have unambiguous rules for coordinating basic terms of digraph theory to empirical phenomena so that its axioms, and hence its derived theorems, produce, when thus interpreted, true statements about the empirical world. Thus, we may hope to benefit from the precision of digraph theory, but this gain requires skill in handling empirical data. In particular, we must have adequate operational procedures for identifying relevant empirical entities and relationships among them. If these are unequivocally identified, then digraph theory specifies structural properties that must be found in the empirical world.

With this general orientation, let us turn now to a consideration of the basic nature of digraph theory.

NETS AND RELATIONS

It is best to begin with fundamentals. The theory of digraphs is based on an axiom system consisting of four primitives (undefined terms), together with four axioms (or postulates) which give us an understanding of the primitives and of their relations to one another. As we shall see, digraph theory can be thought of as growing out of more general mathematical theories about nets and relations. All three theories have the same primitives, but the theory of nets uses only two of the axioms whereas the theory of relations uses three. We shall begin with nets, proceed to relations, and then consider digraphs.

Before stating the primitives and axioms for a net, we describe them more intuitively. The diagram shown in Figure 1.1 is a very simple

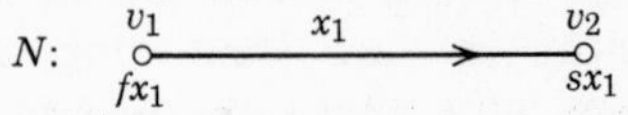

$$N: \quad \overset{v_1}{\underset{fx_1}{\circ}} \xrightarrow{\quad x_1 \quad} \overset{v_2}{\underset{sx_1}{\circ}}$$

FIGURE 1.1

net N, consisting of two points and a directed line. In the picture of a net, the points are conventionally depicted by dots labeled $v_1, v_2, \ldots, v_p$ and the directed lines by arcs labeled $x_1, x_2, \ldots, x_q$. The direction of each line is indicated by an arrowhead. In Figure 1.1, the direction of the line x_1 can also be described by saying that its first point, denoted fx_1, is v_1 and its second point, sx_1, is v_2.

The four primitives of nets (and also of relations and of digraphs) are:

P_1. A set V of elements called "points."

P_2. A set X of elements called "directed lines," or more briefly, "lines."

P_3. A function f whose domain is X and whose range is contained in V.

P_4. A function s whose domain is X and whose range is contained in V.

The first two of these primitives are self-explanatory. The second two relate the lines to the points by means of two functions f and s which serve to identify the "first" and the "second" point of each line, respectively. In the net of Figure 1.1, $V = \{v_1, v_2\}$ and $X = \{x_1\}$. The image fx_1 of the function f is v_1, the first point of x_1. The image sx_1 of the function s is v_2, the second point of x_1. It is in this sense that the line x_1 is "directed" from v_1 to v_2. In general, for any line x of X, the image fx of the function f is called the *first point* of x and the image sx of the function s is the *second point* of x. The line x is *incident with* both its points fx and sx. Thus every line of a net is directed from its first point to its second point.

The axioms for a net are:

A_1. The set V is finite and not empty.

A_2. The set X is finite.

The first axiom excludes consideration of an empty net with no points at all and of a net with an infinite number of points. Then the second axiom avoids nets with a finite number of points but an infinite number of lines. Thus these two axioms impose no restrictions on the structure of a net other than the number of its points and lines.

Figure 1.2(a) shows a net N which is a bit more complicated than the previous one. In this case, N has three points and six lines. We see that the first point of line x_1 is v_3 and its second point is v_1, that is, $fx_1 = v_3$ and $sx_1 = v_1$. We also find that $fx_3 = fx_4 = v_1$ and $sx_3 = sx_4 = v_2$. Moreover, $fx_5 = sx_5 = v_2$, and $fx_6 = sx_6 = v_2$.

Although this picture is drawn on a plane and resembles figures found in Euclidean geometry, a net is quite a different object. For example, the lengths of the arcs and the location of the dots on the page have no significance in the theory of nets. Thus, the net shown in Figure 1.2(b) is the same as that in Figure 1.2(a) even though it looks rather different. All of the statements in the preceding paragraph about part (a) apply equally to part (b) of this figure. In thinking about nets (and digraphs) we shall have to break certain habits built up over years of experience with Euclidean geometry.

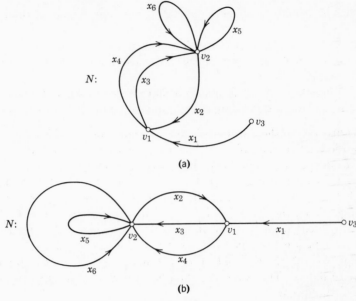

(a)

(b)

FIGURE 1.2

It will be useful now to make certain observations about the lines which a net may contain. A line x of a net is called a *loop* if $fx = sx$, in other words, if it has the same first and second point. The net of Figure 1.2 has two loops: x_5 and x_6. We say that two lines x_i and x_j are *parallel* if $fx_i = fx_j$ and $sx_i = sx_j$. Thus in the net under consideration, the lines x_3 and x_4 are parallel, as also are the loops x_5 and x_6. Note, however, that x_2 and x_3 are not parallel. When a net has parallel lines distinct meanings may be given to the different lines from one point to another. Thus, for example, the two lines from v_1 to v_2 might indicate that person v_1 both likes v_2 and tends to communicate messages to him. It is also possible to let each line indicate a unit of strength of a relationship, in which case we would say that the relationship from v_1 to v_2, perhaps that of liking, is stronger than that from v_3 to v_1 since there are two lines from v_1 to v_2 and only one from v_3 to v_1. We shall see that these complications do not arise in digraphs and shall delay further consideration of them until Chapter 14.

We may now define a relation. A *relation* is a net in which no two distinct lines are parallel.[4] Clearly, every relation is a net, by definition, but not every net is a relation. Figure 1.2(a) shows a net that is not a relation, whereas Figure 1.3 shows one that is.

---

[4] In view of the axiom system, we are dealing here, of course, with a finite relation.

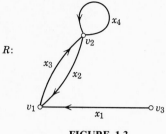

FIGURE 1.3

Since there are no parallel lines in a relation, any line x is determined by specifying its first point fx and its second point sx. And since a relation, by definition, has a finite number of points, it must necessarily have a finite number of lines as well. If u and v are two points of a relation and $fx = u$ and $sx = v$, we may denote the line x by (u, v) to indicate that x is the *ordered pair* whose first element is u and whose second element is v. When (u, v) is in a relation R, we also write uRv. For example, in the relation R of Figure 1.3, we have v_3Rv_1, v_2Rv_1, v_1Rv_2, and v_2Rv_2 to stand for lines x_1, x_2, x_3, and x_4, respectively.

Properties of Relations

In this volume we shall need frequently to refer to certain properties that a relation may have. Since these are presented in most textbooks[5] in logic, we shall treat them quite briefly here.

A relation R is *reflexive* if every point of R is on a loop. We say that R is *symmetric* if whenever uRv, then vRu. A relation R is *transitive* if for any three distinct points u, v, w of R, whenever uRv and vRw, then uRw. And a relation R is said to be *complete* if for every pair of distinct points u and v in R, at least one of the ordered pairs (u, v) or (v, u) is in R.

Each of these properties has a certain kind of opposite property. We shall be concerned primarily with only two of these. A relation R is *irreflexive* if no point of R has a loop. And R is said to be *asymmetric* if uRv precludes vRu for distinct points u and v.

Any particular relation R may possess various combinations of these properties. The reader should verify that the relation R drawn in Figure 1.3 has none of these six properties. Consider the relation "greater than" on the set of integers.[6] Clearly, this relation is irreflexive—

---

[5] For a discussion of properties of relations, see Copi (1954, Ch. 5).
[6] To be strictly consistent, we should speak here, and later, of a finite set of integers. We hope that this slight indiscretion will be forgiven.

no integer is greater than itself. It is asymmetric—for any two integers u and v, if u is greater than v, then v is not greater than u. It is transitive— if it is given that u is greater than v and v is greater than w, it follows that u is greater than w. And it is complete—for any two distinct integers, one is greater than the other.

Certain combinations of properties give rise to a variety of "orders" on a set of points. A relation is called an (*irreflexive*) *complete order* if it is irreflexive, asymmetric, transitive, and complete. As we have just seen, the relation "greater than" on a set of integers has these properties and is therefore such an order.

Upon removing the requirement of completeness from this definition, we obtain a *partial order*, which is an irreflexive, asymmetric, and transitive relation. Consider the employees of a firm and the relation "can give orders to." This relation is a partial order if it satisfies the following three plausible statements: (a) No one can give orders to himself; (b) if person u can give orders to v, then v cannot give orders to u; and (c) if u can give orders to v and v can give orders to w, then u can give orders to w. Since this relation is not necessarily complete, it may happen that there are two people, perhaps foremen in different departments, neither one of whom can give orders to the other.

By a *reflexive complete order* we mean a relation that is reflexive, asymmetric, transitive, and complete. It can be verified that the relation "greater than or equal to" on the set of integers is such an order. And a relation whose only requirement is that it be reflexive and transitive is called a *quasi-order*. We shall see in Chapter 2 that "reachability" is a quasi-order.

In concluding this section, we consider an especially important combination of properties. If a relation R is reflexive, symmetric, and transitive, it is known as an *equivalence relation*. Consider again the set of

R:

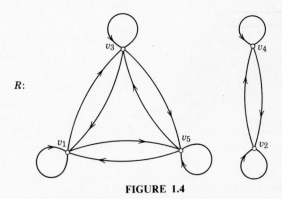

FIGURE 1.4

integers discussed above. Let R be the relation such that uRv if and only if the difference $u - v$ is even. We see that R is reflexive, since every difference $u - u = 0$, which is even. It is symmetric, for if $u - v$ is even, then $v - u$ is even. And R is transitive, for if $u - v$ and $v - w$ are both even, then $u - w$ is even. By definition, then, R is an equivalence relation. We observe that R is not complete because no odd number is in relation R to any even number. Clearly, the relation shown in Figure 1.4 is an equivalence relation. The best known equivalence relation is equality itself.

DIGRAPHS

We are now prepared to consider the axiom system for digraphs. Although the primitives or undefined terms of this system, and some of the axioms, are the same as those for nets and relations, we repeat them here for convenience of reference.

A *digraph* satisfies the following axiom system.

The primitives are:

P_1: A set V of elements called "points."
P_2: A set X of elements called "lines."
P_3: A function f whose domain is X and whose range is contained in V.
P_4: A function s whose domain is X and whose range is contained in V.

The axioms[7] are:

A_1: The set V is finite and not empty.
A_2: The set X is finite.
A_3: No two distinct lines are parallel.
A_4: There are no loops.

Comparing the axioms for nets and for digraphs, we see that a digraph is a net with no loops and no parallel lines. In other words, a digraph is an irreflexive relation.

In discussing digraphs we shall denote points and lines in the manner developed for nets. Sometimes we refer to points by the letters u, v, w, and at other times by the notation $v_1, v_2, \ldots, v_p$. The lines of a digraph are often indicated by $x_1, x_2, \ldots, x_q$. When we wish to denote a line in terms of its two points, we write uv for a line *from u to v* or v_1v_2 for a line from v_1 to v_2. In Figure 1.5 we show a digraph D with its customary notation. Here the number of points in the set V is $p = 3$, and the number of lines in the set X is $q = 3$. The three points are

---

[7] It is easily seen that axioms A_1 and A_3 together imply axiom A_2. Therefore A_2 could have been omitted from this list and derived as the first theorem.

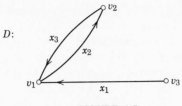

D:

FIGURE 1.5

denoted v_1, v_2, v_3 and the three lines are $x_1 = v_3v_1$, $x_2 = v_1v_2$, and $x_3 = v_2v_1$.

Let us summarize what we have learned thus far about nets, relations, and digraphs. Every digraph is a relation, and every relation is a net, but there are nets that are not relations and there are relations that are not digraphs. In this book we shall concentrate on digraphs. This means that we exclude from consideration loops and parallel lines. In doing so we simplify the mathematical theory and focus upon structural properties. At the end of the book we shall return to a consideration of loops and parallel lines. The exclusion of loops does not prevent our using digraphs to analyze relations that have loops. In dealing with such a relation we form its digraph simply by ignoring the loops. Nearly all the important structural properties are the same whether loops are included or not. And in many relations, such as "can communicate to," or "likes to work with," the question of whether loops are included or not makes no essential difference. Thus, there is ordinarily no difficulty in ignoring the distinction between a digraph and a relation.

By an *interpretation of a digraph*, we mean the coordination of empirical elements to its points and lines. In other words, an interpretation tells what entities are represented by the points and what empirical relationships by the lines. Thus, one interpretation of the digraph of Figure 1.6 might be the following: the points v_1, v_2, v_3 represent three individuals and each line, say $x_1 = v_2v_1$, indicates that individual v_2 is a neighbor of v_1. Since there are no lines in this digraph joining points v_2 and v_3,

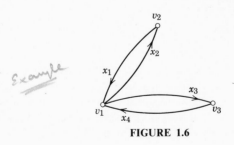

FIGURE 1.6

we may conclude that individuals v_2 and v_3 are not neighbors. If one were to insist that everyone is his own neighbor, then we would be dealing with a relation that is reflexive, and loops would have to be added at every point. It is clear, however, that for most purposes nothing significant is lost by treating the relation as a digraph.

Kinds of Digraphs

Since every digraph is a relation, digraphs may be described in terms of the properties of relations discussed above. The axiom system for digraphs demands only that the relation be irreflexive. If, however, certain additional properties are required, we obtain a particular kind of digraph. We now briefly describe some of the major kinds of digraphs.

A *symmetric digraph* is an irreflexive symmetric relation. Thus, for every line *uv* in a symmetric digraph *D*, there is also a line *vu*. Such a digraph is shown in Figure 1.6. Symmetric digraphs constitute an important special class that correspond to *graphs*. Systematic treatments of the theory of graphs have been provided by König (1936), Berge (1958), and Ore (1962).

A *complete symmetric digraph* is one whose relation is both complete and symmetric. Therefore, every pair of points is joined by two lines, one in each direction. We denote a complete symmetric digraph by K_p, where *p* is the number of points in the digraph. The digraph of Figure 1.7(a) is K_4, while that in Figure 1.6 is symmetric but not complete.

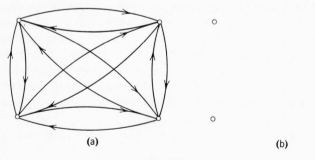

(a)   (b)

FIGURE 1.7

A *complete asymmetric digraph* is both complete and asymmetric, as for example in Figure 1.8. One interpretation of such a digraph arises if we let the points correspond to the players in a chess tournament and each line *uv* indicate that player *u* defeats player *v*. Then, if every player plays every other and no game ends in a draw, the digraph representing the outcome of the tournament is complete and asymmetric. For this reason, such digraphs are commonly called tournaments, and we shall consider these structures in Chapter 11. In Figure 1.8 we see that player v_1 won all his games, whereas v_4 lost all of his.

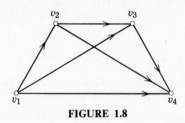

FIGURE 1.8

There is nothing in the axiom system for digraphs that precludes the possibility that a digraph may have no lines at all. A digraph without any lines is called *totally disconnected*, as shown in Figure 1.7(b). A *transitive digraph D* is one which contains a line *uw* whenever lines *uv* and *vw* are in *D*, for any distinct points *u, v, w*. Clearly, a digraph that is transitive and asymmetric is a partial order. If, in addition, the digraph is complete, then it is a complete order. The digraph shown in Figure 1.8, having all these properties, is a complete order. It is possible, of course, for a digraph to be asymmetric and complete but not transitive. Figure 1.9 shows such a digraph representing the outcome of a tiddlywinks tournament among Harvard, Yale, and Princeton. We find that Harvard beat Yale, Yale beat Princeton, and Princeton beat Harvard. The following quotation from a review of the literature on dominance relations among birds and mammals reveals that such inconsistency is not confined to college teams. "Not infrequently, flocks contain triangular pecking relations, that is *A* will dominate *B*, *B* will dominate *C*, which in turn dominates *A*" (Collias, 1951, p. 390).

Certain empirical structures of interest to social scientists may generate a particular kind of digraph. For example, DeSoto and Kuethe (1958, 1959) have investigated the properties which people attribute to various kinds of interpersonal relations. They found, among other things, that

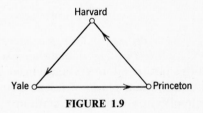

FIGURE 1.9

most people believe that the following relations are likely to be symmetric: trusts, confides in, likes, dislikes, and hates. In other words, people expect structures based on these relations to correspond to symmetric digraphs. DeSoto and Kuethe also report a tendency to attribute transitivity and asymmetry to such relations as dominates and fears. Structures of this kind correspond to a partial order.

Implication Digraphs

There is an interesting interpretation of digraphs which is helpful in proving certain kinds of theorems. Consider a collection of four propositions, p_1, p_2, p_3, p_4. We assume that each of these is either true or false. The propositions themselves might come from any universe of discourse, say Euclidean geometry. For example,

p_1: *ABC* is an equilateral triangle.
p_2: *ABC* is an equiangular triangle.
p_3: *ABC* is a triangle in which at least two sides are equal (an isosceles triangle).
p_4: *ABC* is a triangle in which at least two angles are equal.

It is known from Euclidean geometry that propositions p_3 and p_4 are logically equivalent, that is, each implies the other. It is also known that every equilateral triangle is equiangular, and conversely. This information can be depicted by a digraph in which points represent propositions and lines indicate the relationship of implication, as shown in Figure 1.10(a).

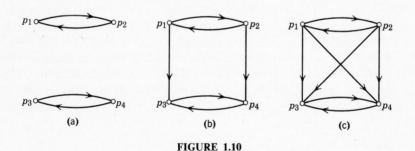

FIGURE 1.10

It is immediately obvious that, in addition, p_1 implies p_3 and p_2 implies p_4. With this further information, we may construct the digraph shown in Figure 1.10(b). But it is known from propositional logic that the relation of implication among propositions is transitive. This applies to the digraph of Figure 1.10(b), in which the lines $p_1 p_3$ and $p_3 p_4$ occur. Thus, it follows that p_1 implies p_4. Similarly, from the presence of lines $p_2 p_4$ and $p_4 p_3$ we conclude that p_2 implies p_3. All of the implications that hold for these four propositions are shown in the digraph of Figure 1.10(c).

A digraph in which the points are interpreted as propositions and the lines as implication is called an *implication digraph*. Therefore, each of the digraphs of Figure 1.10 is an implication digraph. In a *total implication digraph* there is a line from proposition p_i to p_j if and only if p_i implies p_j. Thus, a total implication digraph displays all possible implications between the propositions which constitute its points. For, example, Figure 1.10(c) is a total implication digraph since it is known that p_3 and p_4 do not imply p_1 or p_2. In proving theorems about digraphs, we shall often make use of (implication) digraphs themselves!

Implication digraphs are especially useful in proving that a set of propositions are all logically equivalent. If they are, we know that their total implication digraph is symmetric, transitive, and complete, since the digraph of an equivalence relation has these properties. Suppose that we have four propositions and wish to prove that they are all equivalent. It is sufficient, then, to prove just four implications—for example, those shown in Figure 1.11. Once these are established, we may use the fact that implication is a transitive relation and add a line uw to the digraph whenever lines uv and vw have been established. Repeated applications of this procedure results in a total implication digraph that is complete, symmetric, and hence an equivalence relation.

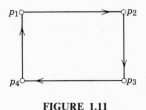

FIGURE 1.11

DIGRAPHS AND MATRICES

In this section we show how digraphs can be represented by means of matrices. An $r \times s$ *matrix* is a rectangular array of rs numbers called the *entries* of the matrix, arranged in r rows and s columns. We denote the entry in the ith row and jth column of a matrix M by m_{ij}. The number m_{ij} is also called the entry of the i, j *cell* of M. A matrix M is often written with square brackets in the form

$$M = \begin{bmatrix} m_{11} & m_{12} & \cdots & m_{1s} \\ m_{21} & m_{22} & \cdots & m_{2s} \\ \cdots\cdots\cdots\cdots\cdots\cdots\cdots \\ \cdots\cdots\cdots\cdots\cdots\cdots\cdots \\ m_{r1} & m_{r2} & \cdots & m_{rs} \end{bmatrix}$$

For brevity we write: $M = [m_{ij}]$.

Given a digraph D, its *adjacency matrix*, $A(D) = [a_{ij}]$, is a square matrix with one row and one column for each point of D, in which the entry $a_{ij} = 1$ if line $v_i v_j$ is in D, while $a_{ij} = 0$ if $v_i v_j$ is not in D.

Consider a digraph of five points, $V = \{v_1, v_2, v_3, v_4, v_5\}$ whose relation consists of the ordered pairs (v_1, v_2), (v_1, v_3), (v_1, v_4), (v_3, v_2), and (v_4, v_3). Figure 1.12 shows this digraph and its adjacency matrix.

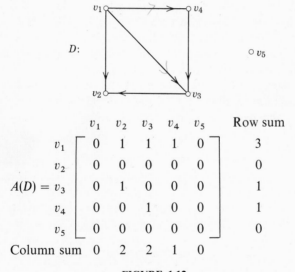

	v_1	v_2	v_3	v_4	v_5	Row sum
v_1	0	1	1	1	0	3
v_2	0	0	0	0	0	0
$A(D) = v_3$	0	1	0	0	0	1
v_4	0	0	1	0	0	1
v_5	0	0	0	0	0	0
Column sum	0	2	2	1	0	

FIGURE 1.12

By an *ordering* of the points of D, we mean their designation as first, second, third, and so on. It should be noted that the adjacency matrix is determined by the particular ordering of the points. Thus, if we were to take a different ordering of the points of the digraph of Figure 1.12, we might obtain a different adjacency matrix. The digraph of Figure 1.13 is the same digraph as in Figure 1.12 but the ordering of the points is different. It can be seen that the matrix of Figure 1.13 is not the same as that of Figure 1.12. Despite the fact that a digraph may have more than one adjacency matrix, we shall usually refer to the adjacency matrix of a digraph when its points have been ordered by means of their subscripts. Therefore, when we speak of *the adjacency matrix of a digraph* we assume that the order of the points is understood.

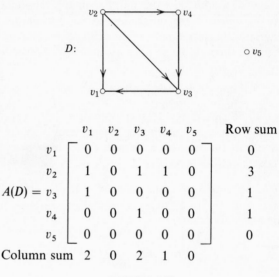

$$A(D) = \begin{array}{c} \\ v_1 \\ v_2 \\ v_3 \\ v_4 \\ v_5 \\ \end{array} \begin{array}{ccccc} v_1 & v_2 & v_3 & v_4 & v_5 \\ \left[\begin{array}{ccccc} 0 & 0 & 0 & 0 & 0 \\ 1 & 0 & 1 & 1 & 0 \\ 1 & 0 & 0 & 0 & 0 \\ 0 & 0 & 1 & 0 & 0 \\ 0 & 0 & 0 & 0 & 0 \\ \end{array}\right] \end{array} \begin{array}{c} \text{Row sum} \\ 0 \\ 3 \\ 1 \\ 1 \\ 0 \\ \end{array}$$

Column sum 2 0 2 1 0

FIGURE 1.13

Certain features of a digraph may be seen in its adjacency matrix. Thus, the symmetry or asymmetry of a digraph is reflected in a definite way. If a digraph is asymmetric, then the existence of a line v_iv_j precludes the existence of the line v_jv_i. Therefore, it follows that in the adjacency matrix of an asymmetric digraph if $a_{ij} = 1$, then $a_{ji} = 0$. It can readily be seen that the digraph of Figure 1.13 is asymmetric. In the adjacency matrix of a symmetric digraph an entry of 1 in the i, j cell implies an entry of 1 in the j, i cell.

The row and column sums of the adjacency matrix indicate the number of lines originating and terminating at each point of the digraph. The *outdegree* of point v, written od(v), is the number of lines from v. It is evident that each row sum of the adjacency matrix gives the out-degree of the corresponding point. Thus, in the digraph of Figure 1.13 od(v_2) = 3. The *indegree* of point v, written id(v), is the number of lines to v. Clearly, each column sum of the adjacency matrix indicates the indegree of the corresponding point.[8] In our example, $\text{id}(v_2) = 0$, there being no lines which terminate at v_2.

A point u is *adjacent to* v if the line uv is in D; u is *adjacent from* v if the line vu is in D. Thus, we may say that $\text{id}(v)$ is the number of points adjacent to v, and that $\text{od}(v)$ is the number of points adjacent from v. The *outbundle* of v is the set of lines from v; the *inbundle* of v is the set of lines to v. Clearly, $\text{od}(v)$ indicates the number of lines in the outbundle of v, and $\text{id}(v)$ indicates the number in the inbundle of v. The *bundle* of v is the union of the inbundle and the outbundle. These are, of course, mutually exclusive sets of lines incident with v. The *total degree* of v, $\text{td}(v)$, is the number of lines incident with v. We immediately obtain the following equation

$$\text{td}(v) = \text{id}(v) + \text{od}(v).$$

The sum of all entries of the adjacency matrix $A(D)$ is the sum of all the row sums of A or the sum of all the column sums of A. This information is contained in the following formulas, in which p and q are the numbers of points and lines of D.

Theorem 1.1. The sum of the indegrees of all the points of any digraph is equal to the sum of the outdegrees, and their common value is the number of lines; symbolically,

$$\sum_{i=1}^{p} \text{id}(v_i) = q, \quad \text{and} \quad \sum_{i=1}^{p} \text{od}(v_i) = q.$$

These two equations can be expressed alternatively by stating the following formula for the average indegree, $\overline{\text{id}}$, and the average outdegree, $\overline{\text{od}}$, of the points of a digraph.

Corollary 1.1a. In any digraph, $\overline{\text{id}} = \overline{\text{od}} = \dfrac{q}{p}$.

It will be useful to classify every point of a digraph according to the combination of its indegree and outdegree. An *isolate* is a point whose outdegree and indegree are both 0. A *transmitter* is a point whose outdegree is positive and whose indegree is 0. A *receiver* is a point whose outdegree is 0 and whose indegree is positive. A *carrier* is a point whose outdegree and indegree are both 1. Any other point is an *ordinary point*.

Each kind of point is illustrated by the digraph of Figure 1.13 and its adjacency matrix. By reference to these, the class of each point can

[8] Unlike most human beings, a point has an id but no superego.

be determined readily:

$$v_5 \text{ is an isolate, } \mathrm{od}(v_5) = \mathrm{id}(v_5) = 0$$
$$v_2 \text{ is a transmitter, } \mathrm{od}(v_2) = 3, \mathrm{id}(v_2) = 0$$
$$v_1 \text{ is a receiver, } \mathrm{od}(v_1) = 0, \mathrm{id}(v_1) = 2$$
$$v_4 \text{ is a carrier, } \mathrm{od}(v_4) = \mathrm{id}(v_4) = 1$$
$$v_3 \text{ is ordinary, } \mathrm{od}(v_3) = 1, \mathrm{id}(v_3) = 2.$$

The product of the indegree and the outdegree of a point contains information concerning its classification. For, if $\mathrm{id}(v) \cdot \mathrm{od}(v) = 0$, then at least one of the two values, $\mathrm{id}(v)$ and $\mathrm{od}(v)$, must be 0: if they are both 0, then v is an isolate; if only $\mathrm{id}(v) = 0$, then v is a transmitter; and if only $\mathrm{od}(v) = 0$, then v is a receiver. If the product $\mathrm{id}(v) \cdot \mathrm{od}(v)$ is *not* 0, then v must be in one of the two remaining classes: if this product is 1, then both $\mathrm{id}(v)$ and $\mathrm{od}(v)$ are 1, and v is a carrier; if $\mathrm{id}(v) \cdot \mathrm{od}(v) > 1$, then both the indegree and outdegree are positive and at least one of them is greater than 1, and v is an ordinary point.

The empirical meaning of the various terms just considered may be illustrated by taking a digraph D to represent a communication network. The outdegree of point v indicates the number of people that person v can communicate to directly, and the outbundle of v corresponds to the communication links going directly from v to other people. The indegree of point v indicates the number of people who can communicate directly to person v, and the inbundle of v corresponds to the links going directly to v from other people. With this interpretation of a digraph, an isolate point corresponds to a person who can neither send nor receive messages in the network, a transmitter to one who can send but not receive messages, a receiver to one who can receive but not send, and the two remaining types to persons who can both send and receive (a carrier being more constrained than an ordinary point).

ISOMORPHISM OF DIGRAPHS

It is possible, of course, for two different communication networks to have the same "structure." Suppose, for example, that there are two groups each consisting of ten people. Suppose, further, that in each group everyone can communicate directly to everyone else. The digraph corresponding to each of these communication networks consists of ten points and is complete and symmetric. These two groups are certainly different since they are composed of different individuals. Nonetheless, the communication networks of these two different groups have the same structure. Or, to give another example, suppose that both of these groups are organized in a hierarchical fashion so that the "top boss" has three subordinates, each of whom has two subordinates. Again, the authority structures of these two different groups are the same; each has one transmitter, three ordinary points, and six receivers.

These examples are special cases of the concept of "isomorphism" of two digraphs. Two digraphs D and E are *isomorphic* if there exists a one-to-one correspondence between their points which preserves their directed lines. That is, D and E are isomorphic if they have the same number p of points and if one can order their points respectively $v_1, v_2, \ldots, v_p$ and $u_1, u_2, \ldots, u_p$ so that for any i and j, line $v_i v_j$ is in D if and only if line $u_i u_j$ is in E. Such a correspondence is called an *isomorphism* between D and E.

It often happens that when drawn, two isomorphic digraphs D and E **have** different appearances. In Figure 1.14 are two such digraphs. It

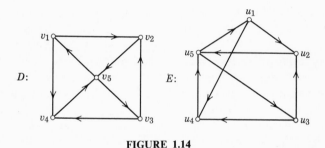

FIGURE 1.14

is easy to verify that these two digraphs are isomorphic, and that corresponding points have the same subscripts. For example, we note that $v_1 v_2$ is in D and that $u_1 u_2$ is in E, while $v_1 v_3$ and $u_1 u_3$ are not in D and E respectively.

Any two complete symmetric digraphs with the same number of points are necessarily isomorphic. Thus we say that there is exactly one complete symmetric digraph of five points, since any two such digraphs are isomorphic, and we speak of it as the complete symmetric digraph of five points. Similarly, we may refer to the totally disconnected digraph of four points in which every point is an isolate, etc.

It is easy to show that the relation of isomorphism between pairs of digraphs has the properties of reflexivity, symmetry, and transitivity and is therefore an equivalence relation. To do this, one verifies that any digraph D is isomorphic to itself; if D_1 is isomorphic to D_2, then D_2 is isomorphic to D_1; and if D_1 is isomorphic to D_2 and D_2 is isomorphic to D_3, then D_1 is isomorphic to D_3.

All the digraphs with three points[9] are shown in Figure 1.15. No matter what digraph with three points anyone will ever construct, it must be isomorphic to exactly one of these. Thus, we may say that there are sixteen digraphs with three points, or that the number of digraphs with three points and two lines is four, and so on.[10]

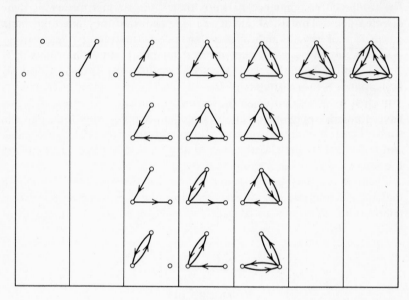

FIGURE 1.15

We now show how the isomorphism of any two digraphs may be determined by their adjacency matrices. Let D_1 and D_2 be digraphs whose adjacency matrices are A_1 and A_2 respectively. From matrix theory, the statement that *two matrices are equal* means that they have the same size (i.e., the same number of rows and of columns) and for every i and j, the i, j entry of one and the i, j entry of the other are equal.

Theorem 1.2. Two digraphs D_1 and D_2 are isomorphic if and only if for any ordering of the points of D_1, there is an ordering of the points of D_2 such that their adjacency matrices are equal, that is, $A_1 = A_2$.

This theorem may be proved in the following way. If there is an isomorphism between D_1 and D_2, take any ordering of the points of

[9] Mandler and Cowan (1962) use the digraphs shown in Figure 1.15 to generate items in a learning experiment.
[10] A formula for the number of digraphs with a given number of points and lines appears in Harary (1955b).

D_1 and reorder the points of D_2 in accordance with this isomorphism. Since by definition isomorphism entails the preservation of lines, there is a line from the ith point of D_1 to its jth point if and only if there is also a line from the ith point of D_2 to its jth point. This is guaranteed by the fact that the points of D_2 have been ordered in accordance with the isomorphism. Translated into matrix terms, this means that the i, j entry of A_1 and the i, j entry of A_2 must both be 1 or both be 0. Then $A_1 = A_2$ by the definition of equality of matrices.

Conversely, if $A_1 = A_2$, then clearly D_1 and D_2 are isomorphic.

If digraphs D_1 and D_2 are isomorphic, then any transmitter of D_1 corresponds to a transmitter of D_2. Similarly any receiver of D_1 corresponds to a receiver of D_2, and so forth. Since, by Theorem 1.2, two isomorphic digraphs have equal adjacency matrices, it follows that the sums of corresponding rows and columns of the two matrices are equal, and consequently the classification of any two corresponding points are the same.

Theorem 1.2 may be illustrated by the following example. Suppose that we are interested in three persons u, v, and w, who display liking relationships as shown by digraph D_1 of Figure 1.16. As an empirical

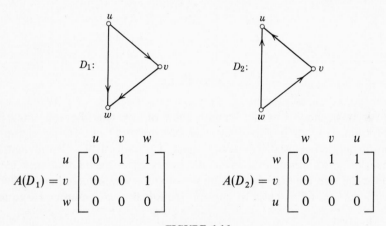

FIGURE 1.16

axiom, assume that whenever one person likes a second person, then the second person can influence the first. From this assumption, we obtain an influence structure for persons u, v and w, as represented by digraph D_2 of Figure 1.16. Clearly, we may order the points of each digraph so as to obtain the adjacency matrices $A(D_1)$ and $A(D_2)$, and it is evident that these two matrices are equal. By Theorem 1.2, D_1 and D_2 are isomorphic. This means that the liking and the influence relationships among these three people have the same structure. And, both digraphs have one transmitter, one receiver, and one carrier. It should be noted, however, that the transmitter in the liking structure is the receiver in the influence structure, and conversely. Thus, if two isomorphic digraphs are interpreted as two different empirical relations on the same set of empirical entities, it does not necessarily follow that a given entity will correspond to a point of the same class in the two digraphs.

STRUCTURAL MODELS

We noted earlier that the social scientist may hope to gain certain benefits from employing digraph theory as a mathematical model. This possibility arises from the fact that he is interested in such empirical structures as groups of people, organizations, networks of communication, and systems of attitudes, beliefs, or alternatives, while digraph theory deals with structural properties in the abstract. As we have seen, the basic terms of digraph theory are point and line. Thus, if an appropriate coordination is made so that each entity of an empirical system is identified with a point and each relationship is identified with a line, then for all true statements about structural properties of the obtained digraph there are corresponding true statements about structural properties of the empirical system. The availability of a formal theory of structure, therefore, provides the researcher with conceptual tools for his analysis of empirical structures.

What empirical terms, or concepts of social science theory, can properly be coordinated to point and line? Consider first the term, point. In order to give an empirical interpretation of point, it is necessary to decide upon the appropriate unit of empirical data. Although the possibilities are almost limitless, five classes of entities may be suggested: persons, objects, places, events, and propositions. Entities from any of these classes may be identified with points. Thus, for example, the set of points V of a particular digraph D may correspond to the students enrolled in a course, the commodities in a market, the positions (offices) of an organization, the alternatives in a decision situation, or the propositions of an argument.

Suppose, then, that we have selected a set of empirical entities and have identified them with a set V of points. In order to obtain a digraph D, we must have some way of identifying its set X of lines. As we have seen, every line x consists of an ordered pair (u, v) of points, $fx = u$ and $sx = v$. An empirical relation on a set of people, such as liking, consists of a set of ordered pairs of people such that (u, v) is in the relation if

and only if person u likes person v. Thus, if we have sufficient information about the liking relation on a particular group of people, we may
construct a digraph D of this empirical relation. Then, the presence of
a line uv in D means that the person corresponding to point u likes the
person corresponding to point v, and the absence of line uv means that
person u does not like v. It is clear that other empirical relations on
the same set of people may be treated in a similar fashion.

Essentially the same procedure may also be used to construct digraphs
when points and lines are given other interpretations. Thus, the digraph
of the competition structure of a market may be constructed by letting
points stand for commodities and a line uv indicate that commodity u
competes with commodity v. The digraph of the authority structure of
an organization may be constructed so that each point corresponds to
a position and each line uv means that position u can exercise authority
over position v. In a realization where points stand for alternative
outcomes, a line uv may represent the fact that alternative u is preferred
to alternative v. And, if points represent propositions, then line uv may
indicate that proposition u implies proposition v.

The empirical scientist clearly has great latitude in what empirical
phenomena he coordinates to the primitives of digraph theory. Just
how he proceeds will depend in part upon the nature of the phenomena
he is studying. If his interests are in the social behavior of individuals,
he may want to interpret points as persons and lines as interpersonal
relationships of a type that interests him. Obviously, too, he will want
to select an interpretation which will help him reach conclusions of
significance for some theory about the world of empirical data. While
we shall not attempt here to specify which interpretations should be
made in order to achieve theoretical significance, it may be useful to
discuss briefly some of the alternatives that must be faced in deciding
upon a particular interpretation.

In interpreting point and line, the social scientist may be interested
in relationships that indicate the possibility, the necessity, or the actual
occurrence of an event. These different kinds of criteria are reflected
by the words "can," "must," and "does," that is, by the use of the
potential, imperative, and indicative moods. Thus, a line uv may be
interpreted as "person u can communicate to person v," "u must communicate to v," or "u does communicate to v." There is nothing in the
nature of digraph theory which requires that the interpretation refer to
any particular modality.

Consider a simple digraph consisting of points v_1, v_2, v_3 and two
lines v_1v_2 and v_2v_3. If the interpretation of a line is "can communicate
message M," it follows that message M can go from v_1 to v_3 but not

that it will necessarily do so. If the interpretation is "must communicate," then if message M originates at v_1 it must reach v_3. And if the interpretation is "does communicate," the digraph describes the actual transmission of the message. In most social psychological research on communication networks the interpretation has been "can communicate." And in this research it has become apparent that, in order to be able to predict completely the actual flow of communication, we must state certain "operating procedures" which people employ when working in any given network of potential communication.[11]

Considerations of this sort suggest that a distinction should be made between descriptive and predictive interpretations of digraphs. The nature of this distinction may be illustrated by an example. Suppose that we have obtained friendship choices from a group of people. We can then describe the "friendship structure" of this group in terms of digraph theory by interpreting points as persons and lines as friendship choices. The concepts of digraph theory will apply to this structure, and its theorems will give factual information about this or any other structure. For example, a theorem to be presented in Chapter 12 asserts that if every point of a digraph D has outdegree 1, then D must have one of a very limited number of configurations. In fact, it follows from this theorem that every such digraph with four points must be isomorphic with one of those shown in Figure 1.17. We may conclude, then, that in a group of four people in which each person has exactly one friend, the only possible friendship structures are those shown in Figure 1.17. Factual information of this sort is of real value, but it does not lead to further predictions about the behavior of people unless

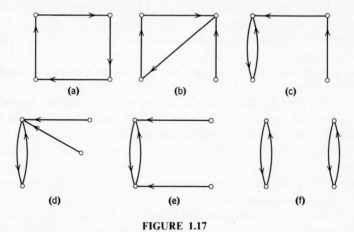

(a)   (b)   (c)

(d)   (e)   (f)

FIGURE 1.17

[11] See, for example, Guetzkow (1960).

it is taken as an empirical axiom that "friendship choice" implies some particular resultant behavior. If, to achieve a predictive interpretation, an empirical axiom is set up so that "*u* chooses *v*" implies that *u* and *v* will tend to engage in social activities together, then we may draw the empirical conclusion that in a group of four people each of whom has exactly one friend, all will tend to engage in social activities together if and only if there are not two pairs of mutual friends. Although this conclusion appears obvious in such a small group, more complex conclusions may be derived in the same manner for groups of any size.

We see, then, that digraph theory will be useful to the social scientist in his efforts to describe the structural properties of empirical phenomena but that digraph theory, in and of itself, is not sufficient to derive empirical tendencies or laws from structural properties. Throughout this volume, in discussing the strictly structural properties of digraphs, we suggest a few rather simple empirical axioms which, when combined with digraph theory, result in certain empirical consequences. These are intended merely to illustrate how, in principle, empirical consequences may be derived. The reader will wish to consider for himself the consequences which he may deduce from other empirical axioms of interest to him.

SUMMARY

In this chapter we have been concerned with matters lying at the foundation of digraph theory. We began by considering an axiom system for the very general theory of nets. This system has four primitive terms: P_1: a set V of points, P_2: a set X of lines, P_3: a function f whose domain is X and whose range is contained in V, and P_4: a function s whose domain is X and whose range is contained in V. The system has two axioms: A_1: the set V is finite and not empty, and A_2: the set X is finite.

We next showed that an axiom system for relations is obtained simply by adding the axiom, A_3: no two distinct lines are parallel. Certain properties of relations were then defined and illustrated, and we saw how different kinds of orders on a set of points arise from various combinations of these properties.

With this background, we were able to place digraph theory in its more general mathematical context. The axiom system for digraph theory consists of that for relations with one additional axiom, A_4: There are no loops. Thus, a digraph is an irreflexive relation. We then saw how various properties of relations may be employed to generate different kinds of digraphs. These will be encountered throughout the remainder of the book.

Many of the properties of digraphs are more conveniently handled in terms of matrices. In particular, there is a correspondence between a digraph and its adjacency matrix which allows a classification of points in terms of outdegree and indegree. It was shown that the sum of the outdegrees of all points, the sum of their indegrees, and the number of lines of a digraph are all equal. A detailed discussion of digraphs and matrices is given in Chapter 5.

Next, we considered the fundamental concept of isomorphism of two digraphs. With this concept we were able to give precise meaning to the notion that two empirical systems have the same structure. A theorem was then given, showing how the determination of the isomorphism of two digraphs can be obtained by means of their adjacency matrices.

At the beginning and the end of the chapter we discussed how the empirical scientist can use digraph theory. We pointed out that digraph theory is concerned with structural properties of sets of abstract elements called points and lines, whereas the empirical scientist is interested in empirical structures made up of empirical entities and relationships. If an appropriate coordination is made so that each empirical entity is identified with a point and each empirical relationship is identified with a line and if this is done in such a way that the axioms of digraph theory become true statements about the empirical world, then all true statements of digraph theory correspond to true statements about the empirical phenomena. When these requirements are met, the scientist may use the results of digraph theory in his treatment of empirical data. It was noted that the empirical scientist also needs empirical axioms, in addition to those of digraph theory, in order to derive empirical tendencies or laws from structural properties.

In the next chapter we take up the fundamental properties of joining and reaching within digraphs.

EXERCISES

1. Among the digraphs of Figure 1.15, how many are symmetric? Asymmetric? Transitive? Complete? Disconnected?

2. Draw a digraph that contains an ordinary point and has a minimum number of points and lines. Draw another such digraph. Are there any others?

3. Draw a transitive digraph of three points and three lines. What is the classification of each point? Can one construct a transitive digraph whose points are all carriers?

4. Construct a 4 × 4 matrix which corresponds to an irreflexive, asymmetric, transitive relation. Draw the corresponding digraph. What kind of empirical situation might this digraph represent?

5. Construct a digraph and its corresponding adjacency matrix for the children's game "Paper, Rock, and Scissors" in which paper defeats rock, rock defeats scissors, and scissors defeats paper. (a) Characterize the relation in terms of reflexivity, symmetry, and transitivity. (b) What is the indegree and out-degree of each point?

6. Draw a digraph containing six points and five lines such that all these lines constitute the outbundle at the first point v_1. Write its adjacency matrix.

7. Verify that the two digraphs of Figure 1.14 are isomorphic by writing their adjacency matrices in such a way that they are equal.

8. Show that the two digraphs of Figure 1.18 are isomorphic. (a) Assign orderings to the points of D_2 so that the two adjacency matrices are equal. (b) Can this be done in more than one way?

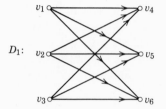 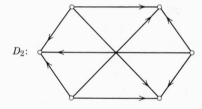

FIGURE 1.18

9. Let an asymmetric digraph D have three points and three lines. (a) Prove: If D has exactly one carrier, then D has one transmitter and one receiver. (b) Prove: If D has one transmitter and one receiver, then D is transitive. (c) Prove: If D is transitive, then D has exactly one carrier. (d) Construct an implication digraph for these three previous statements. (e) Use the fact that the relation of implication is transitive, and show from the implication digraph that the following statements are true: (1) If D is transitive, then D has one transmitter and one receiver. (2) If D has exactly one carrier, then D is transitive. (3) If D has one transmitter and one receiver, then D has exactly one carrier.

APPENDIX

In this book we make use of certain concepts of set theory. For the reader who wishes to refresh his memory of set-theoretic terminology and notation, we present the following very brief summary. Here, "set," "element," and "is an element of" are taken to be undefined terms with a natural intuitive meaning.

The *universal set U* is the set of all elements under consideration. The *empty set* ∅ is the set which does not contain any elements. The set *B* is a *subset* of a set *A*, written $B \subset A$, if every element of *B* is in *A*. Two sets are called *equal* if each is a subset of the other. We say that *B* is a *proper* subset of *A* if *B* is a nonempty subset of *A* and *B* does not equal *A*. Clearly every set is a subset of the universal set.

There are several important operations on sets. The *union* of two sets *A* and *B*, written $A \cup B$, is the set consisting of all those elements which are in *A* or *B* (or both). The *intersection* of *A* and *B*, denoted $A \cap B$, consists of those elements in both *A* and *B*. If the intersection of *A* and *B* is empty, the sets are said to be *disjoint*. The *difference A − B* contains all elements of *A* which are not in *B*. The *symmetric difference*, written $A \oplus B$, is the set containing those elements in exactly one of the sets *A* and *B*. Their symmetric difference can be thought of as the elements in *A* or *B* but not in both: $A \oplus B = (A \cup B) - (A \cap B)$. It can also be

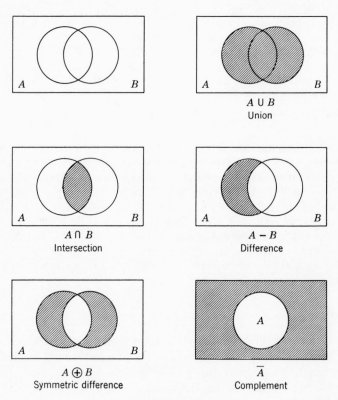

$A \cup B$
Union

$A \cap B$
Intersection

$A - B$
Difference

$A \oplus B$
Symmetric difference

$\overline{A}$
Complement

FIGURE 1.19

thought of as the elements of A not in B together with those in B not in A: $A \oplus B = (A - B) \cup (B - A)$, whence the name "symmetric difference." The *complement* of a set A, denoted $\bar{A}$, consists of the elements of U not in A: $\bar{A} = U - A$. These operations and their resulting sets are illustrated in Figure 1.19 by what are usually called Venn diagrams, in which the universal set U is a rectangular region of the plane and where the hatched area is the set resulting from the operation.

Some of the most useful set theoretic identities, whose validity may be readily verified by Venn diagrams, are as follows:

$A \cup U = U$ $A \cap U = A$

$A \cup \varnothing = A$ $A \cap \varnothing = \varnothing$

$A \cup \bar{A} = U$ $A \cap \bar{A} = \varnothing$

$A \cup A = A$ $A \cap A = A$

$A \cup B = B \cup A$ $A \cap B = B \cap A$

$A \cup (B \cup C) = (A \cup B) \cup C$ $A \cap (B \cap C) = (A \cap B) \cap C$

$A \cap (B \cup C) = (A \cap B) \cup (A \cap C)$ $A \cup (B \cap C) = (A \cup B) \cap (A \cup C)$

2 • Joining and Reaching

In every modern corporation
are channels of communication
along which lines, from foot to crown,
reports flow up and vetoes down.*

KENNETH E. BOULDING

Suppose that we are interested in studying the communication system of an industrial organization and that we have data indicating for every pair of people whether it is possible for each to give information about some topic directly to another. From these data about the communication system we may construct a digraph in which each point corresponds to a person and each line uv indicates that person u can communicate directly to person v. Given this digraph, we may ask whether information possessed by one person (for example, a particular foreman) can reach another person (for example, the president). If there is a line in the digraph from the foreman to the president, the answer is, of course, straightforward. But if the foreman is not adjacent to the president, we need to examine the digraph further, for it is possible that information can reach the president from the foreman indirectly through a sequence of communications. Considerations of this sort make it clear that two points u and v of a digraph D may be "joined" in some sense even though D has no line uv.

If in our study of the communication system we find that information can get in some way from person u to person v, we may regard v as reachable from u. Considering the foreman and the president, we may

* Reprinted by permission from the March, 1958, issue of the *Michigan Business Review*, published by the Graduate School of Business Administration, The University of Michigan.

discover that neither can reach the other, only one can reach the other, or each can reach the other. It would not be at all surprising to find that the president can reach the foreman whereas the foreman cannot get through to the president. Clearly, then, reachability may, or may not, be symmetric.

There is another, and "weaker," way in which two persons u and v may be joined in a communication system. Suppose it is found that neither can reach the other but that each can reach a third person w. Since w is reachable from both u and v, we may regard u and v as joined, albeit weakly, by the communication system even though neither can get information to the other.

This brief discussion of the various ways in which two people may be joined serves to illustrate the need for carefully defined terms. In this chapter we consider concepts from digraph theory which are useful in making precise such intuitive notions as "joining" and "reaching." The fundamental concept for this purpose is semipath, a term defined broadly enough so as to be able to deal with the various kinds of joining suggested above. We shall see that there are two different kinds of semipaths and that the difference between them depends in a fundamental way upon the inclusion in them of the different classes of points discussed in the preceding chapter.

Closely related to the concept of joining is that of distance. If, for example, we know that two foremen can reach the president but that one can talk to him directly whereas the other must go through several people, we would regard the former as much "closer" to the president than the latter. By the same token, if the president can get information directly to the second foreman, we would say that the distance from the president to this foreman is less than the distance from this foreman to the president. In the following discussion we give precise meaning to the notion of the "distance" from one point to another in a digraph.

The material presented in this chapter is basic to all that follows in this volume. In particular, an understanding of the nature of semipaths will give the background needed for consideration, in the next chapter, of how the connectedness of complex structures may be characterized.

SEMIPATHS AND PATHS

A *semipath joining* v_1 *and* v_n is a collection of distinct points, $v_1, v_2, \ldots,$ v_n, together with $n - 1$ lines, one from each pair of lines, v_1v_2 or v_2v_1, v_2v_3 or $v_3v_2, \ldots, v_{n-1}v_n$ or v_nv_{n-1}. Such a semipath is sometimes called a $v_1 - v_n$ semipath.

A (*directed*) *path from* v_1 *to* v_n is a collection of distinct points, $v_1, v_2, \ldots, v_n$, together with the lines $v_1v_2, v_2v_3, \ldots, v_{n-1}v_n$, considered in the following order: $v_1, v_1v_2, v_2, v_2v_3, v_3, \ldots, v_{n-1}v_n, v_n$.

In Figure 2.1 there is a path from v_1 to v_3. There is also a semipath joining v_1 and v_3. In fact, every path is a semipath. A semipath which

FIGURE 2.1

is not a path is called a *strict semipath*. Accordingly, in Figure 2.1 there is a strict semipath joining v_1 and v_4. Clearly, there is no semipath joining v_5 and any other point of the digraph. If there is a path from u to v, we say that v is *reachable from u*. The following statements can therefore be made concerning the digraph of Figure 2.1: Points v_1 and v_4 are joined by a semipath but neither point is reachable from the other; v_1 and v_3 are joined, v_3 is reachable from v_1, but v_1 is not reachable from v_3; v_1 and v_5 are not joined and hence neither is reachable from the other.

The number of lines in a path is called its *length*. A *geodesic* from u to v is a path from u to v of minimum length. If there is a path from u to v in a digraph, then the *distance from u to v*, denoted $d(u, v)$, is the length of a geodesic from u to v. It is important to note that in general the distance from u to v need not be equal to the distance from v to u. For example, in Figure 2.2, $d(v_1, v_2) = 1$ and $d(v_2, v_1) = 2$. If there is no path from u to v, the distance from u to v is called infinite, for there is no way to get from u to v in a finite number of steps. Symbolically, we write $d(u, v) = \infty$.

For completeness, we note that a single point v is a path of length 0, called a *trivial path*. This is consistent with the definition of path for the following reasons: the single point v is a collection of distinct points and directed lines which begins and ends with a point and has the property (satisfied vacuously) that every line in this collection is preceded by its first point and followed by its second point. Since the length of a

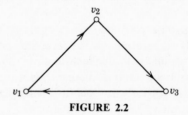

FIGURE 2.2

path is the number of lines in it, the length of this path is 0. The distance from a point v to itself is, therefore, equal to zero: $d(v, v) = 0$.

The following theorem resembles the theorem of Euclidean geometry that the length of one side of a triangle is at most the sum of the lengths of the other two sides. It is known as the Triangle Inequality.

Theorem 2.1. If in a digraph, v is reachable from u and w is reachable from v, then $d(u, w) \leq d(u, v) + d(v, w)$.

By the hypothesis of this theorem, there are paths from u to v and from v to w. By following these paths in succession, one gets from u to w in $d(u, v) + d(v, w)$ steps. But since the distance $d(u, w)$ is the fewest number of steps required to get from u to w, $d(u, w) \leq d(u, v) + d(v, w)$.

A *subpath* of a path L is a path contained in L. Clearly, any subpath of a geodesic is itself a geodesic from its first point to its last point.

One may often want to find a geodesic from one point to another. If the digraph is small, this is easily done by inspection. However, in larger digraphs the following procedure may be helpful. Suppose we wish to find a geodesic from u to v in the digraph of Figure 2.3. First,

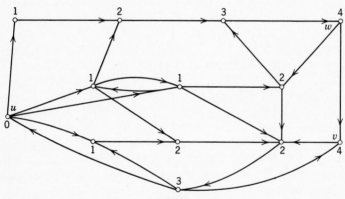

FIGURE 2.3

we assign to u the number 0 and to each point adjacent from u the number 1. Then the number 2 is assigned to every unnumbered point adjacent from a point marked 1, thereby designating the set of points at distance 2 from u. If we continue in this manner, point v is eventually assigned a number which is its distance from u. The numbers shown in Figure 2.3 are obtained in this way, so we know that $d(u, v) = 4$. Hence a geodesic from u to v will have four lines. Let v_3 be any point at distance 3 from u such that $v_3 v$ is a line of D. Let v_2 be a point at distance 2 from u such that v_2v_3 is in D, and let v_1 be any point such that both lines uv_1 and v_1v_2 are in D. Then we have a geodesic from u to v, whose points are u, v_1, v_2, v_3, v.

In our example, there is only one geodesic from u to v. Of course, it may happen that there is more than one geodesic from one point to another, as for example from u to w in the digraph of Figure 2.3. However, the procedure is still applicable, and if we take all feasible choices for v_3, v_2, and v_1, we shall find all geodesics from u to w. The procedure is stated in general terms in the following theorem.

Theorem 2.2. (Geodesic algorithm.[1]) Let v be reachable from u with $d(u, v) = n$. The following algorithm can be used to construct any geodesic from u to v. First, find a point v_{n-1} such that $d(u, v_{n-1}) = n - 1$ and line $v_{n-1}v$ is in D. Then find a point v_{n-2} such that $d(u, v_{n-2}) = n - 2$ and $v_{n-2}v_{n-1}$ is in D. Continue this process until finding a point v_1 such that $d(u, v_1) = 1$ and v_1v_2 is in D. Then the path $uv_1v_2 \dots v_{n-1}v$ is a geodesic from u to v.

In order to gain a deeper understanding of the nature of semipaths, let us examine more closely how semipaths are constituted. For this purpose the classification of points presented in Chapter 1 will be employed. The semipath in Figure 2.4(a) is, of course, the primordial building block of any digraph, for it consists of a single directed line. If we construct semipaths containing exactly two lines, we find that the only possible configurations are those shown in Figure 2.4(b), (c), and (d). The letters t, r, and c, indicated at the points, stand for transmitter, receiver, and carrier respectively. It is clear that the sequences of letters *tcr*, *rtr*, and *trt*, indicating the classification of successive points, contain all the information required to draw each of these semipaths. It must be understood that when any of these sequences is "spelled backwards," the result still determines exactly the same semipath. Thus, both *tcr* and *rct* determine the semipath of Figure 2.4(b). These considerations lead to the following conclusion.

Theorem 2.3. A sequence of letters consisting of c's, r's, and t's describes a nontrivial semipath if and only if neither the first nor the last is c, there is an r between any two occurrences of t's, and there is a t between any two r's.

As an illustration of this theorem we note that the v_1–v_4 semipath in the digraph of Figure 2.1 can be described by *tcrt* or by *trct*.[2] Between the two occurrences of t there is an r.

---

[1] This algorithm is due to Moore (1959).

[2] Since the "word" describing a semipath of length 3 contains four letters, we have carefully selected our alphabet so as to avoid any possible embarrassment.

Corollary 2.3a. A nontrivial semipath is a path if and only if it can be described with a sequence of letters containing exactly one t and one r. It is a strict semipath if and only if its description requires at least two t's or at least two r's.

We see that the character of a semipath is to a large extent determined by its r-points and t-points. It is often convenient therefore to suppress the c-points. The suppression of the carriers of a semipath L corresponds to "erasing" all c's from the sequence of letters describing L. The semipath resulting from the suppression of all carriers of L is called its *suppressed semipath.* Thus, for example, the digraph of Figure 2.4(a) is the suppressed semipath of the digraph of Figure 2.4(b). The next statement follows immediately from Theorem 2.3 and the definition of suppression.

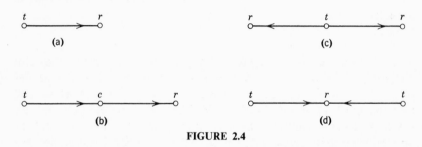

FIGURE 2.4

Corollary 2.3b. The suppression of the carriers in a semipath results in a semipath consisting entirely of t-points and r-points in alternation, and the numbers of t-points and r-points are unchanged by suppression.

A *maximal path in a semipath* L is a path contained in L but is not a subpath of any longer path in L. A maximal path in a semipath must have one r-point and one t-point of the given semipath; its other points are all c-points. Clearly, each line of a suppressed semipath corresponds to a maximal path in the original semipath. Two maximal paths in a semipath L can have but one point in common, which must be a t-point of both or an r-point of both, since it must be a t-point or an r-point of L. Such a point common to two paths in L is called a *linking point.* Thus in any strict semipath there are at least two maximal paths and at least one linking point.

A semipath can be regarded as built up from its maximal paths. If L is a semipath joining u and v, then it can be thought of as constructed from maximal paths $L_1, L_2, \ldots, L_m$ and linking points $v_1, v_2, \ldots, v_{m-1}$, where L_1 joins u and v_1, L_2 joins v_1 and $v_2, \ldots, L_m$ joins v_{m-1} and v.

The points u, v_1, v_2, ..., v_{m-1}, v are alternately receivers and transmitters. Only the linking points lie on more than one maximal path, and linking point v_i lies only on L_i and L_{i+1}. We note that the number of maximal paths exceeds the number of linking points by 1. The following corollary is a particular case of some of these remarks.

Corollary 2.3c. If two transmitters are joined by a semipath L that contains no other transmitter, then L has exactly one receiver. Furthermore, for any point v in L there is a path from v to the receiver.

DIRECTIONAL DUALITY

In this section we study the operation of taking the "converse" of any digraph. We shall see that this operation, which involves reversing the direction of every line of a given digraph, sets the stage for a powerful principle called "directional duality." This principle will enable us to establish certain theorems without effort once we have proved other corresponding theorems.[3]

Note, first, that the digraphs of Figures 2.4(c) and (d) are related to each other in a particular way: either one can be obtained from the other simply by reversing the directions of all lines. Given a digraph D, its *converse* D' is the digraph with the same set of points such that for any two points u and v the line uv is in D' if and only if vu is in D. The digraphs of Figures 2.4(c) and (d) are converses of each other, and the digraph of Figure 2.2 is isomorphic to its own converse.

Theorem 2.4. The converse of the converse of a digraph D is D itself; symbolically, $D'' = D$.

To prove this statement observe that D and D'' have the same set of points. We must show that they have the same lines. By the definition of D', vu is a line of D' if and only if uv is a line of D. Since D'' is the converse of D', uv is a line of D'' if and only if vu is a line of D'. Thus uv is in D'' if and only if it is in D. Therefore, they have the same lines.

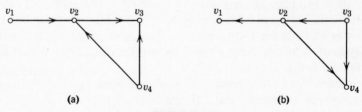

(a)   (b)

FIGURE 2.5

[3] The approach employed here is that presented by Harary (1957).

The two digraphs shown in Figure 2.5 serve to illustrate this theorem. Note that the digraph of Figure 2.5(b) is the converse of that in Figure 2.5(a). In addition, the digraph of Figure 2.5(a) is the converse of the one in Figure 2.5(b). Thus, in accordance with Theorem 2.4, the converse of the converse of the digraph in Figure 2.5(a) is itself the digraph in Figure 2.5(a).

A *dual operation* means an operation on digraphs which, when applied twice, results in the original digraph. Thus, Theorem 2.4 tells us that one dual operation is that of taking converses. For each dual operation there is an associated collection of dual concepts; in the particular case of the converse operation, these are called converse concepts. More specifically, *the converse of a concept* concerning digraphs is one which results in place of the concept, when the operation of converse is applied to a digraph. The following theorem specifies some of the more frequently occurring converse concepts. In each case, the words before the verb "becomes" refer to the original digraph *D*, while the words after "becomes" refer to the converse digraph *D'*. Each of the statements in the theorem follows at once from the definition of the operation of converse.

Theorem 2.5. The following ten statements specify what happens to certain parts of a digraph *D* when the converse digraph *D'* is formed.

1. Every point v of D becomes exactly the same point v in D'.
2. Every line uv becomes line vu; every path from u to v becomes a path from v to u.
3. Every strict semipath joining u and v becomes a strict semipath joining these same two points.
4. Every transmitter becomes a receiver.
5. Every receiver becomes a transmitter.
6. Every isolate becomes an isolate.
7. Every carrier becomes a carrier.
8. Every ordinary point becomes an ordinary point.
9. The indegree of v, id(v), becomes the outdegree of v, od(v).
10. The outdegree of v becomes the indegree of v.

A *concept* is *self-dual* with respect to a dual operation if it remains the same after the operation is performed on the digraph. We observe that certain concepts, such as point, isolate, and carrier, are self-dual directionally, that is, they remain the same under the operation of taking the converse of a digraph.

The dual of a statement about a digraph refers to that statement obtained upon replacing each concept in the statement by the dual concept. For example, the directional dual of the statement that v is a transmitter of a digraph is that v is a receiver, and the directional dual of the statement that there is a path from u to v is that there is a path from v to u. In both of these examples, we see that in forming the directional dual of a statement about a digraph, we replace each concept by its converse concept, that is, its directionally dual concept.[4]

In general, any *duality principle* has the following two properties: (a) The dual of the dual of a statement is the original statement. (b) The dual of a true statement is true. We now state and prove the directional duality principle.

Directional Duality Principle. For each theorem about digraphs, there is a corresponding theorem obtained by replacing every concept by its converse concept.

In order to prove this principle we consider the nature of a theorem about digraphs. Ultimately, any such theorem can be recast in the following form: For any digraph D, if P is a true statement, then Q is a true statement, that is, P implies Q. Let us denote the respective dual statements by P' and Q'. The directional duality principle asserts that if the statement "P implies Q" holds for any digraph D, then the statement "P' implies Q'" also holds for any digraph D. We begin the proof by taking as a given theorem, whose proof is already known, the following statement:

(1) For any digraph D, if P is true then Q is true.

It is obvious that if P is true for D, then P' holds for D'. Likewise if P' holds for D', then P'' holds for D''. Obviously $P'' = P$, and by Theorem 2.5, $D'' = D$. Thus, P holds for D if and only if P' holds for D'; and of course, the same is true for statement Q. Statement (1) can be reworded, therefore, in a logically equivalent way:

(2) For any digraph D, if P' is true for D' then Q' is true for D'.

The preceding statement can now be stated a bit more briefly by not mentioning digraph D explicitly:

(3) For any digraph D', if P' is true then Q' is true.

Thus, statement (1) is equivalent to saying that for any digraph which is the converse of some digraph, if P' is true then Q' is true. But every digraph is the converse of some digraph; therefore, we have the following logically equivalent form of statement (3):

(4) For any digraph D, if P' is true then Q' is true.

---

[4] When he married, he jumped into the frying pan out of the fire.

This last statement (4) is the theorem corresponding to statement (1) obtained by replacing every concept in the original theorem by its converse concept. Since each of the statements (2)–(4) is logically equivalent to the preceding one, it follows that statements (4) and (1) are equivalent to each other. But statement (1) is the given theorem which is known to be true; hence statement (4) is also true and the directional duality principle is proved.

The way in which the directional duality principle is employed in digraph theory may be illustrated by reference to Corollary 2.3c. This corollary asserts that any semipath L with exactly two transmitters which joins these two points has exactly one receiver, and that for any point v in L there is a path from v to the receiver. On interchanging the words "to" and "from," and the words "transmitter" and "receiver," we obtain the following dual corollary.

Corollary 2.3c'. If two receivers are joined by a semipath L that contains no other receiver, then L has exactly one transmitter. Furthermore, for any point v in L there is a path to v from the transmitter.

It may happen that the directional dual of a statement is the very same statement. If this is true for a theorem, we say that the theorem is *self-dual*. Consider, for example Theorem 2.3, which asserts that a sequence of letters consisting of c's, r's, and t's describes a nontrivial semipath if and only if neither the first nor the last is c, there is an r between any two occurrences of t's, and there is a t between any two r's. Strictly speaking, the directional dual of this theorem is the following statement: A sequence of letters consisting of c's, r's, and t's describes a nontrivial semipath if and only if neither the first nor the last is c, there is a t between any two occurrences of r's, and there is an r between any two t's. Even though the order of stating r's and t's is changed in this converse statement, the logical meaning of the two statements is exactly the same, and Theorem 2.3 is therefore self-dual.

THE JOINING OF PAIRS OF POINTS

In this section we investigate various ways in which pairs of points can be joined in a digraph. The analysis of joining relations is fundamental to much that follows in this book. Joining relations will be used in Chapter 3 to define the kinds of connectedness which digraphs may display. In order to make this analysis we need to generalize the concepts of path and semipath to allow repetition of their points and lines.

A (point-line) *sequence* is an alternating sequence of points and lines which begins and ends with a point and has the property that each line is preceded by its first point and followed by its second point. Thus a sequence may be written in the form: $v_1, v_1 v_2, v_2, v_2 v_3, \ldots, v_{n-1} v_n, v_n$. This sequence is determined by its points $v_1, v_2, \ldots, v_n$ or by its lines $v_1 v_2, v_2 v_3, \ldots, v_{n-1} v_n$. For brevity it is sometimes indicated by $v_1 v_2 \ldots v_n$. The point v_1 is the *initial point* of this sequence; v_n is the *terminal point*. We say that this is a sequence *from v_1 to v_n*. There is no restriction on the number of times a point or line may be repeated in the same sequence. Thus, even though we have used different symbols (given by subscripts) for the points, it is not necessary that these indicate distinct points. A sequence is called *open* if v_1 and v_n are distinct points. The difference between an open sequence and a path is that in a path all points and lines must be distinct.

Theorem 2.6. A sequence from u to v contains a path from u to v.

To prove this theorem, let L be a sequence from u to v and let w be any point of L. If w occurs more than once in L, remove from L all points and lines between the first and last occurrence of w and also remove this last occurrence of w. The result of repeated applications of this procedure is a path from u to v contained in L.

Corollary 2.6a. If there is a sequence from u to v, then v is reachable from u.

These concepts may be illustrated by reference to Figure 2.6. Consider the sequence L from v_1 to v_5:

$$L = v_1, v_1 v_2, v_2, v_2 v_3, v_3, v_3 v_4, v_4, v_4 v_2, v_2, v_2 v_5$$

By application of the procedure described in the proof of Theorem 2.6, we see that there is a path $v_1 v_2 v_5$ from v_1 to v_5. And by Corollary 2.6a, v_5 is reachable from v_1. It is also evident that there is no sequence from v_1 to v_6. Thus, v_6 is not reachable from v_1.

If the initial and terminal points of a sequence are the same point, the sequence is said to be *closed*. If the sequence L from u to v in Theorem 2.6 is closed, then $u = v$ and the construction in the proof of this theorem leaves the single point u, which as we have seen is a path of length 0. Another example of a closed sequence is the following one of the digraph

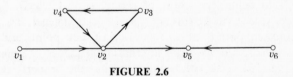

FIGURE 2.6

in Figure 2.6: $v_2, v_2v_3, v_3, v_3v_4, v_4, v_4v_2, v_2$. This sequence has v_2 as both its initial and terminal points and is therefore closed.

A *cycle* is obtained from a nontrivial path on adding a line from the terminal point to the initial point of the path. For example, consider in Figure 2.6 the path $v_2v_3v_4$. Upon adding the line v_4v_2 to this path, we obtain the cycle $v_2v_3v_4v_2$. This cycle is precisely the same as the closed sequence of the preceding paragraph.

We note that a single point v is a (trivial) closed sequence, for it begins and ends with v and vacuously satisfies the definitional requirement concerning lines.

The next theorem states a result for closed sequences which is analogous to Theorem 2.6.

Theorem 2.7. If v is a point of a nontrivial closed sequence L, then v is in a cycle contained in L.

A *semisequence* is an alternating sequence of points and lines which begins and ends with a point and has the property that each line is incident with the point before it and the point after it. Unlike a sequence, it is not necessary that two consecutive lines of a semisequence have consistent directions. Thus a semisequence joining v_1 to v_n may be written in the form: v_1, either v_1v_2 or v_2v_1, $v_2, \ldots, v_{n-1}$, either $v_{n-1}v_n$ or v_nv_{n-1}, v_n. Note that neither the points nor the lines of a semisequence need be distinct. In the digraph of Figure 2.6 there is a semisequence beginning with v_1 and ending with v_6 which consists of the sequence L from v_1 to v_5 listed above together with the line v_6v_5 and the point v_6.

Theorem 2.8. A semisequence joining u and v contains a semipath joining them.

A *semicycle* is obtained from a semipath on adding a line joining the terminal point and the initial point of the semipath. Note that every cycle is a semicycle, since every path is a semipath. The digraph in Figure 2.7 contains three semicycles: Z_1, the semipath $v_2v_3v_1$ together with line v_1v_2; Z_2, the semipath $v_1v_3v_4$ together with v_4v_1; and Z_3, the semipath $v_1v_2v_3v_4$ together with the line v_4v_1. Clearly, Z_1 is not a cycle, whereas Z_2 and Z_3 are.

The *length* of a sequence or a semisequence is the number of occurrences of lines in it. Thus, in particular, the length of a path, cycle, semipath, or semicycle is the number of lines in it. If any of these contains all the points of the digraph D, it is said to be *complete*. Thus the semisequence $v_1v_2v_3v_4v_2v_5v_6$ of the digraph of Figure 2.6 is complete and of length 6. There is no complete sequence, path, semipath, semicycle, or cycle in Figure 2.6.

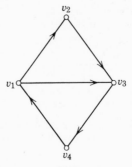

FIGURE 2.7

We may now consider a method for describing different ways in which a pair of points may be joined in a digraph. We say, for convenience, that every pair of points u and v of any digraph are *0-joined*. They are *1-joined* if there is a semisequence joining them, *2-joined* if there is a sequence from one to the other, and *3-joined* if there is a sequence from each to the other. By using Theorems 2.6 and 2.8, we see at once that these definitions can be stated equivalently in terms of semipaths and paths.

In Figure 2.8 five digraphs are shown. These illustrate the different kinds of joining that pairs of points may have. The kinds of joining in each digraph are presented in Table 2.1, which is constructed in the following manner. Since, by definition, every pair of points of a digraph is 0-joined, we enter 0 for every pair in each digraph. Since there are no lines in digraph D_1, these are the only entries for this digraph. For any two points joined by a semipath, we enter 1, and for any two points joined by a path we enter 2. Thus, for example, we enter both 1 and 2 for each pair of points in D_4 and D_5, but we enter only 1 for the pair v_1, v_3 in D_3 since they are joined by a semipath but not a path. Finally, we enter 3 for every pair of points that are mutually reachable. This last condition is met only in D_5, which consists of a cycle and therefore has a path in each direction between every pair of points.

Table 2.1

Pairs of Points	Kinds of Joining				
	D_1	D_2	D_3	D_4	D_5
v_1, v_2	0	0, 1, 2	0, 1, 2	0, 1, 2	0, 1, 2, 3
v_1, v_3	0	0	0, 1	0, 1, 2	0, 1, 2, 3
v_2, v_3	0	0	0, 1, 2	0, 1, 2	0, 1, 2, 3

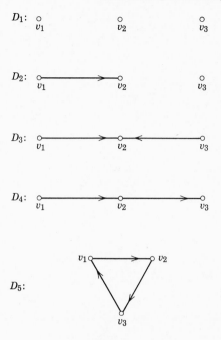

FIGURE 2.8

It is evident from the definitions and from Table 2.1 that if two points are 3-joined they are also 2-joined, if they are 2-joined they are also 1-joined, and if they are 1-joined they are 0-joined. For this reason, we frequently indicate the kind of joining of a pair of points simply by writing the highest degree of joining.

REALIZATIONS OF REACHABILITY AND JOINING

The concepts of reachability and joining are so fundamental in digraph theory that it will be useful at this point in our study to examine them more closely.

Reachability

As we have seen, point v is reachable from u in a digraph D if and only if there is a sequence from u to v. It will be fruitful to conceive of reachability as a relation on the set of points V of a digraph D. Clearly, this is a different relation from that of adjacency, which corresponds to the set of lines of D. What properties does the relation of reachability have? First, reachability is reflexive since every point of V is reachable from itself by a path of length 0. Second, it is transitive, for if there is a sequence L_1 from u to v and a sequence L_2 from v to w, then there is a sequence L_3 from u to w, namely the union of L_1 and L_2. Finally, it need be neither symmetric nor asymmetric, for if there is a sequence from u to v, there may, or may not, be a sequence from v to u. As mentioned in Chapter 1, a reflexive and transitive relation is known as a quasi-order. Thus, the relation of reachability is a quasi-order.

The properties of the reachability relation must be kept in mind when we consider possible realizations of digraphs. Let us illustrate what is involved by means of a communication network of a group of people.[5] This network may be represented by a digraph if we let each person of the group correspond to a point of a digraph D and let the relationship "u can transmit message M directly to v" correspond to the line uv of D.

In order to draw conclusions about the flow of message M through this network, we need to make precise empirical assumptions about the way in which the network operates. For convenience, we state the following simple assumptions.

E2.1. A person may possess message M only by originating it or receiving it from another person in the group.

E2.2. If a person possesses message M, he will transmit it to all persons possible (that is, all persons adjacent from him in the digraph of the network).

We see immediately that if person v_1 possesses message M and there is a sequence in the digraph of the network of the form $v_1v_2 \ldots v_n$, then message M will eventually reach every person in this sequence. Thus, the empirical relationship "message M will reach v from u" can be co-ordinated to the graphical relationship "v is reachable from u."

In general, we represent an empirical relation on a set of empirical entities by a digraph, where each relationship of the relation corresponds to a line. If we wish in the realization to make use of reachability in digraphs, we must be able to make the coordination between a sequence in D and some underlying relation in the empirical world.

Let us return now to empirical assumptions E2.1 and E2.2 to see how these, together with the concept of reachability, lead to certain empirical conclusions. The first conclusion merely makes explicit the consequences of E2.2 noted above.

---

[5] The use of graphs to represent the communication structure of a group was first employed by Bavelas (1950). For a review of subsequent work, see Glanzer and Glaser (1961).

C2.1. If person v possesses M, then M will reach everyone reachable from v in the digraph of the network.

The next two conclusions follow immediately from this, when taken together with the definitions of 2-joining and 3-joining.

C2.2. Let persons u and v be 2-joined in the digraph of a communication network. Then at least one of the following statements is true: (a) Person u is reachable from v, and if v originates M it will reach u. (b) Person v is reachable from u, and if u originates M it will reach v.

C2.3. If in the digraph of a communication network u and v are 3-joined, then u and v can engage in two-way communication; that is, if u originates M it will reach v, and if v originates M it will reach u.

From C2.1 and the definition of a closed sequence, we obtain the next conclusion.

C2.4. Let D be the digraph of a nontrivial communication network such that v lies in a closed sequence L. Then, if v originates M, he will also receive it from another person in L.

Finally, with the aid of the definition of a complete sequence we obtain the next conclusion.

C2.5. If in the digraph of a communication network there is a complete sequence L, then M will reach everyone in the network if it originates with the person corresponding to the initial point of L.

It should be evident that analogous conclusions can be obtained from any empirical realization in which an empirical relationship can be coordinated to a line of a digraph and an underlying empirical relationship can be coordinated to the reachability of pairs of points.

Joining

We saw above that two points u and v are joined in a digraph if and only if there is a semisequence, or semipath, between them. The difference between reachability and joining is that in the latter instance we ignore the direction of lines. Just as in the case of reachability, we may conceive of joining as a relation on the set of points V of a digraph D. Joining is reflexive, for every point of V is joined to itself by a semipath of length 0. It is transitive, for if there is a semipath L_1 between u and v and a semipath L_2 between v and w, then there is a semipath L_3 between u and w. But joining differs from reachability in that it is symmetric, for if a semipath joins u and v, the same semipath obviously joins v and u. From the theory of relations, we may conclude that joining is an equivalence relation, since it is reflexive, transitive, and symmetric.

These observations have implications for realizations that make use of the joining of points in a digraph. Consider, for example, the communication network shown in Figure 2.9. (Note that the entire figure is one digraph, that is, the group consists of six people.) We see that v_1 and v_3 are joined by a semipath, as are v_4 and v_5. However, v_1 and v_4 are not joined in the digraph. Even if we ignore the direction of the lines of this digraph, we observe that v_1 and v_3 are in the same piece of the network, v_4 and v_5 are in the same piece, but v_1 and v_4 are in different pieces. The underlying empirical relation which is expressed by joining, then, is "being in the same piece of the network." Clearly, this is an equivalence relation and appropriately coordinated to joining in a digraph.

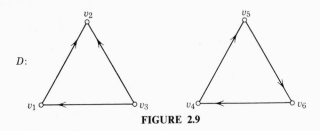

FIGURE 2.9

In comparing the relations of reachability and joining, it appears that joining is the weaker one. This observation is reflected in the fact that the more interesting realizations are ordinarily concerned with reachability. Joining, nevertheless, is an important feature of digraphs, and we shall encounter it repeatedly throughout this book. In the next chapter, we shall develop in greater detail an empirical realization that makes use of joining.

UNIPATHIC DIGRAPHS

A digraph is called *unipathic* if, whenever v is reachable from u, there is exactly one path from u to v. Obviously, every path in a unipathic digraph is a geodesic. Clearly a digraph is unipathic if and only if it has no semicycle which is the union of two paths from one point to another. Although every digraph with no semicycles is unipathic, the converse is not true, as shown by a digraph consisting of a single cycle. We illustrate unipathic digraphs by Figure 2.10. In Figure 2.10(a) there are no semicycles at all. Figure 2.10(b) consists of a single semicycle which is, however, unipathic. In Figure 2.10(c) there are three cycles, but no two of these cycles have a line in common.

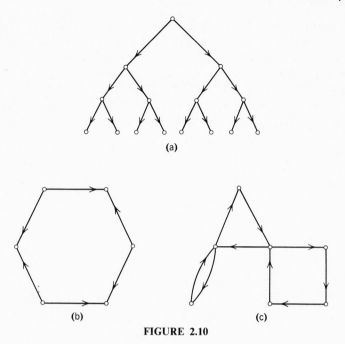

(a)

(b)   (c)

FIGURE 2.10

Theorem 2.9. If D is unipathic, then no two cycles of D have a common line.

Assume that there is a line x in two different cycles Z_1 and Z_2 of the unipathic digraph D. Then there is a path in D from sx to fx along Z_1 and another such path along Z_2, contrary to the hypothesis.

Theorem 2.10. If D is unipathic and Z is a cycle, there is no line in D joining any two points of Z which does not lie in Z.

If there is a line x joining two points of Z such that x is not in Z, the line x itself is one path from fx to sx, and there is another path from fx to sx along the cycle Z, contradicting the hypothesis that D is unipathic.

SUMMARY

In this chapter we have examined different ways in which two points u and v of a digraph may be joined. If there is a path from u to v, then v is reachable from u. If they are joined only by a strict semipath, neither is reachable from the other. We showed that a strict semipath contains a series of maximal subpaths linked together by linking points, each of which is a transmitter or a receiver of the semipath.

After discussing the operation of taking the converse of a digraph, we provided a powerful tool known as the directional duality principle. With the aid of this principle new theorems and corollaries can be obtained immediately from proven theorems and corollaries.

We then defined four kinds of joining that pairs of points may display. Examples were provided to show how the concepts of this chapter may be employed in empirical realizations. It was seen that the graphical concepts of reachability and joining may be coordinated to underlying empirical relations once a primary coordination has been made for the concepts of point and line. In the next chapter we shall show how the concepts of this chapter may be employed to define different kinds of connectedness which more complex structures may possess.

EXERCISES

1. Consider the digraph D in Figure 2.11.

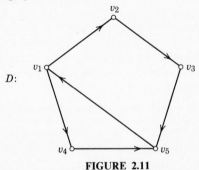

FIGURE 2.11

(a) Write a sequence from v_1 to v_3 that is not a path. (b) How many paths are there from v_3 to v_4? From v_4 to v_3? (c) How many semipaths are there joining v_3 and v_4? (d) How many semicycles are there in D? How many cycles? (e) Write a semisequence beginning with v_1 and ending at v_3 that is not a sequence or a semipath.

2. Consider the following propositions.

p_1: L is a semisequence joining v_1 and v_n.
p_2: L is a sequence from v_1 to v_n.
p_3: L is a semipath joining v_1 and v_n.
p_4: L is a path from v_1 to v_n.

(a) Verify that the digraph D shown in Figure 2.12 is the total implication digraph for these propositions. (b) Why is there no line p_1p_2? p_1p_3? p_2p_4? (c) Why are there no lines joining p_2 and p_3?

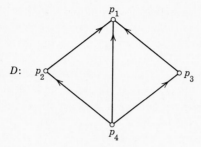

FIGURE 2.12

3. Consider the digraph D of Exercise 1. (a) Construct the converse digraph of D, $D' = E$. (b) Identify the paths from v_1 to v_5 in D; in E. (c) What is the value of $d(v_1, v_5)$ in D? In E? (d) What is the value of $d(v_5, v_1)$ in D? In E? (e) What is the digraph E'?

4. Prove that D is symmetric if and only if D and its converse D' have exactly the same lines.

5. What is the directional dual of each of the following statements? (a) If every two points of a digraph are joined by exactly one line, then there is a point v whose distance to any other point is at most 2. (b) If a semipath has the property that given any two of its points at least one is reachable from the other, then this semipath is a path.

6. Use Theorem 2.3 to show that a semipath is a path if and only if it contains exactly one maximal path.

The last four exercises involve the following terminology: Given a semipath L, let P be the number of maximal paths in L, let R and T be the number of r-points and t-points, respectively. Let R_1 and R_2 be the number of r-points with total degree 1 and 2, respectively; and let T_1 and T_2 be defined similarly.

7. Show that $P = R + T - 1 = R_2 + T_2 + 1$.

8. Show that the following three statements are equivalent: P is even; the difference between R_2 and T_2 is 1; and the difference between R and T is 1.

9. Show that the following statements are equivalent: P is odd; $R_2 = T_2$; and $R = T$.

10. Let L be a semipath for which $T_1 = 2$, $T_2 = 1$, and $R_2 = 2$. (a) What is the directional dual of this statement? (b) Find P, the number of maximal paths in L. (c) How many maximal paths does the directional dual of L have? (d) What is the smallest number of points L can have? Can L have 12 points?

3 • Connectedness

The head bone's connected to the neck bone.
The neck bone's connected to the shoulder bone.
The shoulder bone's connected to the back bone.
Now hear the word of the Lord.

ANON., *Dry Bones*

In the preceding chapter, we found that there are several ways in which two points of a digraph may be joined. Since each pair of points may be joined in these several ways, it would seem that digraphs themselves might be classified according to how strongly their points are inter-connected. For example, a digraph in which every two points are mutually reachable might be thought of as strongly connected, whereas one in which there are two points not joined by any semipath might be thought of as disconnected. Is there some general way in which to characterize the degree of connectedness of any digraph?

In this chapter, we present such a classificatory scheme. The various ways in which two points can be joined, discussed in Chapter 2, lead readily to a definition of four kinds of connectedness that a digraph may have. We then introduce the concepts of component and con-densation of a digraph. These, together with knowledge about certain properties of acyclic digraphs, allow us to present the major results of this chapter, namely, a development of equivalent criteria for each kind of connectedness. Discrete categories of connectedness are then defined so that digraphs can be categorized unambiguously according to their strength of connectedness, and results are presented concerning the number of lines which digraphs in the various categories may possess.

KINDS OF CONNECTEDNESS

A digraph D is *strongly connected*, or *strong*, if every two points are mutually reachable; D is *unilaterally connected*, or *unilateral*, if for any two points at least one is reachable from the other. We say that D is *weakly connected*, or *weak*, if every two points are joined by a semipath. A digraph is *disconnected* if it is not even weak. For completeness, we note that a digraph D consisting of exactly one point is strong, for since it does not contain two distinct points, the definition is vacuously satisfied. A digraph with just one point is called *trivial*.

Clearly, every strong digraph is unilateral and every unilateral digraph is weak, but the converses of these statements are not true in general. Hence these three kinds of connectedness for digraphs, namely strong, unilateral, and weak, are overlapping. Later in this chapter we shall consider nonoverlapping categories.

The next theorem, which follows immediately from the definitions of the concepts involved, states the relationship between the kinds of joining of pairs of points and the kinds of connectedness of digraphs.

Theorem 3.1. The digraph D is strong if and only if every pair of its points is 3-joined; D is unilateral if and only if every pair of its points is 2-joined; and D is weak if and only if every pair of its points is 1-joined.

An example of each kind of connectedness is given by the digraphs of Figure 3.1. The digraph D_1 is disconnected because some of its pairs of points are not 1-joined, namely, v_1, v_4; v_2, v_4; and v_3, v_4. In D_2 these pairs are 1-joined, and since all other pairs are 2-joined (and thus 1-joined), this digraph is weak. Since all pairs of points of D_3 are 2-joined, this digraph is unilateral (and, of course, also weak). Finally, D_4 is strong (and unilateral and weak) since all of its pairs of points are 3-joined.

The following examples illustrate how the various kinds of connectedness can be interpreted empirically.

Example 1. Suppose that we are interested in predicting which residents of a housing project will tend to associate in social activities. All residents have given answers to a sociometric question: With whom do you like to spend your leisure time? A digraph may be constructed from these answers by letting each point represent a resident and a line from u to v indicate that resident u chose v. In order to draw any empirical conclusion from the information in such a digraph, we must make some assumption about the behavior of each pair of residents

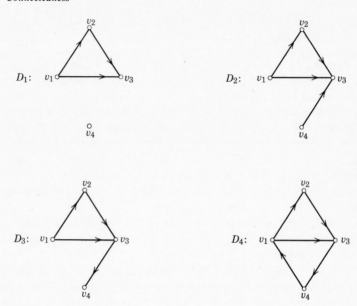

FIGURE 3.1

involved in a sociometric choice. For purposes of illustration, we make the following oversimplified empirical assumption.

E3.1. Residents u and v will tend to engage in social activities together if in the digraph of their sociometric choices there is a line from u to v or from v to u.

In this example, it is assumed that the absence of a line indicates "indifference" rather than active "avoidance." Thus, if u chooses v but v does not choose u, they will nevertheless tend to associate. The representation of both "attraction" and "avoidance" in the same digraph would require the use of signed digraphs, a topic discussed in Chapter 13.

Given a sociometric structure like that represented by digraph D_1 in Figure 3.1, we would expect, then, to find residents v_1, v_2, and v_3 together in social affairs, but no one would associate with v_4. Suppose, however, that the obtained digraph were D_2 of Figure 3.1. Then, v_1 and v_4 would tend to engage in the same social activities, since each wants to associate with v_3.

In general, we conclude that any two residents will tend to associate in social activities if they are 1-joined in the digraph of their sociometric choices. By a simple application of assumption E3.1 and Theorem 3.1, we can make the more general assertion that if the sociometric structure of the residents forms a weak digraph, then all residents will tend to associate in social activities. On the other hand, if the sociometric structure does not form a weak digraph, then the social life of the housing project will display separate subgroups, some of which may be single individuals.

Example 2. Observation of the clerks in a certain business office has shown that every clerk always tells exactly the same people every rumor she hears. We may represent this rumor network by a digraph in which each point corresponds to a clerk and each line uv means that clerk u will relay any rumor she hears to clerk v. (This example is a specific instance of the communication realization presented in Chapter 2.) Consider the digraphs of Figure 3.1 as rumor networks and assume that v_1 starts a rumor. Clearly, v_4 will hear it only in the networks represented by D_3 and D_4.

In general, we may say that v will hear a rumor started by u if and only if u and v are 2-joined and u is the initial point of some sequence from u to v. Moreover, if u and v are 3-joined, then each will be sure to hear any rumor started by the other. From the definition of a unilateral digraph we know that if the rumor network is unilateral, then for every pair of clerks in the office, a rumor can go from one of them to the other. If the rumor network is strong, then for every pair of clerks a rumor can go from either to the other. Moreover, since every two points of a strong digraph are mutually reachable, any originator of a rumor in such a network (containing more than one clerk) will eventually hear the same rumor from someone else.

COMPONENTS

To know that a particular digraph has a certain kind of connectedness is useful, but it is possible to go more deeply into the matter. Thus, although it is true that digraph D_1 of Figure 3.1 is disconnected, we may also observe that the digraph obtained by deleting point v_4 from it is unilateral. The simple statement, then, that the entire digraph is disconnected leaves out of account important information about its connectedness. A more complete characterization of the connectedness of digraphs can be achieved by concentrating on certain of their subgraphs. By a *subgraph of a digraph D* we mean a digraph whose points and lines are points and lines of D. In the present section, we consider several kinds of subgraphs which are of interest because of their connectedness properties.

First, some preliminary definitions are required. *The subgraph $\langle S \rangle$ generated by a set S of points* is the subgraph whose point set is S, containing all lines of D that join two points of S. A subgraph with a certain special property is said to be *maximal with respect to that property* if no larger subgraph (i.e., with more points or lines) contains it as a subgraph and has the property. For example, consider the digraph of Figure 3.2. One of its subgraphs is generated by the point set $\{v_3, v_4, v_5\}$, and we denote this subgraph by $\langle v_3v_4v_5 \rangle$. Clearly, the subgraph $\langle v_3v_4v_5 \rangle$ is maximal with respect to weak connectedness because any subgraph with more points containing this subgraph must contain v_1 or v_2. But neither v_1 nor v_2 is 1-joined with any of the points v_3, v_4, v_5. Therefore, any subgraph generated by the points v_3, v_4, v_5, together with either v_1 or v_2, is not weak. It can be seen by the same reasoning that the subgraph $\langle v_1v_2 \rangle$ generated by the point set $\{v_1, v_2\}$ is also maximal with respect to weak connectedness.

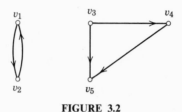

FIGURE 3.2

Three different kinds of components of a digraph may now be given precise definition. A *strong component* of a digraph is a maximal strong subgraph; a *unilateral component* is a maximal unilateral subgraph; and a *weak component* is a maximal weak subgraph.

We have just seen that the digraph of Figure 3.2 contains two subgraphs, $\langle v_1v_2 \rangle$ and $\langle v_3v_4v_5 \rangle$, which are maximal with respect to weak connectedness. Each of these subgraphs is, therefore, a weak component. It can be shown, by a similar process of reasoning, that the two subgraphs, $\langle v_1v_2 \rangle$ and $\langle v_3v_4v_5 \rangle$, are also maximal with respect to unilateral connectedness and are, therefore, unilateral components. To discover the strong components, we note that the subgraph $\langle v_1v_2 \rangle$ is maximal with respect to strong connectedness and is, therefore, a strong component. However, each of the trivial subgraphs, $\langle v_3 \rangle$, $\langle v_4 \rangle$, $\langle v_5 \rangle$, is maximal with respect to strong connectedness, and each of these points constitutes a strong component of the digraph.

The entire digraph of Figure 3.3 is weak; it thus consists of one weak component. It can be seen that it contains two unilateral components: $\langle v_1v_2v_3 \rangle$ and $\langle v_2v_3v_4v_5v_6 \rangle$. And it has three strong components: $\langle v_1 \rangle$, $\langle v_2v_3 \rangle$, and $\langle v_4v_5v_6 \rangle$. In general, every strong component of a digraph is contained in a unilateral component and every unilateral component is in a weak component.

The following theorem, in three parts, gives the distribution of points and lines into the various kinds of components.

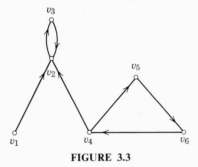

FIGURE 3.3

Theorem 3.2. Let D be a digraph.

(1) Every point and every line of D is contained in exactly one weak component.

(2) Every point and every line lies in at least one unilateral component.

(3) Every point is contained in exactly one strong component; each line is contained in at most one strong component. Furthermore, a line is in a strong component if and only if it is in a cycle.

The proof of each part of this theorem will be given separately.

(1) Any point v is itself a weak subgraph and hence lies in a maximal weak subgraph. We assume that v lies in two weak components W_1 and W_2. Let v_1 be any point of W_1 and v_2 be any of W_2. Then D contains a $v-v_1$ and a $v-v_2$ semipath, and hence a v_1-v_2 semipath. Therefore v_1 and v_2 are in the same weak component, so that W_1 and W_2 must be the same weak component. A similar argument holds for any line x of D.

(2) Any line x of D is itself a unilateral subgraph; hence it lies in a maximal unilateral subgraph. A similar statement holds for any point v of D.

(3) Starting with any point v of D, consider the set S of all points mutually reachable with v, which includes v itself. The subgraph $\langle S \rangle$ generated by this set of points is a strong component since it is both strongly connected and a maximal subgraph with this property. Every point therefore lies in at least one strong component. If v lies in more than one strong component, then any two points in the union of these components are mutually reachable through v. Hence v lies in a unique

strong component, namely $\langle S \rangle$. Similarly, any line in $\langle S \rangle$ lies in exactly one strong component, namely $\langle S \rangle$. A line in a cycle is, of course, in a strong component. On the other hand, if line uv is in a strong component, then there is a path from v to u, which together with uv forms a cycle.

We know by the preceding theorem that every point of any digraph D lies in exactly one strong component. Thus we say that *the strong component $S(v)$ determined by v* is the unique strong component containing v. It contains and is generated by all points of D mutually reachable with v. Clearly, a strong component is determined by any one of its points.

By the same theorem, every point of any digraph lies in exactly one weak component, and we say that *the weak component $W(v)$ determined by v* is the unique weak component containing v. Thus, $W(v)$ contains and is generated by all points of D that are 1-joined with v, and a weak component is determined by any of its points.

The digraph of Figure 3.3 shows that it is not always meaningful to speak of *the* unilateral component containing a certain point. We have already observed that this digraph has two unilateral components $\langle v_1 v_2 v_3 \rangle$ and $\langle v_2 v_3 v_4 v_5 v_6 \rangle$. Both of these contain the points v_2 and v_3.

Example 1 (again). We concluded above, on the basis of assumption E3.1 and Theorem 3.1, that if the sociometric structure of a housing project corresponds to a weak digraph, all residents will tend to associate in the same social activities. With the aid of the concept of weak component, we may now generalize this conclusion and state that the residents will associate in groupings which correspond to the weak components of their sociometric structure. Thus, a structure like that represented by the digraph of Figure 3.2 will produce two social groupings, whereas that of Figure 3.3 will produce only one. Since by Theorem 3.2 every point and every line of a digraph are contained in exactly one weak component, we may conclude that no resident will be in more than one social grouping and that there will be no sociometric choices from a member of one group to a member of another. This conclusion, which may seem to violate common experience, is a necessary consequence of the restricted assumption made in setting up this example.

Example 2 (again). In discussing the spread of a rumor among the clerks of a business office, we noted that for every pair of clerks in a unilateral network it is possible for a rumor to go from at least one of the pair to the other. The same statement can now be made concerning unilateral components of a rumor network. By Theorem 3.2, every clerk will be in at least one unilateral component and perhaps in more than one. Thus, identification of the unilateral components of a network will tell us for which pairs of clerks it is true that a rumor will spread from at least one clerk to the other. Later we shall see how more definite statements can be made about the transmission of rumors in a unilateral network.

When a rumor network is strong, a rumor started by any clerk will spread to every other. Since the same statement holds for strong components of a network, it is evident that a rumor will reach every clerk in a strong component if it is "planted" with at least one clerk of that strong component. Now, Theorem 3.2 guarantees that every clerk is in exactly one strong component, and it follows that the minimum number of clerks with whom a rumor must be planted in order to reach all clerks in the entire office will never exceed the number of strong components of the rumor network. But Theorem 3.2 permits some lines of a digraph not to lie in any strong component. In such a network a rumor may spread from one strong component to another via such lines, thus reducing the minimum number of clerks with whom a rumor must be planted in order to reach everyone. This conclusion is illustrated by the digraph of Figure 3.4 which contains two strong components, $\langle v_1 v_2 v_3 \rangle$ and $\langle v_4 \rangle$. If a rumor were planted with any member of the larger strong component, it would spread to the other strong component via each of the lines not contained in either strong component.

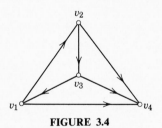

FIGURE 3.4

CONDENSATION

An especially effective way of gaining insight into the structural properties of a digraph D is to construct a simpler one from it by replacing certain subgraphs of D by points, and joining the new points by lines induced from those of D in a specified manner now to be described. First, we define *a partition of a set S* as a decomposition of S into pairwise disjoint nonempty subsets whose union is all of S. Thus each element of S is in exactly one subset. Consider the set V of points of a digraph D, and let V be partitioned into subsets $S_1, S_2, \ldots, S_n$. The *condensation of D with respect to this partition* is the digraph whose points are these n subsets (each point being labeled by the symbol used for its corresponding subset) and whose lines are determined by the following rule: There is a line from point S_i to point S_j in the new digraph if and only if in D there is at least one line from a point of S_i to one of S_j.

There are many different ways in which the points of digraphs may be partitioned. Consider, for example, the digraph of Figure 3.5(a), which contains nine points. Let us assume that this digraph represents the rumor network of the employees of a small business firm. We have, however, certain additional information about these people. For example, it is known that the company has three units: (1) v_1 and v_3 who are supervised by v_2, (2) v_4 and v_5 who are supervised by v_6, and (3) v_7, v_8, and v_9 who have no supervisor. On the basis of this information it is possible to partition the set of employees according to the units of the firm. Let $S_1 = \{v_1, v_2, v_3\}$, $S_2 = \{v_4, v_5, v_6\}$, and $S_3 = \{v_7, v_8, v_9\}$. The condensation of the digraph of Figure 3.5(a) with respect to this partition is shown in Figure 3.5(b). It can be verified that there is at least one line in Figure 3.5(a) from a point of S_3 to a point of S_2, at least one line from a point of S_3 to one of S_1, at least one from a point of S_1 to one of S_2, no lines from a point of S_2 to one of S_1, none from S_2 to S_3, and none from S_1 to S_3. The digraph of Figure 3.5(b) summarizes this information. From inspection we may

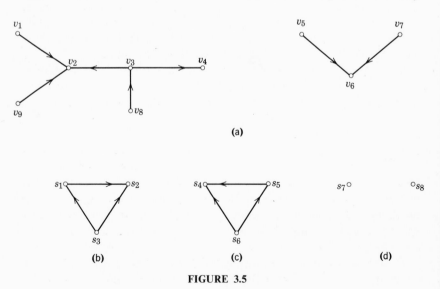

(a)

(b)   (c)   (d)

FIGURE 3.5

conclude that it is possible for a rumor to go from some unsupervised employee to some member of each of the other units, but no rumor will spread from either unit to any of the unsupervised employees. It can be seen, further, that a rumor can go from some member of unit S_1 to some member of S_2 but not in the other direction.

Another way of partitioning the employees of this firm is as follows: $S_4 = \{v_2, v_6\}$, the supervisors; $S_5 = \{v_1, v_3, v_4, v_5\}$, the subordinates; and $S_6 = \{v_7, v_8, v_9\}$, the independents. Figure 3.5(c) shows the condensation of Figure 3.5(a) with respect to this partitioning and summarizes the following information: A rumor can go from at least one independent to at least one supervisor and at least one subordinate, but it cannot go from any supervisor or subordinate to an independent; and a rumor can go from at least one subordinate to at least one supervisor, but not from any supervisor to any subordinate.

We now consider a third way of partitioning the employees of the firm. Assume that v_5, v_6, and v_7 are the only female employees. There are then two sets: $S_7 = \{v_5, v_6, v_7\}$, the females and $S_8 = \{v_1, v_2, v_3, v_4, v_8, v_9\}$, the males. The digraph of Figure 3.5(d) is the condensation of Figure 3.5(a) with respect to this partitioning. Clearly, no rumor will spread from any male to any female, or vice versa.

Two observations should be emphasized concerning these various condensations of the digraph of Figure 3.5(a). First, there is a line from S_i to S_j in a condensed digraph if and only if there is at least one line in the original digraph from a point of S_i to a point of S_j. Second, from each condensed digraph we can draw no conclusions about the spread of a rumor within a set S_i. We must be careful, therefore, not to take the presence of a line from S_i to S_j as evidence that a rumor planted with any member of S_i will spread to every member of S_j.

It is possible to condense a digraph in such a way that the presence of a line from S_i to S_j will guarantee that every pair of points within S_i or within S_j are mutually reachable and that every point of S_j is reachable from every point of S_i. This is accomplished by condensing a digraph with respect to its strong components. We know that such a condensation is always possible because Theorem 3.2 shows that the strong components of any digraph serve to partition its set of points. Since this kind of condensation is so useful and will be employed so frequently, whenever we speak of *the condensation* of a digraph (without mentioning any underlying partition) we shall mean its condensation with respect to strong components, and we shall denote by D^* this condensation of D.

To illustrate condensation with respect to strong components, let us consider the digraph D of Figure 3.6. It can be seen that the points of

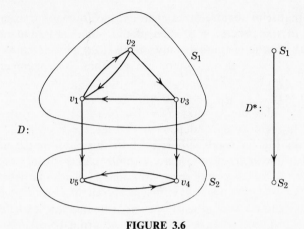

FIGURE 3.6

the strong components of this digraph are $S_1 = \{v_1, v_2, v_3\}$ and $S_2 = \{v_4, v_5\}$. The condensation D^* of D is the digraph of Figure 3.6 containing points S_1 and S_2. This digraph is very simple. And if D were taken to be a rumor network, D^* informs us that if a rumor starts anywhere in S_1 it will reach every member of S_1 and every member of S_2, but if it starts in S_2 it will reach every member of S_2 but none of S_1.

In order to provide a slightly more complicated illustration of condensation, we now consider the digraph D of Figure 3.7. The strong components of D are encircled and labeled S_1, S_2, and S_3. The strong components are shown as points of the digraph D^* in Figure 3.7. There is a line from S_i to S_j in D^* if and only if there is a line in D from a point of S_i to one of S_j. If we consider the digraph D as a rumor network, the condensation D^* of this network makes it easier to see one of its important features: A rumor will reach every member of the group if and only if it originates with person v_6.

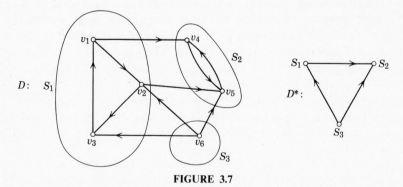

FIGURE 3.7

It will be useful to know that certain features of any digraph are preserved in the process of condensing it with respect to its strong components. Some of these are indicated by the next three theorems.

Theorem 3.3. In a digraph D, let v_1 and v_2 be in strong components S_1 and S_2, respectively. Then there is a path from v_1 to v_2 in D if and only if there is a path from S_1 to S_2 in D^*.

First, we take as given that there is a path L from v_1 to v_2 in D. If L is of length 1, the result follows from the definition of condensation. The proof proceeds by an inductive argument that shows how to find the path in D^* that corresponds to L. As the inductive hypothesis, it is assumed that the theorem holds for any path in D of length $n - 1$. Let L have length n, say $L = v_1 u_1 \ldots u_{n-1} v_2$. By the inductive hypothesis, there is a path L^* in D^* from S_1 to the strong component $S(u_{n-1})$. Now there are two possibilities: (1) if u_{n-1} is in S_2, then L^* is itself a path from S_1 to S_2 in D^*, (2) if u_{n-1} is not in S_2, then there is a line in D^* from $S(u_{n-1})$ to S_2. Hence in either case there must be a path from S_1 to S_2.

The proof of the converse is straightforward and will not be presented here. We can illustrate it, however, using Figure 3.7. Note that there is in D^* a path $S_3 S_1 S_2$. This means that there is a line from a point of S_3 to one of S_1 and a line from a point of S_1 to one of S_2. In the same way, there is a line $v_6 v_3$ and a line $v_1 v_4$. Since v_3 and v_1 are both in S_1, there must be a path from v_3 to v_1—in this case the line $v_3 v_1$. Thus, we have a path $v_6 v_3 v_1 v_4$ in D corresponding to the path $S_3 S_1 S_2$ in D^*.

Corollary 3.3a. In a digraph D, let v_1 and v_2 be in distinct strong components S_1 and S_2. Then there is a strict semipath but no path joining v_1 and v_2 in D if and only if there is a strict semipath but no path joining S_1 and S_2 in D^*.

Figure 3.8 serves to illustrate this corollary. We see that there is in D a path from any point of S_1 to any point of S_2 and a path from any

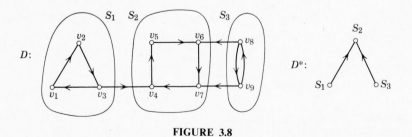

FIGURE 3.8

point of S_3 to any point of S_2. If we choose a pair of these paths having in common only one point of S_2 (for example, $v_1v_2v_3v_4$ and $v_8v_6v_7v_4$), we obtain a strict semipath joining a point of S_1 and a point of S_3 (in this case, $v_1v_2v_3v_4v_7v_6v_8$). And, in keeping with Theorem 3.3, there are paths in D^* from S_1 to S_2 and from S_3 to S_2 which, together, form a strict semipath $S_1S_2S_3$.

Theorem 3.4. In a digraph D, let v_1 and v_2 be in strong components S_1 and S_2. Then S_1 and S_2 are i-joined in D^* if and only if v_1 and v_2 are i-joined in D.

By Theorem 3.3, there is a path from S_1 to S_2 if and only if there is a path from v_1 to v_2. By definition, then, S_1 and S_2 are 2-joined in D^* if and only if v_1 and v_2 are 2-joined in D. We see immediately that this equivalence can be extended to 3-joining, for two points are 3-joined if and only if they are joined by paths in both directions.

To prove this theorem for $i = 1$, we recall that v_1 and v_2 are 1-joined if and only if there is a semipath between them. Since every semipath is a path or a strict semipath, we see from Theorem 3.3 and Corollary 3.3a that S_1 and S_2 are 1-joined in D^* if and only if v_1 and v_2 are 1-joined in D.

The proof for $i = 0$ is trivial, since every pair of points of any digraph is 0-joined, by definition.

Corollary 3.4a. The condensation D^* of any digraph D has the same kind of connectedness as D.

This corollary follows at once from Theorem 3.4 together with Theorem 3.1. It is illustrated for unilateral and weak connectedness in Figures 3.7 and 3.8.

Theorem 3.5. All transmitters, receivers, and isolates of D become transmitters, receivers, and isolates of D^*, respectively.

The proof of this theorem is straightforward. If v is a transmitter of D, then v is the only point in its strong component since there is no other point mutually reachable with v. There must, therefore, be a line in D from v to a point of another strong component, and the point in D^* corresponding to v must have an outdegree of at least one. Since v is a transmitter, there are no lines to it. The corresponding point in D^* will thus have no lines to it. Similar observations hold for receivers and isolates.

The digraphs D and D^* of Figure 3.9 illustrate this theorem. The transmitter v_1 of D is the only point of its strong component S_1, the receiver v_4 is the only point of S_2, and the isolate v_6 of D is the only point of the set S_3. In D^* the point S_1 is a transmitter, S_2 is a receiver,

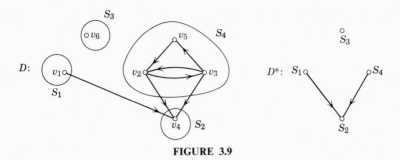

FIGURE 3.9

and S_3 is an isolate. Figure 3.9 also serves to show that the converse of Theorem 3.5 is not true in general, for the remaining strong component S_4 is a transmitter of D^* but does not correspond to a transmitter of D.

The next theorem establishes an important property of all condensed digraphs, namely that they have no cycles. A digraph is said to be *acyclic* if it has no cycles.

Theorem 3.6. The condensation D^* of any digraph D is acyclic.

This theorem may be proved by contradiction. Assume that in D^* there is a cycle. Then, D^* has a line S_1S_2 in this cycle, and by Theorem 3.2, this line lies in a strong component. Thus, points S_1 and S_2 are 3-joined. By Theorem 3.4 there are in D two points v_1 in S_1 and v_2 in S_2 which are also 3-joined. Thus, they lie in the same strong component of D, and $S_1 = S_2$. But then, by construction of D^*, S_1 and S_2 are the same point in D^*, and D^* can have no line S_1S_2. This contradicts the assumption that D^* has a cycle, and the theorem is proved.

In the remaining discussion of condensed digraphs, we need to use the fact that they are acyclic. While we shall give a more thorough study of acyclic digraphs in Chapter 10, we introduce here some of the properties displayed by acyclic digraphs in general. The next theorem presents several equivalent conditions for a digraph to be acyclic.

Theorem 3.7. The following properties of a digraph D are equivalent.
(1) D is acyclic, that is, has no cycles.
(2) Every strong component of D consists of one point.
(3) D^* is isomorphic to D.
(4) D and D^* have the same number of points.
(5) Every sequence of D is a path.

To prove this theorem, we observe first that conditions (2), (3), and (4) are equivalent because of the definition of D^*, which asserts that two points in D are condensed into the same point of D^* if and only if they are in the same strong component in D. Conditions (1) and (5) are equivalent since a sequence is a path if and only if it contains no cycles. We shall prove that conditions (1) and (2) are equivalent, and thereby establish the theorem.

By definition of strong component, two distinct points u and v are in the same strong component of D if and only if D contains a path from u to v and one from v to u. Together two such paths form a closed sequence, and by Theorem 2.7, a closed sequence contains a cycle. Therefore, D has no cycles if and only if every strong component consists of one point.

Corollary 3.7a. The only strong acyclic digraph is the one consisting of exactly one point.

The corollary follows immediately from condition (2), since a strong digraph consists of exactly one strong component.

Figure 3.10 shows three examples of acyclic digraphs. The first is unilateral, whereas the others are weak but not unilateral. From

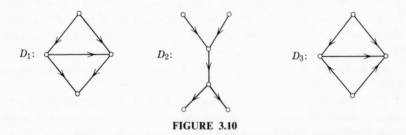

FIGURE 3.10

Theorem 3.7 we know that for each of these digraphs, D^* is isomorphic to D. (This may be verified by condensing each of these digraphs.) Furthermore, we see that every sequence in these digraphs is a path. Finally, we note that in each digraph there is at least one point of indegree zero and at least one of outdegree zero. This is a general property of acyclic digraphs.

Theorem 3.8. An acyclic digraph D has at least one point of outdegree zero and at least one of indegree zero.

The proof proceeds by contradiction. Assume that D is acyclic and has no points of outdegree zero. By starting with any point v_1, we can construct an arbitrarily long sequence $v_1 v_2 v_3 \ldots$. Since the number of points of D is finite, in a sufficiently long sequence some point v_i must appear twice. Thus, it is contained in a closed sequence, and by

Theorem 2.7 v_i is also in a cycle. But this contradicts the assumption that D is acyclic. Hence, D must have at least one point of outdegree zero. The remainder follows by directional duality.

This theorem has three immediate corollaries, the last of which will be used in later chapters.

Corollary 3.8a. A nontrivial unilateral acyclic digraph has a unique receiver and a unique transmitter.

Corollary 3.8b. If a digraph is unilateral but not strong, its condensation D^* has a unique receiver and a unique transmitter.

Corollary 3.8c. If every point of a digraph has positive outdegree, it contains a cycle.

CONNECTEDNESS CRITERIA

In this section we formulate criteria for each of the kinds of connectedness. Three theorems give several criteria which are met by any strong, unilateral, or weak digraph respectively. Since each of these criteria gives a necessary and sufficient condition for a digraph to be of a specified kind of connectedness, any one of them could be taken as a definition. The definitions given earlier are stated as the first criterion in each theorem.

Theorem 3.9. (Criteria for strong digraphs.) The following statements are equivalent for any digraph D.

(1) D is strong, that is, any two points are mutually reachable.

(2) D has a complete closed sequence.

(3) D^* consists of exactly one point.

That the three statements are equivalent may be shown by proving first the equivalence of (1) and (3) and then the equivalence of (1) and (2).

Equivalence of (1) and (3). Clearly, D is strong if and only if D^* is a single point, since a strong digraph consists of a single strong component.

(1) Implies (2). Let D be a strong digraph whose points are $v_1, v_2, v_3, \ldots, v_p$. By definition, D contains paths from v_1 to v_2, from v_2 to $v_3, \ldots$, from v_{p-1} to v_p, and from v_p to v_1. The successive points and lines of these paths form a closed sequence containing all points of D.

(2) Implies (1). We take as given that D has a complete closed sequence L. It is sufficient to show that *any* point u can reach *any other* point v. Since L is complete, it contains both u and v. Since L is closed, it contains an open sequence from u to v. By Corollary 2.6a, v is reachable from u.

Theorem 3.10. (Criteria for unilateral digraphs.) For any nontrivial digraph D the following statements are equivalent.

(1) D is unilateral, that is, for any two points, at least one is reachable from the other.

(2) D has a complete open sequence.

(3) D^* has a unique complete path.

We prove the equivalence of these conditions in a cyclic manner.

(*1*) *Implies* (*2*). We first establish an auxiliary result: In any subset of the points of a unilateral digraph D, there is some point which can reach the others. If this were not true, then there must be a smallest set U of which no point can reach the rest. And if U has n points, say v_1, $v_2, \ldots, v_n$, then $U - \{v_n\}$ has a point v_i which can reach the others. Now v_i cannot reach v_n since then v_i could reach every point of U. Similarly v_n cannot reach v_i. But this implies neither v_i nor v_n can reach the other, contradicting the fact that D is unilateral, and hence proving the result.

We now use repeated applications of this result. Let D be unilateral and let u_1 denote a point which can reach the rest. Among the remaining points, let u_2 be one which can reach the others, and so on. In this way, one gets an ordering of the points of D as $u_1, u_2, \ldots, u_p$ so that each u_i can reach u_{i+1} ($i = 1, 2, \ldots, p - 1$). Thus there is a path from u_i to u_{i+1}. These paths in succession determine a complete sequence of D.

(*2*) *Implies* (*3*). Let $w_1 w_2 \ldots w_n$ be a complete open sequence of D. Since for each $i = 1, 2, \ldots, n - 1$, w_i can reach w_{i+1}, there is a path from $S(w_i)$ to $S(w_{i+1})$ by Theorem 3.3. These paths determine a complete sequence in D^*. Since D^* is acyclic, by Theorem 3.7, this sequence is a path. Now assume D^* has two different complete paths L_1 and L_2. Then there must be two distinct points S_i and S_j of D^* such that S_i precedes S_j in L_1 but S_j precedes S_i in L_2. But then S_i and S_j are mutually reachable, and hence not distinct components, which is a contradiction. Therefore D^* has a unique complete path.

(*3*) *Implies* (*1*). Let L be the complete path of D^*. Then for any two points of D^*, there is a path from the one occurring first in L to the other. Hence D^* is unilateral; and by Corollary 3.4a, D is unilateral.

This theorem is illustrated in Figure 3.11 in which D is unilateral, $v_1 v_2 v_3 v_4 v_5 v_6 v_7$ is a complete open sequence of D and $S_1 S_2 S_3 S_4$ is the unique complete path in D^*.

With the aid of Theorem 3.10 we are now able to make more definite statements about the transmission of rumors in a unilateral network. Every point of a sequence is reachable from the initial point of the sequence. Now Theorem 3.10 informs us that every unilateral digraph contains a complete open sequence. It follows, therefore, that every unilateral network contains at least one person from whom a rumor will reach everyone. The third criterion of Theorem 3.10 helps us locate such people, for they must lie in the strong component corresponding to the initial point of the unique complete path of D^*. Thus, if the digraph D of Figure 3.11 is taken as a rumor network, we can readily determine that a rumor starting with either v_1 or v_2 will reach every person in the network.

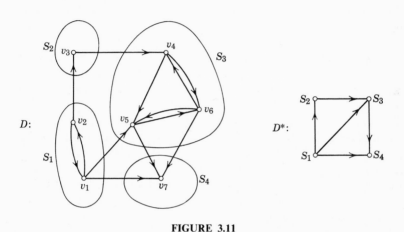

FIGURE 3.11

These observations are also true, of course, for each unilateral component of any network. Since by Theorem 3.2 every point of a digraph lies in at least one unilateral component, we may conclude that the minimum number of people with whom a rumor must be planted so that it reaches everyone in the network does not exceed the number of unilateral components of the network. Since a point may lie in more than one unilateral component and be the initial point of a complete open sequence in these components, it is possible in some networks for a rumor to reach everyone when planted with fewer people than the number of unilateral components.

We turn now to the criteria for a digraph to be weak. In order to state the theorem, we require one more definition. The *symmetrized digraph of D*, written D^s, is the symmetric digraph obtained from D by adding a directed line uv whenever this line does not already occur in D but the line vu does appear in D. Figure 3.12 shows a digraph D and its symmetrized digraph D^s.

Theorem 3.11. (Criteria for weak digraphs.) For any digraph D the following statements are equivalent.

(1) D is weak, that is, there is a semipath joining any two points.

(2) D has a complete semisequence.

(3) For any partition of the points of D into two subsets, there is at least one line of D joining a point of one subset with a point of the other.

(4) D^s is strong.

We prove this theorem by showing that each of (2), (3), and (4) is in turn equivalent with (1).

(*1*) *Implies* (*2*). By definition, the point v_1 is joined by a semipath to each of the other points $v_2, v_3, \ldots, v_p$. Take in succession a v_1–v_2 semipath followed by a v_2–v_1 semipath, a v_1–v_3 semipath followed by a v_3–v_1 semipath, and so on. The result is clearly a complete semisequence.

(*2*) *Implies* (*1*). Proof of this implication is immediate, for if two points are contained in a semisequence, there is a semipath joining them.

(*1*) *Implies* (*3*). Assume that the weak digraph D has a partition of its points into two subsets U and W such that no line joins two points of distinct subsets. Then for any two points u in U and w in W, there is no semipath in D joining them, contradicting the hypothesis.

(*3*) *Implies* (*1*). Suppose D is not weak. Then D has more than one weak component. Let U be the set of points in one weak component and let W be the remaining points. Then U and W partition the points of V and there is no line joining points of U and W, contradicting (3). Therefore D must be weak.

Equivalence of (*1*) *and* (*4*). By definition of a symmetrized digraph, there are two lines, one in each direction, joining two points of D^s if and only if there is a line joining them in D. From this it follows that two points in D^s are mutually reachable if and only if they are joined by a semipath in D. Hence D^s is strong if and only if D is weak.

This theorem is illustrated by the weak digraph of Figure 3.12. Here it can be seen that $v_1v_2v_3v_5v_6v_5v_4$ is a complete semisequence. By application of the procedure presented in the proof it can be verified that for any partition of the points of this digraph into two subsets there is at least one line joining a point of one subset with a point of the other. Finally, consider the symmetrized digraph D^s of D. It can be seen readily that D^s meets the criteria of a strong digraph presented in Theorem 3.9. Thus, for example, the points v_1, v_2, v_3, v_5, v_6, v_5, v_4, v_2, v_1, which are contained in a complete closed semisequence of D, correspond to similarly labeled points of D^s, which are contained in a complete closed sequence of D^s.

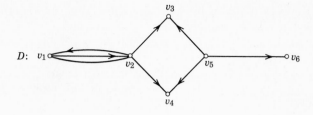

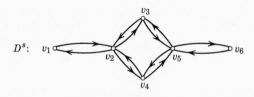

FIGURE 3.12

We note in passing that every weak symmetric digraph is strong.

CATEGORIES OF CONNECTEDNESS

The classification of digraphs according to kinds of connectedness results, as we have seen, in overlapping classes. For many purposes, however, it is desirable to be able to place a digraph in exactly one category of connectedness. To accomplish this objective, we adopt the following definitions and notation.

Let C_0 be the set of all disconnected digraphs.

A digraph is *strictly weak* if it is weak but not unilateral. The set of all strictly weak digraphs is denoted C_1.

A digraph is *strictly unilateral* if it is unilateral but not strong; the set of all such digraphs is denoted C_2.

Finally, the set of all strong digraphs is denoted C_3.

Hence, the notation D is in C_i means that D is a digraph whose disjoint connectedness category is of the ith kind, for $i = 0, 1, 2, 3$. In the following discussion, whenever we refer to the *category of a digraph* we mean its strict connectedness category. We say that a digraph in C_i is *stronger* than one in C_j whenever $i > j$ and that it is *weaker* if $i < j$. Figure 3.13 shows four digraphs, one of each category. In this figure, digraph D_i is in category C_i. Thus, D_3 is stronger than D_2, and D_1 is weaker than D_2.

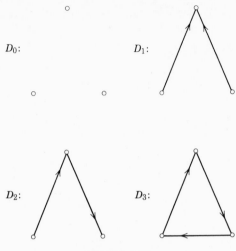

D_0: D_1:

D_2: D_3:

FIGURE 3.13

The definition of kinds of joining given in Chapter 2 resulted in overlapping classes of pairs of points. To obtain nonoverlapping categories for classifying the connectedness of pairs of points, we define the *i-connectedness of two points*. Points v_1 and v_2 are *0-connected* if they are not joined by a semipath. They are *1-connected* if they are joined by a semipath but not by a path. They are *2-connected* if they are joined by a path in one direction but not in the other, and they are *3-connected* if they are 3-joined. Thus, v_1 and v_2 are *i*-connected if they are *i*-joined but not $(i + 1)$-joined. Symbolically, we can state that u and v are *i*-connected by writing $c(u, v) = i$.

In Figure 3.14, we have the following categories of connectedness of pairs of points: $c(v_3, v_5) = 0$, $c(v_1, v_3) = 1$, $c(v_2, v_4) = 2$, and $c(v_3, v_4) = 3$.

As an immediate consequence of these formal definitions we have the following result.

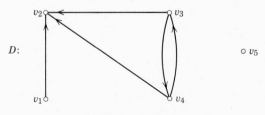

D:

FIGURE 3.14

Theorem 3.12. A digraph is in C_i if and only if every two points are i-joined and at least one pair of points is i-connected.

The criteria for a digraph to be in any category of connectedness can be obtained from Theorems 3.9, 3.10, and 3.11. Thus, for example, we can make the following statements: A digraph D is in C_1 if and only if it has a complete semisequence but no complete sequence; D is in C_2 if and only if it has a complete open sequence but no complete closed sequence; and D is in C_3 if and only if it has a complete closed sequence. We also see that if D is in C_2 then D^* has a unique complete path consisting of at least two points, and conversely. If we think of a single copy of a memorandum being routed through an organization, we may say: If the digraph of the route is in C_1, it is impossible for the memorandum to reach everyone in the organization no matter where it starts; if the digraph is in C_2, the memorandum can be initiated at a place from which it will reach everyone, but after reaching everyone it cannot return to the originator; if the digraph is in C_3, it can originate with anyone, reach everyone, and then return to the originator, regardless of where it starts.

NUMBER OF LINES IN A DIGRAPH OF EACH CATEGORY

One might be inclined to guess that if he had a collection of digraphs with a fixed number of points which fall into different categories of connectedness, the stronger ones would tend to have more lines than the weaker ones. If we know that a digraph D is in C_i, can we in fact state any upper or lower limits upon the number of lines that D may have? Theorems 3.13–3.17 present formulas which give bounds on the number of lines in a digraph in each category. For any given digraph D, let p be the number of points and q be the number of lines in it. It is convenient to have the following preliminary result.

Theorem 3.13. The number of lines in a complete symmetric digraph with p points is $p(p - 1)$.

Since each of the p points is the first point of a directed line to each of the other $p - 1$ points, the number of lines in a complete symmetric digraph is $p(p - 1)$.

Theorem 3.14. If D is in C_0, then $0 \leq q \leq (p - 1)(p - 2)$.

The smallest possible number of lines in a disconnected digraph is obviously 0, since this is the number of lines in any totally disconnected digraph. It is clear that the greatest number of lines among all disconnected digraphs with p points will occur in a digraph in which each weak component is complete symmetric. A simple argument shows that this maximum number of lines will occur in a digraph having exactly two weak components, one of which consists of a single isolate and the other consists of a complete symmetric digraph having $p - 1$ points. Now by Theorem 3.13, the number of lines in this weak component, and hence in the digraph, is $(p - 1)(p - 2)$.

Figure 3.15 shows two disconnected digraphs with four points, one of which has the smallest possible number of lines, $q = 0$, and the other has the greatest, $q = 6$.

$D_1:$ $D_2:$

FIGURE 3.15

The next theorem gives bounds on the number of lines in a digraph in C_1. Strangely enough, the maximum here is the same as for digraphs in category C_0.

Theorem 3.15. If D is in C_1, then $p - 1 \leq q \leq (p - 1)(p - 2)$ and $p \geq 3$.

Obviously, there are no digraphs in C_1 with $p < 3$. It is evident that the smallest possible number of lines in a strictly weak digraph occurs in one which consists of a strict semipath. The number of lines in such a digraph is $p - 1$. The greatest possible number of lines can be determined by the following reasoning. In a strictly weak digraph, there must be at least two points u and v neither of which is reachable from the other. We set these two points aside for the moment and construct a complete symmetric digraph with the remaining $p - 2$ points, which, by Theorem 3.13, has $(p - 2)(p - 3)$ lines. In order to join u and v to the remaining points with as many lines as possible and still have a strictly weak digraph, it is necessary to have both u and v as transmitters or both as receivers. In either case, there will be no line joining u and v. Hence, the total number of lines in the digraph just constructed is given by $(p - 2) + (p - 2) + (p - 2)(p - 3) = (p - 1)(p - 2)$. The first term of the left side of this equation is the number of lines from (or to) u to (or from) the $p - 2$ points of the complete symmetric subgraph we have constructed; the second term is the corresponding number for v.

The remaining term on the left is the number of lines in this complete symmetric subgraph. The right-hand member is then obtained at once by algebraic manipulation.

In Figure 3.16 there are two strictly weak digraphs of four points which illustrate this theorem. The digraph D_1 contains the smallest possible number of lines, $q = 3$, and D_2 contains the greatest possible number, $q = 6$.

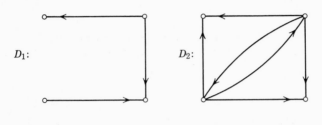

FIGURE 3.16

Theorem 3.16. If D is in C_2, then $p - 1 \leq q \leq (p - 1)^2$.

The smallest number of lines in any strictly unilateral digraph obviously occurs in the digraph which consists of a single path. Since the length of this path is $p - 1$, the smallest number of lines possible in any strictly unilateral digraph is $p - 1$. The following reasoning indicates the greatest possible number of lines. In order for a digraph D to be strictly unilateral, there must exist in its condensation D^* exactly one transmitter and exactly one receiver (by Corollary 3.8b). It can be shown (just as in the proof of Theorem 3.14) that D will have the greatest number of lines in its strong components when D^* has exactly two points, one of which is condensed from a single point of D and the other from a complete symmetric subgraph of D having $p - 1$ points. The single point will be either a transmitter or a receiver; it does not matter which. We find, then, that the number of lines in this digraph is $(p - 1) + (p - 1)(p - 2) = (p - 1)^2$. The first term of the left-hand member is the number of lines from the transmitter (or to the receiver) of D, while the second term is the number of lines in the complete symmetric subgraph of $p - 1$ points (by Theorem 3.13). The right side is obtained by algebraic manipulation.

The two digraphs shown in Figure 3.17 contain the smallest number, $q = 3$, and the greatest number, $q = 9$, of lines possible in a strictly unilateral digraph with four points.

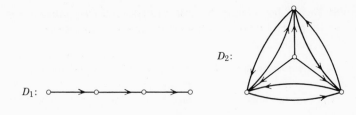

D_2:

D_1:

FIGURE 3.17

A comparison of Theorems 3.15 and 3.16 shows that the minimum number of lines in a digraph of p points is the same whether it is in C_1 or C_2.

Theorem 3.17. If $p > 1$ and D is in C_3, then $p \le q \le p(p-1)$.

The smallest number of lines in any strong digraph can be ascertained by using the result of Theorem 3.9 that a strong digraph must contain a complete closed sequence. It can be seen that the smallest possible number of lines in any complete closed sequence occurs in a digraph consisting of a single cycle of length p. Hence, the smallest number of lines among all nontrivial strong digraphs is p. The greatest possible number of lines among all strong digraphs with p points is given by the number of lines in the complete symmetric digraph of p points, which by Theorem 3.13 is $p(p-1)$.

This theorem is illustrated by the two digraphs of Figure 3.18 which are strong and contain four points. The digraph D_1 contains the smallest possible number of lines, $q = 4$, and D_2 contains the greatest possible number, $q = 12$.

The results of this section are summarized in Table 3.1. Numerical examples are also provided for digraphs containing 3, 5, and 7 points.

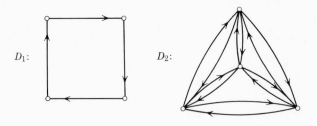

D_1: D_2:

FIGURE 3.18

Table 3.1. The Smallest and the Greatest Possible Number of Lines in a Digraph of *p* Points for Each Category of Connectedness

Category	Minimum Number of Lines	Maximum Number of Lines	Illustrative Ranges		
			$p = 3$	$p = 5$	$p = 7$
0	0	$(p-1)(p-2)$	0–2	0–12	0–30
1	$p-1$	$(p-1)(p-2)$	2–2	4–12	6–30
2	$p-1$	$(p-1)^2$	2–4	4–16	6–36
3	p	$p(p-1)$	3–6	5–20	7–42

It is evident from Table 3.1 that only under limited conditions can we infer the category of a digraph from knowing how many points and lines it has. We do know that if $q < p - 1$, D is in C_0 and that if $q > (p - 1)^2$, D is in C_3. This means, for example, that for a digraph with 7 points the following conclusions can be drawn: If D has less than 6 lines, D is in C_0, and if D has more than 36 lines, D is in C_3. However, for all other values of q we cannot infer a unique category of D. In fact, there is a broad range, $p \leq q \leq (p - 1)(p - 2)$, where D may be in any category. Consider, for example, a digraph with 7 points. If all we know is that its number of lines falls in the range from 7 through 30, we can draw no conclusion about its category. These facts have a clear implication: Any index of the density of a digraph (i.e., one based on the number of its lines) will be a poor indicator of its connectedness properties.

REALIZATIONS OF CONNECTEDNESS

In order to interpret the abstract ideas presented in this chapter, we have introduced two examples at appropriate places. We now bring together some of the empirical conclusions drawn from these examples and state them more formally. It may have been noticed that Example 1, dealing with sociometric choices and the tendency to associate socially, was employed when discussing weak connectedness, whereas Example 2, dealing with the spread of rumors, was introduced to illustrate unilateral or strong connectedness. The reason for this is that the underlying relation of Example 1 is one of "joining" while that of Example 2 is "reachability." Let us examine each of these examples a bit more closely.

The empirical axiom for Example 1 is E3.1, which asserts that residents *u* and *v* will tend to associate socially if there is a line *uv* or a line *vu* in the digraph of their sociometric choices. Since the tendency to associate is assumed to depend upon the presence of a line, regardless of its direction, we are concerned with joining rather than reaching within the digraph. The equivalence classes generated by the relation of joining on the digraph correspond to sets of people who will tend to associate socially in the housing project. And since these equivalence classes generate the weak components of the digraph, we conclude that the residents will tend to associate in groups which correspond to the weak components of the digraph of their sociometric choices.

The following conclusions, then, illustrate empirical propositions that can be derived from empirical assumption E3.1 and the property of weak connectedness.

C3.1. The residents of a housing project will tend to associate in groupings which correspond to the weak components of the digraph of their sociometric choices.

C3.2. The number of social groupings will equal the number of weak components of the digraph of their sociometric choices.

C3.3. No resident will be in more than one grouping brought about by the sociometric structure of the housing project.

C3.4. If there are p residents in a housing project and the number of choices made by them is less than $p - 1$, then there will tend to be more than one social grouping.

It is possible, of course, to construct other joining realizations by coordinating points to other empirical entities, by coordinating joining to other kinds of empirical association, or by employing a different relation on a set of points.

For Example 2, the critical empirical assumption is E2.2. This assumption states that if a person possesses message M, he will transmit it to all people adjacent from him in the digraph of the communication network. Since this assumption applies to all people in the network, we may conclude that if person v possesses M, it will eventually be possessed by everyone in the network reachable from v. Thus, the critical concept for this realization is sequence (rather than semisequence, as in Example 1) and its related concepts of 2-joining and 3-joining. For purposes of studying the transmission of messages in a communication network, we are therefore concerned with unilateral or strong digraphs since these are defined in terms of 2-joining or 3-joining of pairs of points.

We now list some empirical conclusions which may be drawn concerning transmission of a message in communication networks that operate in accordance with assumptions E2.1 and E2.2. In order to simplify the statement of conclusions about communication we introduce a new concept. A *commune*[1] is a part of a communication network corresponding to a strong component of the digraph of the network. Thus, a commune contains a maximal collection of people who are mutually reachable in a communication network, that is, who can engage one another in two-way communication. Each commune is represented by a point of D^*, where D is the digraph of the network. If this point is a transmitter, we speak of a *sending commune*; if it is a receiver, we refer to a *receiving commune*; and if it is an isolate, we have an *isolated commune*.

C3.5. Every communication network contains an isolated commune or both a sending commune and a receiving commune.

C3.6. Consider a network with p persons in which every pair of people can engage in one-way communication but there is at least one pair who cannot engage in two-way communication. Then, (a) the network contains exactly one sending commune and exactly one receiving commune; (b) message M can reach everyone from a single person if and only if it originates with a person in the unique sending commune; and (c) the network has at least $p - 1$ and at most $(p - 1)^2$ links.

C3.7. Consider a network with p persons in which every pair of people can engage in two-way communication. Then, (a) the network consists of an isolated commune, (b) if M originates with any person, it will reach everyone and will return to its originator; and (c) the network has at least p and at most $p(p - 1)$ links.

C3.8. Consider a network with p persons. (a) If the network has more than $(p - 1)(p - 2)$ links, it is possible for M to reach everyone from a single person. (b) If it has more than $(p - 1)^2$ links, wherever M originates it will reach everyone and will return to its originator.

C3.9. In any network, the minimum number of people with whom M must originate so as to reach everyone is at most the number of unilateral components of its digraph.

C3.10. Consider a network in which every person who possesses M will transmit it to at least one other person. Then there is a subgroup of at least two people such that if M originates with one of them it will eventually return to its originator.

Other reachability realizations can, of course, be constructed by different interpretations of points and lines and by different coordinations of reachability. Thus, for example, one could use the results of this chapter in analyzing the transmission of neural impulses in a nervous

---

[1] To whom it may concern: No political connotations are intended.

system, the ramifications in a cognitive structure of changing one of its elements, the flow of personnel through the positions of an organization, or the flow of traffic through the corridors of a building.

COMPLEMENTARY DIGRAPHS

In Chapter 2 we considered the operation of taking the converse of a digraph. We now discuss briefly another operation that may be performed on a digraph. Given a digraph D, its *complement* $\bar{D}$ is the digraph with the same set of points such that for any two points u and v, the line uv is in $\bar{D}$ if and only if it is not in D. Figure 3.19 shows a digraph D and its complement $\bar{D}$. From the definition of the complement of a digraph, it is clear that the union of a digraph with p points and its complement is the complete symmetric digraph K_p, also shown in Figure 3.19.

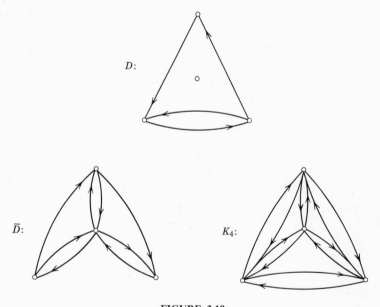

FIGURE 3.19

As shown in Chapter 2, taking the converse of a digraph is a dual operation. It is readily apparent that taking the complement is also a dual operation; and this kind of duality[2] is known as *existential duality*, since it is concerned with the existence of lines in a digraph.

[2] For a further discussion of existential duality, see Harary (1957).

Theorem 3.18. The complement of the complement of a digraph D is D itself; symbolically, $\bar{\bar{D}} = D$.

The digraph D of Figure 3.19 is disconnected whereas its complement $\bar{D}$ is strong. We may ask in general: Given a digraph in category C_i, what can be said about the category of its complement?

Theorem 3.19. The relation between the category of a digraph D and of its complement $\bar{D}$ is as follows:
(1) If D is in C_0, $\bar{D}$ is in C_3.
(2) If D is in C_1 or C_2, $\bar{D}$ is not in C_0 but may be in C_1, C_2 or C_3.
(3) If D is in C_3, $\bar{D}$ may be in any category.

To prove the first statement, we take as given that D is disconnected. Now, if u and v are in distinct weak components of D, then uv and vu are both in $\bar{D}$. Hence, they are mutually reachable in $\bar{D}$. If on the other hand u and v are in the same weak component of D, there must be a point w in a different weak component. Then the lines uw, wu, vw, and wv are in $\bar{D}$. Therefore, in $\bar{D}$ there are paths from u to v and from v to u, and u and v are mutually reachable. We see, then, that every two points of $\bar{D}$ are mutually reachable, proving the first statement.

The contrapositive of the first statement asserts that if a digraph is not in C_3 then its complement is not in C_0. In particular, then, if D is in C_1 or C_2, $\bar{D}$ is not in C_0. That all other combinations of connectedness between D and $\bar{D}$ are possible is shown by the digraphs in Figure 3.20, completing the proof of the theorem.

The digraphs in Figure 3.20 are displayed in a matrix, so that the digraph in the ith row and jth column is in category i; the digraph in the jth row and the ith column is its complement. Thus the digraphs on the main diagonal are self-complementary.

From the proof of the first statement of Theorem 3.19 it is evident that if D is disconnected, every path in $\bar{D}$ is of length 1 or 2. Moreover, if D is not totally disconnected, there are two points joined only by paths of length 2. These observations are stated in the following corollary.

Corollary 3.19a. If D is in C_0, the largest distance in $\bar{D}$ from any point to any other is at most 2. It is exactly 2, unless D is totally disconnected.

As a simple illustration of this theorem and its corollary, consider a committee of five members who want by unanimous vote to select one of two alternative policies. It is known that members v_1 and v_2 favor policy A whereas v_3, v_4, and v_5 favor policy B. Digraph D of Figure 3.21

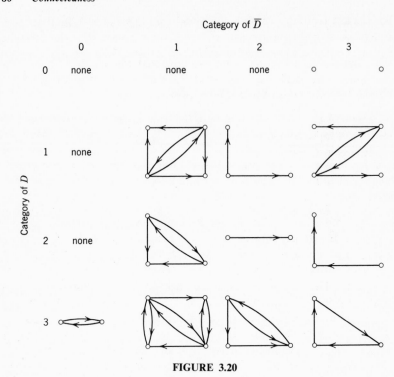

FIGURE 3.20

is constructed so that there is a line from v_i to v_j if and only if v_i favors the same policy as v_j. Let us assume that v_i will attempt to influence v_j if and only if v_i and v_j favor different alternatives. The digraph of attempted influence, then, is $\bar{D}$, the complement of D. From Theorem 3.19 we know that the digraph of attempted influence is strong. Moreover, since in this example we have assumed that at least two people

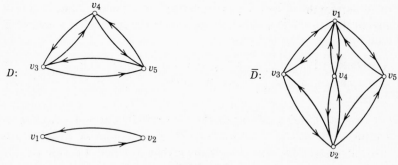

FIGURE 3.21

favor the same policy, we may conclude from Corollary 3.19a that there are at least two people (in this case v_1 and v_2) such that the distance from one to the other in the digraph of attempted influence is 2.

CONNECTEDNESS OF RELATIONS

In Chapter 2 we saw that every digraph has relations of joining and reaching induced on its set of points. In this chapter we have seen how these induced relations give rise to various structural properties of digraphs, such as kinds of connectedness, components, and condensation. Thus, for example, the relation of joining, which is reflexive, symmetric, and transitive, is an equivalence relation and its equivalence classes generate the weak components of a digraph. The relation of reaching, which is only reflexive and transitive, is a quasi-order. But mutual reaching is reflexive, symmetric, and transitive, and hence an equivalence relation whose equivalence classes generate the strong components of a digraph.

A digraph is an irreflexive relation. We asserted in Chapter 1, however, that a digraph can be used to represent a reflexive relation simply by ignoring loops and that all important structural properties are the same whether loops are included or not. We now justify this assertion for the structural properties considered in the present chapter by showing that the definitions of joining and reaching in digraphs can be extended to any relation.

If u and v are points of a relation R, then v *is reachable from* u if there is a sequence of points $u, v_1, v_2, \ldots, v$ such that uRv, v_1Rv_2, and so forth. In addition, we say that any point is reachable from itself. This definition is analogous to that for digraphs. And indeed, if we form a digraph from R on the same set of points by deleting all loops from R, we see that v is reachable from u in R if and only if it is reachable from u in D. Similarly, two points of R are mutually reachable if and only if they are mutually reachable in D. Formulating the definition of joining in R analogously to that in a digraph, we find that u and v are joined in R if and only if they are joined in D.

Thus, for any relation R, the induced relations of joining, reaching, and mutual reaching are respectively an equivalence relation, a quasi-order, and an equivalence relation, just as in the case of a digraph. Accordingly, we can speak of a strong, unilateral, weak, or disconnected relation, we can find its strong and weak components, and we can form its condensation. The condensation R^* of a relation R is defined as an irreflexive relation induced on the strong components of R by the following rule: If S_1 and S_2 are distinct strong components of R, then

$S_1R^*S_2$ if and only if for some point v_1 in S_1 and for some v_2 in S_2, v_1Rv_2. The proof that the resulting relation R^* is acyclic is identical to that given for digraphs. And if again we let D be the digraph formed from R by deleting all loops, we see that $D^* = R^*$.

SUMMARY

In this chapter, we have investigated the connectedness of digraphs. We first discussed four kinds of connectedness (three of which are overlapping) that digraphs may possess, and we related these to the kinds of joining of pairs of points. Next, we explored how a subgraph may be generated by a subset of the set of points of the digraph and identified three kinds of components of digraphs. One of these, a strong component, was used to define the condensation D^* of a digraph D. It was demonstrated that certain features of D (notably its kind of connectedness) are preserved in the process of forming D^*.

With this background, we were able to formulate several equivalent criteria for each kind of connectedness. The problem of obtaining nonoverlapping categories of connectedness was then raised. Four discrete categories of connectedness of digraphs, and of pairs of points, were defined, and theorems were provided which state upper and lower limits on the number of lines there can be in a digraph with p points in each category of connectedness. These theorems demonstrate that only under limited conditions is it possible to infer the category of a digraph from knowing how many points and lines it has.

We next illustrated some of the ways in which the findings of the chapter may be given empirical meaning. Then, we considered briefly the concept of the complement $\bar{D}$ of a given digraph D and the relation between the connectedness of D and $\bar{D}$. In the final section, we showed that the concepts of connectedness may be extended from a digraph to any relation.

EXERCISES

1. (a) What is the category of the digraph of Figure 3.14? (b) List its strong, unilateral, and weak components. (c) If this were a rumor network, who would be likely to hear the most rumors? Why? (d) If v_4 started a rumor, who would hear it?

2. Disprove: If a digraph has a unique point of indegree 0, it is weak.

3. Why is it not true that all transmitters, receivers, and isolates of D^* come from transmitters, receivers, and isolates of D, respectively?

4. Prove or disprove: If a digraph D is strictly unilateral, its condensation D^* has a unique receiver and a unique transmitter.

5. Show that in a nontrivial strong digraph, every point is on a cycle.
6. (a) Construct a strong digraph which does not contain a complete cycle. (b) If this digraph is interpreted as a communication network, what empirical conclusions can be drawn concerning the transmission of message M?
7. Show that any strictly unilateral digraph D can be made strong by adding exactly one line to D.
8. Assume that D is in C_3. (a) Is D unilateral? (b) Is D in C_2? (c) Is D weak? (d) Is D disconnected?
9. Let D be the digraph of the Figure 3.22. (a) Classify the points of D. (b) Draw D^*. (c) Classify the points of D^*. (d) Determine the connectedness

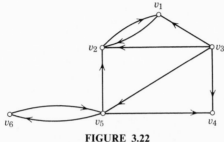

FIGURE 3.22

category of each pair of points of D. (e) Which lines of D, if any, do not lie in any strong component? (f) At how many points of D (considered as a communication network) need a message originate to reach all points?
10. (a) If it is known that the digraph D has some lines which are not contained in any strong component of D, what else can be inferred about D? (b) If such a digraph has p points, can it have $p(p - 1)$ lines? (c) If D has 7 points and 38 lines, does D have any lines not contained in a cycle? How many lines does D^* have?
11. Assume that u and v will transmit to each other any rumors heard if and only if u chooses v sociometrically or v chooses u. Let D represent the sociometric structure of a group of people. Indicate for each of the following conditions whether or not a rumor can reach every member of the group from a single person. (a) D has 3 weak components. (b) D is weak. (c) D has 10 points and 8 lines. (d) D has 10 points and 73 lines.
12. Assume that D represents a communication network. Is it possible that D is in C_1 and a message M can reach everyone from a single person in D?
13. A man has 14 cousins, each living in a different town. He has a photograph of his children which he wants all of his cousins to see, and he wants to get the photograph back. The postage for each mailing is 12 cents. What is the minimum total postage required?
14. Prove: If a digraph has a complete semisequence, it has a complete closed semisequence.

15. Show that every point of D constitutes a strong component if and only if D has no cycles.

16. Assign each 3-point digraph (see Figure 1.14) to its category of connectedness. (a) How many digraphs are there in each category? (b) Verify the bounds on the number of lines for each category as stated in Theorems 3.14–3.17.

17. Prove: Let u, v, w be points of a digraph. If u and v lie on a cycle, then $c(u, w) = c(v, w)$.

18. Prove: If D is a complete asymmetric digraph, then $D' = \overline{D}$. Are there any other digraphs such that $D' = \overline{D}$?

4 • Point Bases

Great floods have flown
From simple sources.

WILLIAM SHAKESPEARE
All's Well That Ends Well

With the results of the preceding chapters, we can now examine reachability within a digraph more closely. Fundamental to this analysis are the concept of condensation by strong components, discussed in Chapter 3, and the principle of directional duality, introduced in Chapter 2.

Suppose we are interested in those sets of points which can reach all the points of a digraph D. Since every point is reachable from itself, the set V of all points is such a set. But if the digraph contains even one line, a smaller set will do. The central problem of this chapter is to find, among those sets of points which can reach all points of D, the ones having no proper subset with this property. Such a minimal set is known as a point basis of D. Once this problem is solved, we shall know immediately the solution to its directional dual: how to find a minimal set of points of D that is reachable from all points of D. Stated in terms of communication networks, these two problems are: (1) how to find a minimal collection of people required for a message to reach everyone, and (2) how to find a minimal collection of people who, together, will learn of any message originating in the network.

POINT BASES AND HOW TO FIND THEM

Let v be any point of a digraph D. The *reachable set $R(v)$ of a point v*, is the collection of all points reachable from v. In other words, the reachable set of v consists of all points u for which D contains a path from v to u. For example, in Figure 4.1, $R(v_1) = \{v_1, v_2, v_3, v_5\}$, $R(v_4) = \{v_4, v_5\}$, and $R(v_6) = \{v_5, v_6, v_7, v_8, v_9\}$. Since every point of a digraph is reachable from itself, we note that v is always in its own reachable set $R(v)$.

The notion of a reachable set of a point can be extended. The *reachable set* $R(S)$ *of a set S of points*, is the collection of points reachable from any point of S. Thus, $R(S)$ is the union of the sets $R(v)$ for v in S. In Figure 4.1 if we denote by S the set of points in squares, then $R(S) = \{v_1, v_2, v_3, v_5, v_8, v_9\}$. We see that $R(S)$ is the union of $R(v_3)$ and $R(v_8)$.

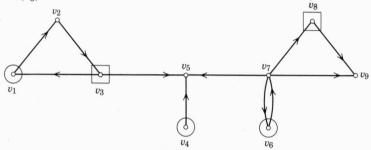

FIGURE 4.1

A *point basis* of a digraph D is a minimal collection of points of D from which all its points are reachable. Thus a set B of points is a point basis for D if $R(B) = V$, the set of all points of D, and if no proper subset of B has this property.

The marked points in Figure 4.1 form a set from which all points of D can be reached, but it does not constitute a point basis because a proper subset of it, the circled points, also has the property that from it all points are reachable. One can verify that the circled points in Figure 4.1 satisfy the definition and therefore constitute a point basis of the digraph. Observe that no circled point is reachable from any other circled point. We shall see in Theorem 4.2 that this is a characteristic of all point bases.

Where a digraph consists of a nontrivial semipath, we know from Chapter 2 that its set of transmitters is the smallest collection of points from which all others can be reached and, hence, is a point basis. In general, however, we cannot expect all points of a digraph D to be reachable from its set of transmitters, as is shown in Figure 4.1. There, v_4 is the only transmitter, and only points v_4 and v_5 are reachable from it. The following theorem generalizes these observations to all points of indegree 0.

Theorem 4.1. In any digraph D all points of indegree 0 are in every point basis.

The proof of this theorem consists essentially of noting that every point of indegree zero is reachable only from itself. It follows from this theorem that every point basis must include all transmitters.

The digraph shown in Figure 4.1 has six point bases: $\{v_1, v_4, v_6\}$, $\{v_1, v_4, v_7\}$, $\{v_2, v_4, v_6\}$, $\{v_2, v_4, v_7\}$, $\{v_3, v_4, v_6\}$, $\{v_3, v_4, v_7\}$. And in accordance with Theorem 4.1 the only transmitter of the digraph, v_4, is in every point basis.

Theorem 4.2. A set S of points of a digraph D is a point basis if and only if it satisfies the following conditions:
1. Every point of D is in $R(S)$, that is, $R(S) = V$.
2. No point of S is reachable from any other.

Since condition (1) is part of the definition of point basis, in order to prove this theorem we need only show that for a set of points satisfying this condition, condition (2) is equivalent to minimality. If condition (2) is satisfied, then surely S is minimal, for if any point were deleted from S then it could not be reached from any other point of S.

Conversely, let S be minimal. We can show that the assumption—for any two points u and v of S, there is a path from u to v—leads to a contradiction, proving condition (2). For if there is a path from u to v, then $R(u)$ contains $R(v)$. Let S' be the set obtained by removing v from S. Then it follows that $R(S')$ also contains all points of D, contradicting the minimality of S.

Corollary 4.2a. Every digraph has a point basis.[1]

Consider the two conditions of Theorem 4.2 for a set S of points of D to constitute a point bases. If $S = V$, then S obviously satisfies the first condition but does not satisfy the second condition in general. Let B be any set of points of D which is minimal with respect to the first condition. Then B must satisfy the second condition, as shown in the proof of Theorem 4.2. Therefore, it follows from the theorem that B is a point basis of D.

Corollary 4.2b. No two points of a point basis lie in the same strong component.

This is an immediate consequence of condition (2) of the theorem.

The next two theorems and their corollaries develop properties of point bases and lead to an algorithm for finding a point basis of a digraph.

[1] This and other results concerning point bases may be found in König (1936).

Theorem 4.3. Every acyclic digraph has a unique point basis consisting of all points of indegree 0.

We begin the proof of this theorem by showing that the set S of points of indegree 0 of an acyclic digraph D is a point basis. Since no point of indegree 0 is reachable from any other point, it follows at once that no two points of S are reachable from each other. Then to show that S is a point basis, we must prove that any point v_0 in D is in $R(S)$. Unless v_0 has indegree 0, there is a point v_1 for which $v_1 v_0$ is a line of D. And unless v_1 has indegree 0, there is a point v_2 for which $v_2 v_1$ is a line of D. In this manner we construct a sequence of points $v_0, v_1, \ldots, v_k$, such that either v_k is in S or there is a point v_{k+1} for which the line $v_{k+1} v_k$ is in D. The points of this sequence are all distinct, since if $v_k = v_m$ for $m < k$ then the points from v_m to v_k lie on a cycle. This is contrary to our hypothesis that D is acyclic. Since the number of points in D is finite, the sequence must stop, and thus its initial point is in S. Denoting the initial point by v_n, it follows that $v_n v_{n-1} \ldots v_1 v_0$ is a path of D. Thus v_0 is reachable from v_n, a point of S, and hence v_0 is in $R(S)$. That S is the only point basis of D follows at once from Theorem 4.1, since it contains only points of indegree 0.

Corollary 4.3a. The condensation D^* of any digraph D has a unique point basis consisting of all its points of indegree 0.

This statement follows at once by applying Theorem 3.6 to Theorem 4.3. In Figure 4.2 we have the condensation D^* of the digraph of

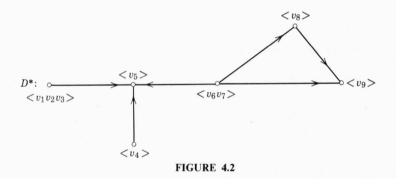

FIGURE 4.2

Figure 4.1. The points of this digraph D^* are the strong components of Figure 4.1. In this digraph there are three points of indegree 0, namely $\langle v_1 v_2 v_3 \rangle$, $\langle v_4 \rangle$, and $\langle v_6 v_7 \rangle$. And in keeping with Theorem 4.3, these points constitute the only point basis B^* of D^*.

The next theorem gives a useful characterization of the concept of point basis. We shall use it in developing an algorithm for finding the point bases of any digraph.

Theorem 4.4. Every point basis of D consists of exactly one point from each of the strong components in the point basis B^* of D^*.

The proof of Theorem 4.4 follows. Let B be a set of points containing exactly one point from each of the strong components in B^*. Since no point of B^* is reachable from any other, the same property holds for B. Let v be any point of D. To complete the proof that B is a point basis, we must show that v is in $R(B)$. Let $S(v)$ be the strong component containing v. Then for some strong component S_0 in B^*, there is in D^* a path L^* from S_0 to $S(v)$. Let v_0 be the point of S_0 in B. By Theorem 3.3, there is a path from v_0 to v. Thus v is in $R(B)$, as was to be shown.

We next show that every point basis B has precisely one point from each member of B^*. By Corollary 4.2b, B cannot have two points from any strong component. On the other hand, if $S(v)$ is in B^*, no point of $S(v)$ is reachable from any point not in it. Hence, for v to be in $R(B)$, B must contain some point of $S(v)$.

Theorem 4.4 shows how to find a point basis of a digraph D. The procedure can be accomplished by following these three steps:
(1) Form D^*.
(2) Find the point basis B^* of D^*, that is, its set of points of indegree 0.
(3) For each point in B^* choose any point in the corresponding strong component of D.

Any set of points obtained in accordance with this procedure constitutes a point basis of D, and all point bases can be obtained in this manner.

We have implicitly used this procedure in finding the point bases of the digraph D of Figure 4.1. More explicitly, we look at its condensation D^* shown in Figure 4.2 and find its point basis B^* to be $\{\langle v_1 v_2 v_3 \rangle, \langle v_4 \rangle, \langle v_6 v_7 \rangle\}$. A point basis for D is then found by choosing any one of v_1, v_2, v_3, together with v_4, and either v_6 or v_7. For example, the point basis shown in Figure 4.1 can be found in this way, as can all the point bases listed following Theorem 4.1.

Corollary 4.4a. Any two point bases of a digraph D have the same number of points.

This corollary is an immediate consequence of the fact stated in Theorem 4.4 that the number of points in each point basis of D is equal to the number of points in the unique point basis B^* of D^*.

THE COMMUNICATION REALIZATION

In Chapter 2 we saw that empirical assumptions E2.1 and E2.2 lead to the conclusion C2.1 that if person v possesses message M, then M will reach everyone reachable from v in the digraph of the network. In the terminology of the present chapter, if v possesses M, everyone in $R(v)$ will receive M. We now give empirical meaning, in terms of communication networks, to the concept of point basis. A *communication basis* of a group is the collection of people corresponding to a point basis of the digraph of the group's communication network.

Theorem 4.2 provides a means for characterizing communication bases of groups. Thus, a set S of people constitutes a communication basis of a group if and only if (1) all members of the group are reachable from at least one person in S, and (2) no person in S is reachable from any other. Suppose that someone wants to plant a rumor with the smallest possible number of people so that everyone in the group will hear the rumor. Clearly, he must plant the rumor with every member of a communication basis, for the rumor will reach everyone in the group if and only if it is possessed by every person in a communication basis of the group. Corollary 4.4a tells us that any communication basis will do, since all communication bases of a group have the same number of people.

To illustrate these observations, consider the rumor network shown by the digraph of Figure 4.3. We want to plant a rumor with as few people as possible and still be sure that it will reach everyone in the group. With whom should the rumor be planted? And with how many people must it be planted? To answer these questions we need to ascertain the communication bases of this group.

Let us follow the three-step procedure, outlined above, for finding the point bases of a digraph. First, we form the condensation D^* of the digraph of Figure 4.3, as shown in Figure 4.4. The second step is to find in D^* all points of indegree 0, and it is readily apparent that the point $\langle v_8 v_{10} \rangle$ is the only such point. This point constitutes the point basis B^* of D^*. Then, the third step is to choose a point from the strong component of D which corresponds to this point of D^*. Since in labeling the points of D^* we have preserved the identity of the strong components of D, this step is easy. One point basis is the single point v_8, and the only other point basis is the single point v_{10}. Thus, there are two communication bases in this group, one consisting of person v_8 and the other person v_{10}. We can be sure that everyone in the group will hear the rumor if it is planted with either of these two people.

It will be recalled that a commune is a maximal subgroup of people

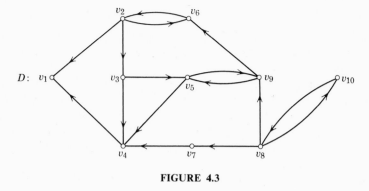

FIGURE 4.3

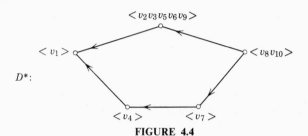

FIGURE 4.4

who are mutually reachable in a communication network. In other words, a commune corresponds to a point of the condensed digraph D^*. From Corollary 4.3a and Theorem 4.4, then, we see that every communication basis consists of exactly one person from each sending and each isolated commune of the network. Moreover, the number of people in any communication basis is equal to the number of such communes.

Finally, we consider the interesting special case covered by Theorem 4.3. This theorem tells us that if a group has no two people who are mutually reachable in its communication network, a rumor will reach everyone in the group if and only if it is planted with all transmitters and isolates.

POINT CONTRABASES

In Chapter 2 it was shown that to each theorem about digraphs, there is a corresponding theorem obtained on replacing every concept by its converse concept. This principle of directional duality is especially useful in dealing with the material under consideration here. In this section we define the converse concepts needed to state the directional duals of the theorems and corollaries presented thus far. Since the statements of these new theorems and corollaries follow from the directional duality principle, their proofs may be omitted.

We first define the directional dual of the concept of reachable set. Let v be a point of D. The *antecedent set $Q(v)$ of v* consists of all points of D from which v is reachable. Similarly, if we let S be any set of points of D, then the *antecedent set $Q(S)$ of the set S* is the collection of points from which some point of S is reachable. In the digraph of Figure 4.5, $Q(v_6) = \{v_1, v_2, v_3, v_6\}$ and $Q(v_5) = \{v_1, v_2, v_3, v_4, v_5, v_9, v_{10}\}$. Moreover, if we let $S = \{v_5, v_6\}$, then $Q(S) = \{v_1, v_2, v_3, v_4, v_5, v_6, v_9, v_{10}\}$. In terms of the communication example, this means that persons v_5 and v_6 together will receive a message originating with any of the persons in this set $Q(S)$. If we want to know what messages may have originated with all of these people together, we need ask only v_5 and v_6.

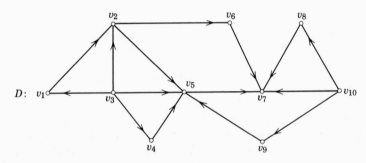

FIGURE 4.5

The following concept is dual to that of point basis. A *point contrabasis* of D is a minimal set S of points such that $Q(S)$ contains all points of D, that is, $Q(S) = V$. In other words, a point contrabasis is a minimal set of points S such that every point of D can reach some point of S. In the digraph D of Figure 4.5 it can be seen that v_7 is reachable from all points of D. Moreover, there is no other point for which this is true. We may conclude, therefore, that D has a unique point contrabasis consisting of the single point v_7.

The following theorems and corollaries are obtained immediately from the preceding section by application of the directional duality principle.

Theorem 4.1′. All points of outdegree 0 are in every point contrabasis of a digraph.

Theorem 4.2'. A set S of points of a digraph D is a point contrabasis if and only if it satisfies the following two conditions:

(1) Every point of D is in $Q(S)$.

(2) No point of S is antecedent to any other.

Corollary 4.2a'. Every digraph has a point contrabasis.

Corollary 4.2b'. No two points of a point contrabasis lie in the same strong component.

Theorem 4.3'. Every acyclic digraph has a unique point contrabasis consisting of all points of outdegree 0.

Corollary 4.3a'. The condensation D^* of any digraph D has a unique point contrabasis consisting of all its points of outdegree 0.

Theorem 4.4'. Every point contrabasis of D consists of exactly one point from each of the strong components in the point contrabasis C^* of D^*.

Corollary 4.4a'. Any two-point contrabases of a digraph D have the same number of points.

Any point contrabasis of a digraph D can be found by means of the following three steps:

(1) Form D^*.

(2) Find the point contrabasis C^* of D^*, that is, its set of points of outdegree 0.

(3) For each point in C^* choose any point in the corresponding strong component of D.

The procedures for finding a point basis and a point contrabasis both begin by forming the condensation D^* of D. After D^* has been obtained, we then find the point basis B^* of D^* by locating the points of indegree 0 in D^* and the point contrabasis C^* of D^* by locating the points of outdegree 0 in D^*. Thus, B^* and C^* can be found at the same time. To illustrate, consider the digraphs D and D^* shown in Figures 4.6 and 4.7. It is clear that B^* consists of three points of D^*, namely, $\langle v_1 v_2 v_3 \rangle$, $\langle v_6 \rangle$, $\langle v_7 \rangle$, and that C^* consists of the two points $\langle v_4 v_5 \rangle$ and $\langle v_8 v_9 \rangle$. Theorems 4.4 and 4.4' tell us that any point basis of D contains exactly

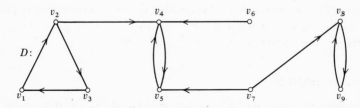

FIGURE 4.6

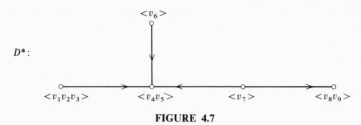

FIGURE 4.7

one point from each of the strong components of B^* and any point contrabasis of D contains exactly one point from each of the strong components of C^*.

The Communication Realization

Interpretation of the concept of point contrabasis in terms of the communication example is strictly analogous to that of its directionally dual concept of point basis and need not be discussed in detail. We define a *communication contrabasis* of a group as a collection of people corresponding to a point contrabasis of the digraph of the group's communication network. This concept is useful in answering such a question as how most economically to monitor a group's communication network so as to learn of any message that originates in the group.

From Theorem 4.2′ we know that a set S of people constitutes a communication contrabasis if and only if (1) all members of the group can reach at least one person in S, and (2) no person in S can reach any other. It follows, then, that one can learn of any message, regardless of where it originates in the group, by monitoring only those people in any communication contrabasis of the group. Thus, the minimum number of people who must be monitored is the number of people in any communication contrabasis.

Corollary 4.3a′ and Theorem 4.4′ lead to the following general conclusion: In order to be sure to learn of any message originating in a group, we must monitor one person from each receiving or isolated commune, and we need not monitor any others. Thus, if digraph D of Figure 4.7 is interpreted as the communication network of a group, we can be certain to learn of any message originating in this group simply by monitoring either v_4 or v_5 and either v_8 or v_9.

POINT DUOBASES

The material presented in the first section of this chapter made use of the concept of the set $R(v)$ of points reachable from a point v. The dual concept of the set $Q(v)$ of points antecedent to a point v was employed in the second section. We now consider these two concepts together.

In the digraph of Figure 4.8 it can be seen that for the point v_2, $R(v_2) = \{v_2, v_3, v_4, v_5\}$ and $Q(v_2) = \{v_2, v_3, v_4, v_1\}$. The intersection of these two sets is $R(v_2) \cap Q(v_2) = \{v_2, v_3, v_4\}$. What can be said about this last set of points? We note that it generates a strong component

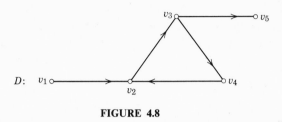

FIGURE 4.8

of D containing v_2, which we denote by $S(v_2)$. Similarly, for v_5: $R(v_5) = \{v_5\}$, $Q(v_5) = \{v_1, v_2, v_3, v_4, v_5\}$, and $R(v_5) \cap Q(v_5) = \{v_5\}$, which generates the strong component $S(v_5)$.

These considerations suggest the following general statement.

Theorem 4.5. The subgraph of D generated by $R(v) \cap Q(v)$ is $S(v)$, the strong component containing v.

Let us return now to the dual concepts of point basis and point contrabasis. Is it possible for a point basis and a point contrabasis of a given digraph D to be identical? To make the question exact, we state the following definition. A *point duobasis* of a digraph D is a set of points S which is both a basis and a contrabasis for D. Thus, all points of D are reachable from a point of S and every point of D can reach some point of S, that is, $R(S) = Q(S) = V$. The next theorem provides a means for characterizing digraphs with point duobases.

Theorem 4.6. A point S of the condensed digraph D^* is in both its point basis B^* and its point contrabasis C^* if and only if S is an isolate.

The proof of this theorem follows directly from Corollaries 4.3a and 4.3a'. Let S be a point of D^* lying in both B^* and C^*. Then in D^*, S has indegree 0 since it is in B^*, and S has outdegree 0 since it is in C^*. Hence S is an isolate. The converse is also immediate. For since S is an isolate, it has indegree 0 and outdegree 0 and, therefore, lies in both B^* and C^*.

Corollary 4.6a. A point v is in both a point basis and a point contrabasis of D if and only if the strong component $S(v)$ corresponds to an isolate of D^*.

We know that v is in both a point basis and a point contrabasis of D if and only if $S(v)$ corresponds to a point of D^* that is in both B^* and C^*. By Theorem 4.6, this point is an isolate of D^*. When D itself is strong, then every point of D is a point duobasis and D^* consists of a single point.

The digraph D and its condensation D^* shown in Figure 4.9 serve to illustrate this theorem and its corollary. The point basis B^* of D^*

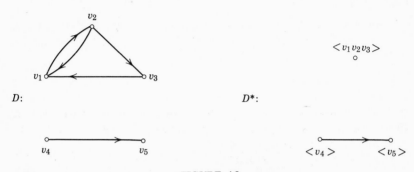

FIGURE 4.9

consists of the two points: $\langle v_1 v_2 v_3 \rangle$ and $\langle v_4 \rangle$. The point contrabasis C^* consists of the two points: $\langle v_1 v_2 v_3 \rangle$ and $\langle v_5 \rangle$. The only point in both is $\langle v_1 v_2 v_3 \rangle$, which is the only isolate of D^*. Looking at D, we see that there are three point bases, each consisting of v_4 together with one of v_1, v_2, v_3. And there are three point contrabases, each made up of v_5 together with one of v_1, v_2, v_3. Therefore, each of the points v_1, v_2, v_3 lies in both a point basis and a point contrabasis, and each of these generates the same strong component, which corresponds to the only isolate of D^*.

Theorem 4.7. The following statements are equivalent:
(1) D has a point duobasis.
(2) Every weak component of D is a strong component.
(3) D^* is totally disconnected.

We show first the equivalence of (3) and (1) and then that of (3) and (2).

(3) Implies (1). If D^* is totally disconnected, then every point is an isolate, having both indegree 0 and outdegree 0. Thus every point of D^* is in both the point basis and the point contrabasis of D^*. Then, by

Corollary 4.6a, the choice of any point in each strong component of D will result in a point duobasis of D.

(1) Implies (3). By hypothesis, D has a point duobasis B. Let v be any point of B. Then by Corollary 4.6a, $S(v)$ corresponds to a point of D^* that is in both B^* and C^*. By Theorem 4.6, this is an isolated point. Applying the procedure to every point in the duobasis, we see that D^* is totally disconnected.

Equivalence of (2) and (3). Clearly, D^* is totally disconnected if and only if each point of D^* constitutes a weak component. But by Corollary 3.4a, the kind of connectedness of a digraph is the same as that of its condensation. Hence, D^* is totally disconnected if and only if every weak component of D is strong.

Corollary 4.7a. Let D be a digraph with a duobasis. Then the number of points in each duobasis equals the number of strong components of D.

By Theorem 4.7, every weak component of D is a strong component, and since every duobasis is obtained by choosing exactly one point from each strong component, there is a one-to-one correspondence between strong components and points in the duobasis.

Theorem 4.7 may be illustrated by comparing the digraphs of Figure 4.9 with those of Figure 4.10. In Figure 4.9 the digraph D does not have

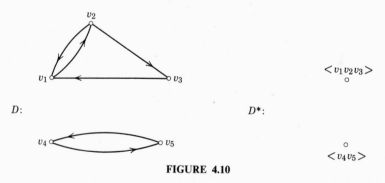

D: D^*:

FIGURE 4.10

a duobasis, one of its weak components $\langle v_4 v_5 \rangle$ is not a strong component, and its condensation D^* is not totally disconnected. But in Figure 4.10 the digraph D does have a duobasis, both of its weak components $\langle v_1 v_2 v_3 \rangle$ and $\langle v_4 v_5 \rangle$ are strong components, and D^* is totally disconnected.

In keeping with Corollary 4.7a, each duobasis of D in Figure 4.10 contains exactly two points, the number of its strong components.

SOURCES AND SINKS

Of particular interest in the study of point bases are digraphs whose point bases consist of a single point. When this is true, every point of the digraph is reachable from a single point. Such a point is known as a source. Its directional dual is called a sink. More formally, a point v is a *source* of D if $R(v) = V$. Dually, v is a *sink* of D if $Q(v) = V$. These concepts are illustrated in the digraph of Figure 4.11 in which points v_1 and v_2 are sources and points v_4, v_5, v_6 are sinks.

A digraph may, of course, have exactly one source and exactly one sink. Such points are called a *unique source* and a *unique sink*, respectively. The digraph of Figure 4.12 has a unique source, S_1, and a unique sink, S_4.

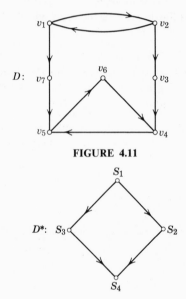

FIGURE 4.11

The next theorem provides a ready means for finding the sources of a digraph.

Theorem 4.8. A digraph D has a source if and only if its condensation D^* has a unique source, that is, exactly one point of indegree 0.

The proof of this theorem is obtained readily from Corollary 4.3a and Theorem 4.4. Assume that D has a source. Then by Corollary 4.3a, D^* has a unique point basis consisting of its single point of indegree 0.

On the other hand, if D^* has a unique source, then by Theorem 4.4 every point basis of D consists of a single point from this unique source of D^*.

From the directional duality principle we obtain the following theorem.

Theorem 4.8′. A digraph D has a sink if and only if its condensation D^* has a unique sink, that is, exactly one point of outdegree 0.

These two theorems are illustrated by means of Figures 4.11 and 4.12. It can be seen that the digraph of Figure 4.12 is the condensation of the digraph of Figure 4.11. From the fact that the digraph of Figure 4.12 has a unique point of indegree 0 and a unique point of outdegree 0, Theorems 4.8 and 4.8′ tell us that the digraph of Figure 4.11 must have a source and a sink. As we have seen, S_1 is the unique source of its digraph, and S_1 corresponds to the sources v_1 and v_2 of the digraph of Figure 4.11. Similarly, the unique sink S_4 corresponds to the sinks v_4, v_5, v_6.

The next theorems relate the concepts of source and sink to that of connectedness of digraphs.

Theorem 4.9. A digraph is strong if and only if every point is both a source and a sink.

This theorem is clearly self-dual. It is merely a restatement of the definition of a strong digraph using the present terminology.

Theorem 4.10. If D is unilateral, then D^* has a unique source and a unique sink.

According to the third criterion of Theorem 3.10, D^* has a unique complete path. The unique point basis of D^* consists of the point of indegree 0 of this path, and the unique point contrabasis consists of the point of outdegree 0 of this path. Thus D^* has a unique source and a unique sink.

It should be noted that the converse of this theorem is not true. For one can easily find digraphs that are not unilateral but that do have a source and a sink. In fact, Figure 4.12 shows such a digraph. The next statement follows immediately from Theorems 4.10, 4.8, and 4.8′.

Corollary 4.10a. If D is a unilateral digraph, then D has at least one source and at least one sink.

Theorem 4.11. For any point v of D, the subgraph generated by $R(v)$ is weak.

Theorem 4.11′. For any point v of D, the subgraph generated by $Q(v)$ is weak.

We need to prove only Theorem 4.11 since 4.11′ follows by duality. Let u and w be any two points in $R(v)$. Then the subgraph generated by $R(v)$ contains a path from v to u and a path from v to w. The union of these two paths contains a semipath joining u and w. Thus this subgraph is weak.

Corollary 4.11a. If the condensation D^* of a digraph D has a unique point of outdegree 0, then D^* is weak.

Corollary 4.11a′. If the condensation D^* of a digraph D has a unique point of outdegree 0, then D^* is weak.

Since we know from Corollary 3.4a that a digraph D and its condensation D^* have the same kind of connectedness, these corollaries could also be phrased to indicate in the conclusion that D is weak.

The proof of Corollary 4.11a follows. Let S be the unique point of D^* of indegree 0 whose existence is known by the hypothesis. By Theorem 4.8, this point is the unique source of D^*. Hence, every point of D^* is in $R(S)$, and by Theorem 4.11, D^* is a weak digraph.

ATTAINING UNANIMITY IN A GROUP

Some of the results presented in this chapter have been employed in a formal theory of social influence developed by French (1956) and Harary (1959b). We shall indicate briefly certain features of this theory. Consider a group of people who hold various opinions about an issue. Under what conditions of interpersonal influence will they attain unanimity? Let us represent the power structure of this group by a digraph D which is constructed so that there is a line $v_i v_j$ in D if and only if v_i can influence the opinion of v_j. The theory makes the following specific empirical assumptions.

E4.1. At time $t = 0$, each of the p members $v_1, v_2, \ldots, v_p$ holds an initial opinion $n_1, n_2, \ldots, n_p$ given by a real number.

E4.2. Power is exerted only at discrete time units denoted by $t = 1$, $t = 2$, etc.

E4.3. If the initial opinions of members v_i and v_j are n_i and n_j and if only v_i exerts influence on v_j, then the opinion of v_j after one unit of time is $\frac{1}{2}(n_i + n_j)$. Similarly if v_i, v_j, and v_k hold opinions n_i, n_j, and n_k

and only v_i and v_j act to influence v_k, then the opinion of v_k after one unit of time is the arithmetic mean $\frac{1}{3}(n_i + n_j + n_k)$, and so on.[2]

It is understood that the attainment of a final common opinion in an infinite number of steps does not require an infinite amount of time, for after the opinions of the different group members come within some preassigned small threshold value, the members will be regarded as holding the same final opinion.

According to this model, then, the opinion of any person v at $t = 1$ is the arithmetic mean of the opinions at $t = 0$ held by v and all persons adjacent to v in the digraph of the power structure. Similarly, the opinion of v at $t = 2$ is the arithmetic mean of the opinions of these people at $t = 1$. Thus, a person directly influences those adjacent from him and indirectly influences all others reachable from him.

As a simple example, let us assume that a committee at Worldwide Widgets, Inc., wishes to reach a unanimous decision concerning the price to charge for a widget. The power structure of this committee is shown in Figure 4.13.

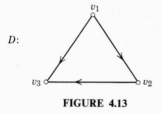

D:

FIGURE 4.13

Let us assume that the initial prices favored by the members are $n_1 = 2¢$, $n_2 = 4¢$, $n_3 = 6¢$. By using the calculations indicated in assumption E4.3, we obtain the following advocated prices at the indicated times:

t	n_1	n_2	n_3
0	2	4	6
1	2	$\dfrac{2+4}{2} = 3$	$\dfrac{2+4+6}{3} = 4$
2	2	$\dfrac{2+3}{2} = 2.5$	$\dfrac{2+3+4}{3} = 3$

---

[2] This is, of course, a strong assumption, which will not ordinarily be satisfied in natural groups. Harary (1959a) has provided a way of modifying it so as to be more realistic and has shown that, even with a weaker assumption, C4.4 is still valid.

Certain observations may be made concerning these values. First, it is clear that the initial opinion of v_1 will remain unchanged since the indegree of v_1 is 0. This holds, of course, for any transmitter or isolate of any digraph. Second, with the passage of time the opinions of v_2 and v_3 will approach the initial opinion of v_1. We note that v_1 is the unique source of the digraph. Since no other point can reach a unique source and all points are reachable from it, we may state the following general conclusions.

C4.1. If v is the unique source of the digraph of a power structure, the members will attain a final common opinion equal to the initial opinion of v.

If the digraph of a power structure is strong, then every person will eventually influence every other person. In this case, the influence processes are more complicated. To illustrate this situation, let us assume that the power structure of Worldwide Widget's committee is that shown in the digraph of Figure 4.14.

D:

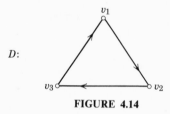

FIGURE 4.14

If we assume that the distribution of initial opinions is the same as before, we may calculate the opinion of the various members at the indicated times as follows:

t	n_1	n_2	n_3
0	2	4	6
1	$\dfrac{2+6}{2} = 4$	$\dfrac{2+4}{2} = 3$	$\dfrac{4+6}{2} = 5$
2	$\dfrac{4+5}{2} = 4.5$	$\dfrac{4+3}{2} = 3.5$	$\dfrac{3+5}{2} = 4$

From these calculations we see that eventually the committee will reach a final common opinion. It is shown in Harary (1959a) that this result may be generalized to any strong digraph, although the proof is beyond the scope of this book.

C4.2. If the digraph of a power structure is strong, the members will reach a final common opinion.

It can be shown that if the structure consists of a cycle, the final common opinion is the arithmetic mean of the initial opinions. In more complicated strong digraphs, the influence of the various members upon the final opinion may vary, but in any group whose digraph is strong the final common opinion is some weighted average of the initial opinions of all members.

We now generalize the analysis to power structures whose digraphs are not necessarily strong. Consider any such digraph D and its condensation D^*. By Corollary 4.3a, D^* has a unique point basis consisting of all points of indegree 0. It is clear that each of these points corresponds to a strong subgroup which will not be influenced by the opinions of anyone outside this subgroup. Thus, we know that this subgroup will attain a final common opinion which is determined only by the initial opinions of its members. Let us call such a subgroup (i.e., one that corresponds to a point of the unique point basis of D^*) a *power subgroup*. If a group has only one power subgroup, then this subgroup is the ultimate source of influence for all members of the group. We may, therefore, state the following conclusion.

C4.3. If a group has exactly one power subgroup, it has a final common opinion which is equal to that of the power subgroup itself.

From Theorem 3.10 we know that a nontrivial digraph D is unilateral if and only if D^* has a unique complete path. Thus, any power structure whose digraph is unilateral has exactly one power subgroup. Conclusion 4.3 therefore implies: Any group whose power structure corresponds to a unilateral digraph has a final common opinion which is equal to that of its unique power subgroup.

Power structures with more than one power subgroup—those whose digraphs are not unilateral—remain to be considered. The strictly weak digraph of Figure 4.15 illustrates a group with two power subgroups: $S_1 = \{v_1, v_2\}$ and $S_2 = \{v_3, v_4\}$.

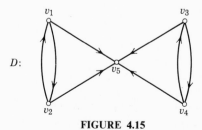

FIGURE 4.15

Let us assume that the initial opinions are as follows: $n_1 = 2$, $n_2 = 4$, $n_3 = 4$, $n_4 = 6$, $n_5 = 8$. It is readily ascertained that at $t = 1$ both S_1 and S_2 attain final common opinions of 3 and 5, respectively. The opinion of v_5 at $t = 1$ is 4.8; at $t = 2$ it is 4.16; and at $t = 3$ it is 4.03. Clearly, in this example, the final opinion of v_5 is the arithmetic mean of the final opinions of S_1 and S_2. In general, a group member who is influenced by more than one power subgroup will have a final opinion that is some weighted average of the final opinions of these power subgroups. The next conclusion follows immediately.

C4.4. A group has a final common opinion if and only if its power subgroups have equal final opinions.

FUNDAMENTAL SETS AND CONTRAFUNDAMENTAL SETS

Closely related to the ideas of reachability and point basis is that of fundamental set. A *fundamental set* is a maximal reachable set. That is, for a point v, $R(v)$ is a fundamental set if there is no point u in D for which $R(v)$ is a proper subset of $R(u)$. The point v is called an *origin* of the fundamental set $R(v)$. Of course, a fundamental set can contain more than one origin.

Any reachable set $R(v)$ is either a fundamental set or else it is properly contained in another reachable set. If $R(v)$ is not fundamental, we can find a fundamental set containing $R(v)$ by taking larger and larger

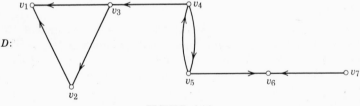

FIGURE 4.16

reachable sets. In Figure 4.16, the reachable set $R(v_3) = \{v_1, v_2, v_3\}$ is contained in the reachable set $R(v_4) = \{v_1, v_2, v_3, v_4, v_5, v_6\}$. Since there is no larger reachable set containing it, $R(v_4)$ is a fundamental set.

The following theorem relates the concept of fundamental set to that of point basis.

Theorem 4.12. Any set of points consisting of exactly one origin from each fundamental set is a point basis, and conversely.

The proof of the direct part of this theorem follows from the facts that every point of D is in at least one fundamental set and that if u and v are origins of distinct fundamental sets, they are mutually non-reachable.

The proof of the converse of this theorem makes use of Theorem 4.4, which tells us that every point basis consists of exactly one point from each of the strong components in the point basis B^* of D^*. We know that each of the points of B^* has indegree 0. Let $S_1, S_2, \ldots, S_n$ be these points, and let $R(S_1), R(S_2), \ldots, R(S_n)$ be their reachable sets. Since no other point of D^* can reach any of $S_1, S_2, \ldots, S_n$, each of their reachable sets is a fundamental set, and conversely. Thus, the selection of one point from each of the strong components in B^* is exactly the same thing as choosing one origin from each fundamental set.

The digraph of Figure 4.16 serves to illustrate this theorem. We noted above that $R(v_4)$ is a fundamental set of this digraph. It can readily be determined that $R(v_5) = R(v_4)$. Thus $R(v_5)$ is also a fundamental set. Finally, $R(v_7)$ is the only remaining fundamental set. According to Theorem 4.12, then, this digraph has two point bases, $\{v_4, v_7\}$ and $\{v_5, v_7\}$. Application of the procedure for finding point bases will confirm this conclusion.

Two corollaries follow immediately.

Corollary 4.12a. A digraph has a source if and only if it has exactly one fundamental set.

Corollary 4.12b. All origins of a fundamental set lie in the same strong component.

The principle of directional duality may now be applied to this material. A *contrafundamental set* is a maximal antecedent set. For a point v, if $Q(v)$ is a contrafundamental set, then v is its *terminus*. We now state the duals of Theorem 4.12 and its corollaries.

Theorem 4.12'. Any set of points consisting of exactly one terminus from each contrafundamental set is a point contrabasis, and conversely.

Corollary 4.12a'. A digraph has a sink if and only if it has exactly one contrafundamental set.

Corollary 4.12b'. All termini of a contrafundamental set lie in the same strong component.

It is sometimes useful to identify the subgraph generated by a fundamental set $R(v)$. Thus, for example, we may be interested in that part of a rumor network which joins all those persons reachable from a particular member of a communication basis of the group. The next theorem and corollary characterize such subgraphs.

Theorem 4.13. Every fundamental set $R(v)$ generates a subgraph which is the union of all unilateral components having v as a source.

Since $R(v)$ is a fundamental set, it is by definition a maximal reachable set. Now consider all the unilateral components in the subgraph generated by $R(v)$. Since v is an origin of $R(v)$, it is also a source of all these unilateral components. Therefore, the subgraph generated by $R(v)$ is the union of these unilateral components.

From inspection of the digraph of Figure 4.16 one can see that its unilateral components are $\langle v_1 v_2 v_3 v_4 v_5 \rangle$, $\langle v_4 v_5 v_6 \rangle$, and $\langle v_6 v_7 \rangle$. The point v_4 is clearly a source of each of the first two components. And we saw above that v_4 is an origin of the fundamental set $R(v_4) = \{v_1, v_2, v_3, v_4, v_5, v_6\}$. According to Theorem 4.12, then, the subgraph generated by $R(v_4)$ is the union of the components $\langle v_1 v_2 v_3 v_4 v_5 \rangle$ and $\langle v_4 v_5 v_6 \rangle$. This conclusion is verified by Figure 4.17, which shows the subgraph of the digraph of Figure 4.16 generated by its fundamental set $R(v_4)$.

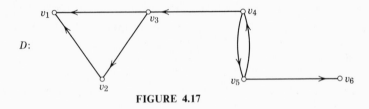

FIGURE 4.17

Combining Theorem 4.13 with Theorem 4.11, we see that every fundamental set generates a weak digraph.

Realizations

The concept of fundamental set is quite useful in describing various sorts of empirical structures, for it designates particular parts of a structure which often have special significance. Consider, for example, the authority structure of an organization. In "rational" conceptions of organizations it is usually assumed that there must be a single "top boss." The digraph of the authority structure of such an organization would contain a source, and the entire organization would constitute a single fundamental set. In actual practice, however, authority structures are often rather different. For example, it is not uncommon to find that authority over certain matters is delegated to autonomous subordinates. Each sub-boss, then, is an origin of a fundamental set containing all his subordinates. In this sense, a fundamental set represents an administrative unit of the organization.

We have seen that a given fundamental set may have more than one origin. But by Corollary 4.12b, all such origins must lie in the same strong component. What might this mean in terms of the authority structure of an organization? Strictly speaking, for every pair of top bosses in the same fundamental set each would have authority over the other. Such a "paradoxical" situation might arise where the top of a unit is governed by a committee. Presumably in such cases of mutual authority some decision-making mechanism is provided so that unitary commands will emanate from the collective source of authority. The strong component would then function as a single unit, and we could represent the authority structure by the condensation D^* of the original digraph.

If a person lies in two or more fundamental sets, then he may be subjected to influence stemming from two or more independent origins (top bosses). An index of potential conflict of authority might, therefore, be constructed on the basis of the number of people located in the intersection of two or more fundamental sets. This number becomes zero, of course, if the organization consists of a single fundamental set. In this case, there is one top boss whose influence can reach everyone in the organization.

If the number of people located in the intersection of two fundamental sets is greater than zero, one way to avoid conflict is to modify the authority structure so that these two fundamental sets become one. This could be accomplished either by placing one top boss over the origins of both fundamental sets or by forming a strong component containing them and establishing an effective decision-making mechanism for the members of the strong component.

In view of the duality principle, it is natural to ask what is the meaning of contrafundamental set of an authority structure. Such a question directs our attention to the bottom of the organization, for a terminus corresponds to a "low man on the totem pole." The antecedent set of a terminus (i.e., the contrafundamental set containing the terminus) corresponds to the terminal person and all those in the organization who can boss him directly or indirectly. If the authority structure of the organization is hierarchical in the sense that everyone except the top boss has exactly one boss, then the contrafundamental set of a terminus contains all those people in the organization lying on a path from the top boss to the terminus. These people might be expected to have special significance for the terminal person.

It would seem promising to employ a similar approach to the structure of a person's attitudes or values. In this case, one would need to identify the elements of an attitude or value system and to determine whether or not each element displays some sort of dependence on every other element. Then fundamental sets could be identified, and each would correspond to a set of elements directly or indirectly dependent upon a "master" attitude or value. From such an analysis it might be possible to give rigorous meaning to such concepts as "integration" and "conflict" of attitudes or value structures.

SUMMARY

In this chapter we have looked more deeply into questions of reachability in digraphs. Two primary concepts were introduced, namely, that of the reachable set $R(v)$ of a point v and that of the antecedent set $Q(v)$ of a point v. With these concepts available we were then able to define point basis, point contrabasis, and point duobasis. In investigating the characteristics of these and their relationships to other properties of digraphs, we found that the task was made much easier by forming the condensation D^* of the digraph D. We then considered two special cases: (1) digraphs in which every point can be reached from a single point, known as a source, and (2) those in which every point can reach a single point, known as a sink. We found that a digraph is strong if and only if every point is both a source and a sink. Moreover, if a digraph is unilateral, it has at least one source and at least one sink. The concepts of point basis and point contrabasis were then related to those of fundamental set and contrafundamental set.

In the next chapter we return to a topic considered first in Chapter 1, namely, how digraphs are related to matrices.

EXERCISES

1. Show that if v is in a point basis of D, then $R(v)$ has at least as many points as $Q(v)$. Is the converse true?
2. Show that if D is symmetric it has a point duobasis. Why is the converse statement not true in general?
3. Show that if v is a point of a digraph which can reach the maximum number of points, then v is in a point basis. Is the converse true?
4. Characterize those points of a digraph D which do not lie in any point basis.
5. Prove or disprove: (a) If D has a source and a sink, then D is unilateral. (b) If D has at least one point which is both a source and a sink, then D is strong. (Compare these statements with Corollary 4.10a and Theorem 4.9.)
6. Let D^* be the condensation of a digraph D of the sociometric choices of the residents of a housing project. If D^* has exactly one point of indegree 0, how many social groupings will there be in the project? (Use assumption E3.1.)

7. Let D be a digraph with c points in a point contrabasis. What is the smallest number of lines that need be added to D so that the resulting digraph has a sink?

8. When does a weak digraph have exactly two different point bases? Exactly four?

9. Show that the number of different point bases of a digraph is the product of the number of points in each strong component of D whose indegree in D^* is zero.

10. List all the point bases of the digraph in Figure 4.18. Verify that this satisfies the formula of Exercise 9.

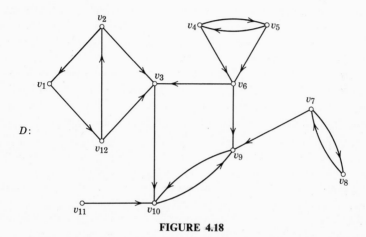

FIGURE 4.18

11. How many point contrabases are there in the digraph of Exercise 10? How many points are there in each?

12. Show that every unilateral component containing a point v is contained in the subgraph generated by $R(v) \cup Q(v)$.

13. Let D be a digraph whose fundamental sets are $F_1, F_2, \ldots, F_n$. Let E be that digraph whose points are these fundamental sets in which F_i is adjacent to F_j whenever $F_i \cap F_j$ is not empty. Show that D is weak if and only if E is strong.

5 • Digraphs and Matrices

In Chapter 1 we saw how the points and lines of a digraph D can be represented by an adjacency matrix $A(D)$ in which the rows and columns correspond to points of D and the entry $a_{ij} = 1$ if line $v_i v_j$ is in D while $a_{ij} = 0$ if $v_i v_j$ is not in D. Then in the following chapters we considered such properties as joining, reaching, connectedness, and distance. We now examine how matrices are useful in the study of these and other properties of digraphs.

Three matrices are of particular value: the reachability matrix $R(D)$, which indicates whether a point v_i can reach a point v_j; the connectedness matrix $C(D)$, which shows the connectedness of every pair of points of D; and the distance matrix $N(D)$, which gives the distance from any point to any other.

The use of matrices makes it possible to exploit matrix algebra, and hence computers, to obtain information concerning digraphs. For the reader unfamiliar with this branch of mathematics, we begin the chapter with an introductory mathematical section reviewing the basic operations on matrices, with some examples giving practice in the use of matrices in work with digraphs.

MATRIX OPERATIONS

Let $A = [a_{ij}]$ and $B = [b_{ij}]$ be two matrices of the same size $m \times n$. The *sum* $A + B$ of these two matrices is that matrix, also of size $m \times n$, whose i, j entry is $a_{ij} + b_{ij}$. Similarly, their *difference* $A - B$ is the matrix of the same size whose i, j entry is $a_{ij} - b_{ij}$. The *elementwise product* $A \times B$ has $a_{ij}b_{ij}$ as its i, j entry. These operations are illustrated by the following matrices.

$$A = \begin{bmatrix} 1 & 0 & 1 \\ 0 & 1 & 0 \end{bmatrix} \qquad A + B = \begin{bmatrix} 1 & 2 & 3 \\ 3 & 2 & 0 \end{bmatrix}$$

$$B = \begin{bmatrix} 0 & 2 & 2 \\ 3 & 1 & 0 \end{bmatrix} \qquad A - B = \begin{bmatrix} 1 & -2 & -1 \\ -3 & 0 & 0 \end{bmatrix}$$

$$A \times B = \begin{bmatrix} 0 & 0 & 2 \\ 0 & 1 & 0 \end{bmatrix}$$

Consider next the operation of multiplication of two matrices A and B. This operation is defined only when the number of columns of A equals the number of rows of B. Thus we let A be $m \times n$ and B be $n \times r$. Their *product* $C = AB$ is defined by the following formula:

$$c_{ij} = a_{i1}b_{1j} + a_{i2}b_{2j} + \cdots + a_{in}b_{nj} = \sum_{k=1}^{n} a_{ik}b_{kj}$$

Thus, c_{ij} is obtained from the ith row of A and the jth column of B.

In particular, the product of a square matrix with itself is always defined. Let A be an $n \times n$ matrix; A is called a square matrix of *order* n. The product AA is denoted A^2 and its i, j entry is written $a_{ij}^{(2)}$. Thus,

$$a_{ij}^{(2)} = a_{i1}a_{1j} + a_{i2}a_{2j} + \cdots + a_{in}a_{nj}$$

In general, A^r denotes the rth power of matrix A and its i, j entry is written $a_{ij}^{(r)}$. It is important to remember that the elementwise product $A \times B$ and the product AB are different operations. Thus, $A \times A \neq A^2$.

Matrix multiplication and its applicability to digraphs are illustrated in Figure 5.1. The adjacency matrix A of the digraph is shown together with its powers A^2 and A^3. Some of the entries of A^2 will now be worked out in detail:

$$a_{12}^{(2)} = a_{11}a_{12} + a_{12}a_{22} + a_{13}a_{32} + a_{14}a_{42}$$

$$= 0 \cdot 0 + 0 \cdot 0 + 1 \cdot 1 + 0 \cdot 0 = 1$$

$$a_{31}^{(2)} = a_{31}a_{11} + a_{32}a_{21} + a_{33}a_{31} + a_{34}a_{41}$$

$$= 0 \cdot 0 + 1 \cdot 1 + 0 \cdot 0 + 1 \cdot 1 = 2$$

$$a_{33}^{(2)} = a_{31}a_{13} + a_{32}a_{23} + a_{33}a_{33} + a_{34}a_{43}$$

$$= 0 \cdot 1 + 1 \cdot 0 + 0 \cdot 0 + 1 \cdot 1 = 1$$

The only nonzero term of $a_{12}^{(2)}$ comes from the product $a_{13}a_{32}$. Both $a_{13} = 1$ and $a_{32} = 1$, which means that the lines v_1v_3 and v_3v_2 both occur in D. Together these lines form a sequence of length 2 from v_1 to v_2, which in this case is a path. The fact that there is in D exactly one sequence of length 2 from v_1 to v_2 is reflected in the value $a_{12}^{(2)} = 1$.

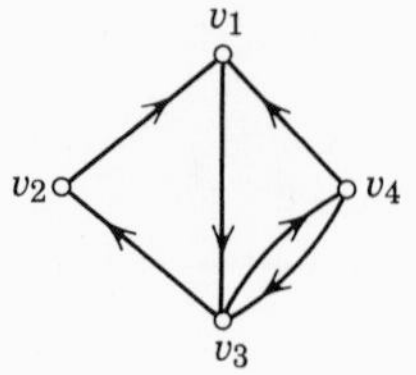

$$A = \begin{array}{c} \\ v_1 \\ v_2 \\ v_3 \\ v_4 \end{array} \begin{array}{cccc} v_1 & v_2 & v_3 & v_4 \\ \left[\begin{array}{cccc} 0 & 0 & 1 & 0 \\ 1 & 0 & 0 & 0 \\ 0 & 1 & 0 & 1 \\ 1 & 0 & 1 & 0 \end{array}\right] \end{array}$$

$$A^2 = \begin{array}{c} \\ v_1 \\ v_2 \\ v_3 \\ v_4 \end{array} \begin{array}{cccc} v_1 & v_2 & v_3 & v_4 \\ \left[\begin{array}{cccc} 0 & 1 & 0 & 1 \\ 0 & 0 & 1 & 0 \\ 2 & 0 & 1 & 0 \\ 0 & 1 & 1 & 1 \end{array}\right] \end{array}$$

$$A^3 = \begin{array}{c} \\ v_1 \\ v_2 \\ v_3 \\ v_4 \end{array} \begin{array}{cccc} v_1 & v_2 & v_3 & v_4 \\ \left[\begin{array}{cccc} 2 & 0 & 1 & 0 \\ 0 & 1 & 0 & 1 \\ 0 & 1 & 2 & 1 \\ 2 & 1 & 1 & 1 \end{array}\right] \end{array}$$

FIGURE 5.1

Similarly, the value $a_{31}^{(2)} = 2$ indicates that there are two sequences of length 2 in D from v_3 to v_1, namely $v_3 v_2 v_1$ and $v_3 v_4 v_1$. On the other hand $a_{33}^{(2)} = 1$ since there is exactly one sequence of length 2 from v_3 to v_3, namely the cycle $v_3 v_4 v_3$. In general, for any digraph D, the diagonal entry $a_{kk}^{(2)}$ of A_2 is the number of cycles of length 2 containing the point v_k. Thus, if the digraph of Figure 5.1 were to represent the sociometric choices of a group of four people, the entry $a_{kk}^{(2)}$ would give the number of mutual choices involving person v_k.

We now illustrate how the entries of A^3 are related to the digraph of Figure 5.1. The value $a_{11}^{(3)} = 2$ reflects the fact that in D there are exactly two sequences of length 3 from v_1 to v_1, $v_1 v_3 v_2 v_1$ and $v_1 v_3 v_4 v_1$. And $a_{13}^{(3)} = 1$ since there is exactly one sequence of length 3 from v_1 to v_3, namely $v_1 v_3 v_4 v_3$.

These observations are summarized and generalized in the following statement.[1]

Theorem 5.1. Let A be the adjacency matrix of a digraph D. Then in A^n the i, j entry is the number of sequences in D of length n from v_i to v_j.

Consider the $m \times n$ matrix $A = [a_{ij}]$ and any real number (scalar) c. The *scalar multiplication* of matrix A by the scalar c is denoted cA and

---

[1] This result was employed by Festinger, Schachter, and Back (1950, pp. 138–147) to find cliques in sociometric structures.

has as its i, j entry the number ca_{ij}. The following matrices illustrate scalar multiplication, where $c = 3$.

$$A = \begin{bmatrix} 1 & 0 & 1 \\ 0 & 1 & 0 \end{bmatrix} \qquad 3A = \begin{bmatrix} 3 & 0 & 3 \\ 0 & 3 & 0 \end{bmatrix}$$

The transpose of a matrix A is the matrix which corresponds to the converse of a relation or of a digraph. It will be recalled that the directional duality principle makes use of the converse of a digraph. Thus, the transpose of the adjacency matrix of a digraph is relevant to problems involving directional duality. The *transpose A' of a matrix A* is obtained from A by interchanging its rows and columns. Thus, the i, j entry of A' is the same as the j, i entry of A. Symbolically, if $A = [a_{ij}]$ and $A' = [a'_{ij}]$ then $a'_{ij} = a_{ji}$. A matrix is called *symmetric* if it equals its own transpose, that is, $A = A'$.

In Figure 5.2 we show the digraph D', which is the converse of the digraph of Figure 5.1. The accompanying matrix A' is its adjacency matrix and is the transpose of the matrix A of Figure 5.1.

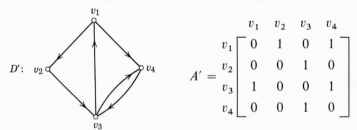

$$A' = \begin{array}{c@{}c} & \begin{array}{cccc} v_1 & v_2 & v_3 & v_4 \end{array} \\ \begin{array}{c} v_1 \\ v_2 \\ v_3 \\ v_4 \end{array} & \begin{bmatrix} 0 & 1 & 0 & 1 \\ 0 & 0 & 1 & 0 \\ 1 & 0 & 0 & 1 \\ 0 & 0 & 1 & 0 \end{bmatrix} \end{array}$$

FIGURE 5.2

Table 5.1 summarizes these six matrix operations.

Table 5.1

Size of A	Size of B	Operation	Notation	Size of Result	i, j Entry of Result
$m \times n$	$m \times n$	sum	$A + B$	$m \times n$	$a_{ij} + b_{ij}$
$m \times n$	$m \times n$	difference	$A - B$	$m \times n$	$a_{ij} - b_{ij}$
$m \times n$	$m \times n$	elementwise product	$A \times B$	$m \times n$	$a_{ij}b_{ij}$
$m \times n$	$n \times r$	product	AB	$m \times r$	$\sum_{k=1}^{n} a_{ik}b_{kj}$
$m \times n$		scalar multiplication	cA	$m \times n$	ca_{ij}
$m \times n$		transpose	A'	$n \times m$	a_{ji}

When we use the adjacency matrix, we can compute many facts about a particular digraph. For example, in a digraph constructed from sociometric choices we may wish to find the number of persons selected by both u and v. The following theorem tells how to find s_{ij}, the number of points to which both v_i and v_j are adjacent. We note that in particular $s_{ii} = \text{od}(v_i)$, the outdegree of v_i.

Theorem 5.2. $[s_{ij}] = AA'$

By using the definitions of transpose and matrix multiplication, we find that the i, j entry of AA' is $a_{i1}a_{j1} + a_{i2}a_{j2} + \ldots + a_{ip}a_{jp}$. If both v_i and v_j are adjacent to v_k, the product $a_{ik}a_{jk} = 1$; and otherwise it is 0. Therefore, the i, j entry of AA' is s_{ij}, the number of points to which both v_i and v_j are adjacent.

Let t_{ij} be the number of points adjacent to both v_i and v_j. The next result follows by directional duality.

Theorem 5.2.' $[t_{ij}] = A'A.$

The matrices illustrating these results for the digraph of Figure 5.1 are

$$
AA' = \begin{bmatrix} 1 & 0 & 0 & 1 \\ 0 & 1 & 0 & 1 \\ 0 & 0 & 2 & 0 \\ 1 & 1 & 0 & 2 \end{bmatrix} \quad \text{and } A'A = \begin{bmatrix} 2 & 0 & 1 & 0 \\ 0 & 1 & 0 & 1 \\ 1 & 0 & 2 & 0 \\ 0 & 1 & 0 & 1 \end{bmatrix}
$$

In most applications of matrix theory in this book, the entries will be integers, and in fact, nonnegative integers. Prior to this chapter, the entries have been even more limited than that, namely just the two integers 0 and 1, since we were concerned only with the adjacency matrix of a digraph.

Two special matrices with entries of just 0 and 1 are important for our work. The *identity matrix* of order n is denoted I_n, or more briefly I when its order is clear by context. Its entries are 1 on the diagonal and 0 elsewhere. The reason for the name of this matrix is that for any matrix C having the same order as I, the product $IC = C$, and also $CI = C$. Thus matrix I is the identity matrix with respect to multiplication. The second special matrix is one in which every entry is 1. This is called the *universal matrix* and is denoted J, where its size is indicated by context. It must be emphasized that I is always a square matrix, while J is not necessarily square. We illustrate scalar multiplication of these two matrices using $I = I_3$ and a universal matrix J of size 2×3.

$$I = I_3 = \begin{bmatrix} 1 & 0 & 0 \\ 0 & 1 & 0 \\ 0 & 0 & 1 \end{bmatrix} \qquad 2I = \begin{bmatrix} 2 & 0 & 0 \\ 0 & 2 & 0 \\ 0 & 0 & 2 \end{bmatrix}$$

$$J = \begin{bmatrix} 1 & 1 & 1 \\ 1 & 1 & 1 \end{bmatrix} \qquad 3J = \begin{bmatrix} 3 & 3 & 3 \\ 3 & 3 & 3 \end{bmatrix}$$

In several uses of matrices we shall require *boolean arithmetic* on the integers 0 and 1. With only one exception, addition and multiplication are exactly the same as for ordinary arithmetic. The exception lies in the stipulation that $1 + 1 = 1$. It follows at once that a sequence of ordinary arithmetic operations on 0 and 1 which leads to any positive integer will yield the element 1 using boolean operations. If x and y are any two nonnegative integers, we indicate their boolean sum by the symbol $(x + y)\#$, so that the sum is either 0 or 1. Since $(1 + 1)\# = 1$, we write $2\# = 1$. Similarly, $3\# = 1$, and so forth. Thus, $(2 + 3)\# = 5\# = 1$.

Suppose that the members of a military unit have been asked the following two sociometric questions: (1) With whom would you like to take a weekend pass? (2) With whom would you like to go on a dangerous assignment? On the basis of the answers to these questions, two diagraphs may be constructed. In Figure 5.3, suppose D_1 is the digraph constructed from the replies to the first question and D_2 that from the second. Matrices A_1 and A_2 give the same information in matrix form. Now, for certain purposes we might wish to study ordered pairs of these persons according to whether the first chooses the second on both questions, on at least one, or on exactly one of the questions.

If, from D_1 and D_2, we form the intersection $D_1 \cap D_2$, there will be a particular line in this new digraph only when this line is in both D_1 and D_2. In our empirical illustration, a line $v_i v_j$ in $D_1 \cap D_2$ means that person v_i chooses v_j on both questions, as shown in Figure 5.3. If the union $D_1 \cup D_2$ is formed, it contains a particular line when that line is in D_1 or D_2. In the digraph $D_1 \cup D_2$ of Figure 5.3 a $v_i v_j$ line means that v_i chooses v_j on at least one of the questions, and the absence of such a line means that v_i chooses v_j on neither question. In the symmetric difference digraph $D_1 \oplus D_2$ a particular line occurs if and only if it is found in exactly one of the given digraphs. In our sociometric example, for each ordered pair of persons, this digraph indicates whether the first chooses the second on exactly one of the questions.

The following theorem states how the adjacency matrices of these three new digraphs can be obtained from those of the given digraphs.

Theorem 5.3. Let D_1 and D_2 be two digraphs having the same set of points with the same ordering, and let A_1 and A_2 be the respective adjacency matrices. Then the adjacency matrices of the intersection, union, and symmetric difference digraphs are as follows:

$$A(D_1 \cap D_2) = A_1 \times A_2,$$
$$A(D_1 \cup D_2) = (A_1 + A_2)\#,$$
$$A(D_1 \oplus D_2) = (A_1 + A_2)\# - (A_1 \times A_2)$$

This theorem is easily verified. The matrix $A_1 \times A_2$ has an i, j entry of 1 if and only if both A_1 and A_2 have; hence it is the adjacency matrix of $D_1 \cap D_2$. Similarly, $(A_1 + A_2)\#$ has an entry of 1 when A_1 or A_2 has; hence $(A_1 + A_2)\# = A(D_1 \cup D_2)$. Since the symmetric difference is the union minus the intersection, it follows that

$$A(D_1 \oplus D_2) = A(D_1 \cup D_2) - A(D_1 \cap D_2) = (A_1 + A_2)\# - (A_1 \times A_2)$$

The theorem is illustrated for our sociometric example in Figure 5.3.

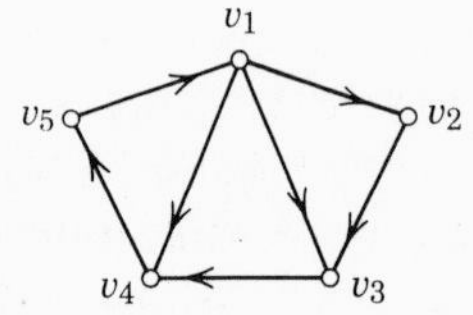

$$A_1 = \begin{bmatrix} 0 & 1 & 1 & 1 & 0 \\ 0 & 0 & 1 & 0 & 0 \\ 0 & 0 & 0 & 1 & 0 \\ 0 & 0 & 0 & 0 & 1 \\ 1 & 0 & 0 & 0 & 0 \end{bmatrix}$$

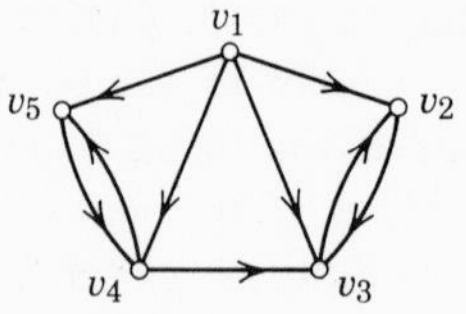

$$A_2 = \begin{bmatrix} 0 & 1 & 1 & 1 & 1 \\ 0 & 0 & 1 & 0 & 0 \\ 0 & 1 & 0 & 0 & 0 \\ 0 & 0 & 1 & 0 & 1 \\ 0 & 0 & 0 & 1 & 0 \end{bmatrix}$$

FIGURE 5.3

$D_1 \cap D_2$:

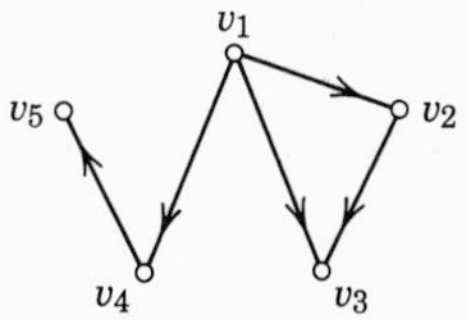

$$A_1 \times A_2 = \begin{bmatrix} 0 & 1 & 1 & 1 & 0 \\ 0 & 0 & 1 & 0 & 0 \\ 0 & 0 & 0 & 0 & 0 \\ 0 & 0 & 0 & 0 & 1 \\ 0 & 0 & 0 & 0 & 0 \end{bmatrix}$$

$D_1 \cup D_2$:

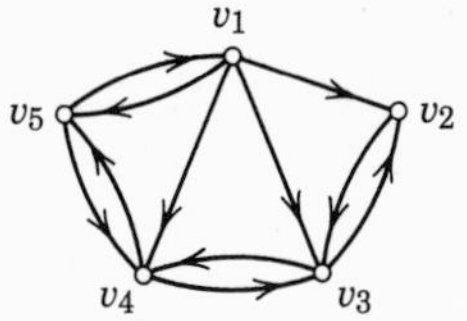

$$(A_1 + A_2)\# = \begin{bmatrix} 0 & 1 & 1 & 1 & 1 \\ 0 & 0 & 1 & 0 & 0 \\ 0 & 1 & 0 & 1 & 0 \\ 0 & 0 & 1 & 0 & 1 \\ 1 & 0 & 0 & 1 & 0 \end{bmatrix}$$

$D_1 \oplus D_2$:

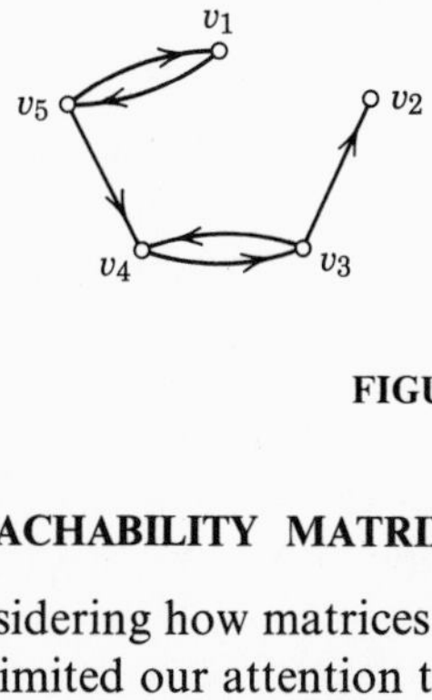

$$(A_1 + A_2)\# - A_1 \times A_2 = \begin{bmatrix} 0 & 0 & 0 & 0 & 1 \\ 0 & 0 & 0 & 0 & 0 \\ 0 & 1 & 0 & 1 & 0 \\ 0 & 0 & 1 & 0 & 0 \\ 1 & 0 & 0 & 1 & 0 \end{bmatrix}$$

FIGURE 5.3 (continued)

THE REACHABILITY MATRIX

In considering how matrices may be associated with digraphs, we have thus far limited our attention to the adjacency matrix. We now consider the *reachability matrix* $R(D)$ whose entries are denoted r_{ij} and defined as follows: $r_{ij} = 1$ if v_j is reachable from v_i; otherwise $r_{ij} = 0$. In other words, if D contains a sequence from v_i to v_j, then $r_{ij} = 1$. In constructing the reachability matrix of a digraph, we use the fact that each point is reachable from itself. The entries on the diagonal of $R(D)$ are, therefore, all 1's.

Figure 5.4 shows a digraph D, together with its adjacency matrix $A(D)$ and its reachability matrix $R(D)$. Obviously, $a_{ij} = 1$ implies $r_{ij} = 1$; thus there is an entry of 1 in the reachability matrix in all those places in which there is an entry of 1 in the adjacency matrix.

Some of the uses of the reachability matrix will be examined in detail in the next section; others are apparent immediately from this figure.

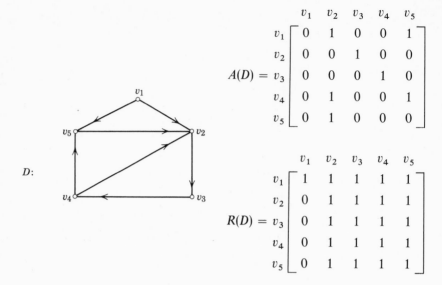

$$
A(D) = \begin{array}{c} \\ v_1 \\ v_2 \\ v_3 \\ v_4 \\ v_5 \end{array}
\begin{array}{ccccc}
v_1 & v_2 & v_3 & v_4 & v_5 \\
\left[\begin{array}{ccccc}
0 & 1 & 0 & 0 & 1 \\
0 & 0 & 1 & 0 & 0 \\
0 & 0 & 0 & 1 & 0 \\
0 & 1 & 0 & 0 & 1 \\
0 & 1 & 0 & 0 & 0
\end{array}\right]
\end{array}
$$

$$
R(D) = \begin{array}{c} \\ v_1 \\ v_2 \\ v_3 \\ v_4 \\ v_5 \end{array}
\begin{array}{ccccc}
v_1 & v_2 & v_3 & v_4 & v_5 \\
\left[\begin{array}{ccccc}
1 & 1 & 1 & 1 & 1 \\
0 & 1 & 1 & 1 & 1 \\
0 & 1 & 1 & 1 & 1 \\
0 & 1 & 1 & 1 & 1 \\
0 & 1 & 1 & 1 & 1
\end{array}\right]
\end{array}
$$

D:

FIGURE 5.4

For example, since the first row contains all 1's, we know that point v_1 can reach every point of D, that is, v_1 is a source. And, since all the off-diagonal entries in the first column are 0's, we know that the point v_1 cannot be reached from any other point of D.

In general, the reachable set $R(v_i)$ can be determined at once from the reachability matrix $R(D)$ by inspection. For $R(v_i)$ consists of those points whose columns in $R(D)$ have a 1 in the ith row. For example, in Figure 5.4, $R(v_2) = \{v_2, v_3, v_4, v_5\}$. Similarly, the antecedent set $Q(v_i)$ is given by the entries of 1 in the ith column of $R(D)$.

It will be recalled from Chapter 1 that a digraph D is transitive if for every three distinct points u, v, w, whenever the lines uv and vw are both in D, then the line uw is also in D. In other words, a digraph is transitive if whenever there is a path of length 2 from one point to another, then there is also a line from the first point to the second. An extension of this point of view will be given as Theorem 5.4 below.

There is a correspondence between the concept of reachability in a digraph and that of transitivity in a binary relation. This may be formalized by introducing the following operation on a digraph. The *transitive closure* D^t of a given digraph D is the minimal transitive digraph containing D and has the same set of points as D. This operation is illustrated in Figure 5.5, along with the adjacency and reachability matrices.

$D:$ 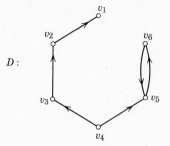 $D^t:$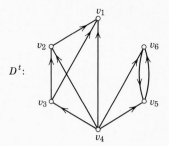

$$
A(D) = \begin{array}{c} \\ v_1 \\ v_2 \\ v_3 \\ v_4 \\ v_5 \\ v_6 \end{array}
\begin{array}{cccccc}
v_1 & v_2 & v_3 & v_4 & v_5 & v_6 \\
\left[\begin{array}{cccccc}
0 & 0 & 0 & 0 & 0 & 0 \\
1 & 0 & 0 & 0 & 0 & 0 \\
0 & 1 & 0 & 0 & 0 & 0 \\
0 & 0 & 1 & 0 & 1 & 0 \\
0 & 0 & 0 & 0 & 0 & 1 \\
0 & 0 & 0 & 0 & 1 & 0
\end{array}\right]
\end{array}
$$

$$
A(D^t) = \begin{array}{c} \\ v_1 \\ v_2 \\ v_3 \\ v_4 \\ v_5 \\ v_6 \end{array}
\begin{array}{cccccc}
v_1 & v_2 & v_3 & v_4 & v_5 & v_6 \\
\left[\begin{array}{cccccc}
0 & 0 & 0 & 0 & 0 & 0 \\
1 & 0 & 0 & 0 & 0 & 0 \\
1 & 1 & 0 & 0 & 0 & 0 \\
1 & 1 & 1 & 0 & 1 & 1 \\
0 & 0 & 0 & 0 & 0 & 1 \\
0 & 0 & 0 & 0 & 1 & 0
\end{array}\right]
\end{array}
$$

$$
R(D) = \begin{array}{c} \\ v_1 \\ v_2 \\ v_3 \\ v_4 \\ v_5 \\ v_6 \end{array}
\begin{array}{cccccc}
v_1 & v_2 & v_3 & v_4 & v_5 & v_6 \\
\left[\begin{array}{cccccc}
1 & 0 & 0 & 0 & 0 & 0 \\
1 & 1 & 0 & 0 & 0 & 0 \\
1 & 1 & 1 & 0 & 0 & 0 \\
1 & 1 & 1 & 1 & 1 & 1 \\
0 & 0 & 0 & 0 & 1 & 1 \\
0 & 0 & 0 & 0 & 1 & 1
\end{array}\right]
\end{array}
$$

FIGURE 5.5

Theorem 5.4. For any two distinct points v_i and v_j of D, the line $v_i v_j$ is in D^t if and only if v_j is reachable from v_i in D.

To prove Theorem 5.4, we construct the transitive closure D^t from D as follows. First we add to D all those lines uv not already in D whenever there is a path of length 2 in D from u to v. We iterate this procedure until no new lines can be added. The resulting digraph is transitive by definition, contains D, and is minimal with respect to these two properties. Hence it is D^t. This construction joins v_i to another point v_j if and only if v_j is reachable from v_i in D, completing the proof.

The following corollaries may be obtained readily from this theorem.

Corollary 5.4a. A digraph D is transitive if and only if it is its own transitive closure.

Corollary 5.4b. A digraph is transitive if and only if it has the following structure: Every strong component S is complete symmetric, and whenever there is a path from a point of S_1 to a point of S_2, there is a line from each point of S_1 to each point of S_2.

The construction of D^t used in the proof of Theorem 5.4 is practical for a small digraph. For a larger one we can use a matrix procedure involving the adjacency matrix $A(D^t)$. This procedure is given by the next corollary.

Corollary 5.4c. For any digraph D, $R(D) = A(D^t) + I$.

From Theorem 5.4 it follows that each diagonal entry of $A(D^t)$ is 0, whereas in $R(D)$ each of these is 1. Otherwise the two matrices are the same. Thus to find D^t we can construct $R(D) - I$ and take the digraph of this matrix.

Usually we shall want to be able to obtain the reachability matrix R of a digraph D from its adjacency matrix A. While R can be obtained from D^t using Corollary 5.4c, the following way is usually easier. By $A^2 \#$ we shall mean the matrix obtained by applying boolean arithmetic to compute the entries of the matrix $A^2 = AA$. Symbolically, $A^2 \# = [a_{ij}^{(2)} \#]$, and in general by $A^n \#$ we shall mean the matrix obtained when A^n is computed using boolean operations. The next statement is an immediate consequence of a combination of Theorem 5.1 with the definition of boolean arithmetic.

Theorem 5.5. The i, j entry $a_{ij}^{(n)} \#$ of $A^n \#$ is 1 if and only if there exists in D at least one sequence of length n from v_i to v_j.

To illustrate this theorem we use the digraph of Figure 5.1. The following matrices, in which the rows and columns have the same ordering as the points of the figure, should be compared with the matrices A^2 and A^3 shown in Figure 5.1:

$$A^2 \# = \begin{bmatrix} 0 & 1 & 0 & 1 \\ 0 & 0 & 1 & 0 \\ 1 & 0 & 1 & 0 \\ 0 & 1 & 1 & 1 \end{bmatrix} \qquad A^3 \# = \begin{bmatrix} 1 & 0 & 1 & 0 \\ 0 & 1 & 0 & 1 \\ 0 & 1 & 1 & 1 \\ 1 & 1 & 1 & 1 \end{bmatrix}$$

Limited reachability

It will be recalled from Chapter 4 that $R(v)$ is the set of all points of D reachable from v, whereas $Q(v)$ is the set of all points of D antecedent to v. We now define the *n-reachable subset* $R_n(v)$ of the set $R(v)$ as the set of all points reachable from v along a sequence whose length does not exceed n. Clearly, $R_n(v)$ consists of all points u of D such that the distance $d(v, u) \leq n$. Dually, the *n-antecedent subset* $Q_n(v)$ of the set $Q(v)$ is the set of all points antecedent to v along a sequence whose length does not exceed n. There will be no ambiguity in denoting the corresponding matrices by $R_n(D)$ and $Q_n(D)$. The following statement interrelates the reachability matrix with matrices of the form $R_n(D)$.

Theorem 5.6. For any digraph D with p points, $R(D) = R_{p-1}(D)$, and further for every integer $n > p - 1$, $R_n(D) = R_{p-1}(D)$.

These two formulas may be justified as follows. Whenever v_j is reachable from v_i in D, there must be a path of length at most $p - 1$ from v_i to v_j. This is immediate since there cannot occur in D any path of length p or greater, there being only p points available.

Some of these matrices may now be illustrated by referring again to the digraph D of Figure 5.1, for which

$$R_0 = I = \begin{bmatrix} 1 & 0 & 0 & 0 \\ 0 & 1 & 0 & 0 \\ 0 & 0 & 1 & 0 \\ 0 & 0 & 0 & 1 \end{bmatrix} \qquad R_1 = I + A = \begin{bmatrix} 1 & 0 & 1 & 0 \\ 1 & 1 & 0 & 0 \\ 0 & 1 & 1 & 1 \\ 1 & 0 & 1 & 1 \end{bmatrix}$$

$$I + A + A^2 = \begin{bmatrix} 1 & 1 & 1 & 1 \\ 1 & 1 & 1 & 0 \\ 2 & 1 & 2 & 1 \\ 1 & 1 & 2 & 2 \end{bmatrix} \qquad \text{so that } R_2 = \begin{bmatrix} 1 & 1 & 1 & 1 \\ 1 & 1 & 1 & 0 \\ 1 & 1 & 1 & 1 \\ 1 & 1 & 1 & 1 \end{bmatrix}$$

Finally, $R = R_3$ by Theorem 5.6 since $p = 4$

$$R = R_3 = \begin{bmatrix} 1 & 1 & 1 & 1 \\ 1 & 1 & 1 & 1 \\ 1 & 1 & 1 & 1 \\ 1 & 1 & 1 & 1 \end{bmatrix}$$

This matrix tells us, then, that in the digraph of Figure 5.1 every point is reachable from every other point, specifically, by a sequence of length 3 or less.

Since $p - 1$ is the length of a longest possible path in a digraph with p points, we shall frequently find the number $p - 1$ occurring in this and later chapters. The next corollary is analogous to the second part of Theorem 5.6.

Corollary 5.6a. Let k be the minimum value of n such that $R_n(D) = R_{n+1}(D)$. Then $R_k(D) = R(D)$.

It is now possible to represent reachability within a certain number n of steps using matrix operations. For brevity, let $R_n = R_n(D)$ and $A = A(D)$. The simplest such matrix, R_0, expresses the fact that each point is reachable from itself and no other point in 0 steps. Thus, R_0 has 1's on the diagonal and 0's elsewhere, i.e., $R_0 = I$. Continuing, v_j is reachable from v_i in at most one step if it is reachable in 0 steps, as shown by I, or in exactly one step, as shown by A. Thus, $R_1 = I + A$. Similarly, we see at once that $R_2 = (I + A + A^2)\#$. To obtain an alternate formula for R_2, note that $(I + A)^2 = I + 2A + A^2$. Since $(2A)\# = A\#$, $(I + A)^2\# = (I + 2A + A^2)\# = (I + A + A^2)\# = R_2$. Hence we may also write $R_2 = (I + A)^2\#$.

The next theorem generalizes these observations.

Theorem 5.7. For every positive integer n,

$$R_n = (I + A + A^2 + \ldots + A^n)\# = (I + A)^n\#$$

Combining Theorems 5.6 and 5.7, we obtain the following corollary.

Corollary 5.7a.

$$R = (I + A + A^2 + \ldots + A^{p-1})\# = (I + A)^{p-1}\#.$$

SOME USES OF THE REACHABILITY MATRIX

How can we find a point basis of a digraph by manipulating its reachability matrix? In Chapter 4 we found that the condensation D^*

of D is of considerable assistance in discovering point bases of D. For this reason, we begin by considering how to find the strong components of D by means of the reachability matrix.

Strong Components of D

Let R be the reachability matrix of D. We form the elementwise product $R \times R'$. Now $r_{ij} = 1$ when v_j is reachable from v_i, and $r'_{ij} = 1$ when v_i is reachable from v_j. Thus, the elementwise product $r_{ij}r'_{ij} = 1$ when v_i and v_j are mutually reachable. In the symmetric matrix $R \times R'$ the entries of 1 in the ith row give all the points mutually reachable with v_i. Thus we have the following theorem.

Theorem 5.8. Let v_i be a point of a digraph D. Then the strong component of D containing v_i is given by the entries of 1 in the ith row (or column) of the matrix $R \times R'$.

To illustrate this theorem, we consider the digraph D shown in Figure 5.6.

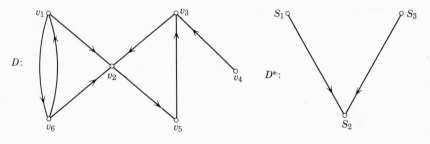

FIGURE 5.6

Starting with the adjacency matrix A, we form the matrices R, R', and $R \times R'$.

$$
A = \begin{array}{c} \\ v_1 \\ v_2 \\ v_3 \\ v_4 \\ v_5 \\ v_6 \end{array}
\begin{array}{c} \begin{array}{cccccc} v_1 & v_2 & v_3 & v_4 & v_5 & v_6 \end{array} \\
\left[\begin{array}{cccccc}
0 & 1 & 0 & 0 & 0 & 1 \\
0 & 0 & 0 & 0 & 1 & 0 \\
0 & 1 & 0 & 0 & 0 & 0 \\
0 & 0 & 1 & 0 & 0 & 0 \\
0 & 0 & 1 & 0 & 0 & 0 \\
1 & 1 & 0 & 0 & 0 & 0
\end{array} \right] \end{array}
$$

$$
R = \begin{array}{c} \\ v_1 \\ v_2 \\ v_3 \\ v_4 \\ v_5 \\ v_6 \end{array}
\begin{array}{cccccc}
v_1 & v_2 & v_3 & v_4 & v_5 & v_6 \\
\begin{bmatrix} 1 & 1 & 1 & 0 & 1 & 1 \\ 0 & 1 & 1 & 0 & 1 & 0 \\ 0 & 1 & 1 & 0 & 1 & 0 \\ 0 & 1 & 1 & 1 & 1 & 0 \\ 0 & 1 & 1 & 0 & 1 & 0 \\ 1 & 1 & 1 & 0 & 1 & 1 \end{bmatrix}
\end{array}
$$

$$
R' = \begin{array}{c} \\ v_1 \\ v_2 \\ v_3 \\ v_4 \\ v_5 \\ v_6 \end{array}
\begin{array}{cccccc}
v_1 & v_2 & v_3 & v_4 & v_5 & v_6 \\
\begin{bmatrix} 1 & 0 & 0 & 0 & 0 & 1 \\ 1 & 1 & 1 & 1 & 1 & 1 \\ 1 & 1 & 1 & 1 & 1 & 1 \\ 0 & 0 & 0 & 1 & 0 & 0 \\ 1 & 1 & 1 & 1 & 1 & 1 \\ 1 & 0 & 0 & 0 & 0 & 1 \end{bmatrix}
\end{array}
$$

$$
R \times R' = \begin{array}{c} \\ v_1 \\ v_2 \\ v_3 \\ v_4 \\ v_5 \\ v_6 \end{array}
\begin{array}{cccccc}
v_1 & v_2 & v_3 & v_4 & v_5 & v_6 \\
\begin{bmatrix} 1 & 0 & 0 & 0 & 0 & 1 \\ 0 & 1 & 1 & 0 & 1 & 0 \\ 0 & 1 & 1 & 0 & 1 & 0 \\ 0 & 0 & 0 & 1 & 0 & 0 \\ 0 & 1 & 1 & 0 & 1 & 0 \\ 1 & 0 & 0 & 0 & 0 & 1 \end{bmatrix}
\end{array}
$$

Now, with the aid of Theorem 5.8, we find the strong components of D. Since in $R \times R'$ the first row has a 1 in the first and sixth columns, one strong component is $S_1 = \langle v_1 v_6 \rangle$. Similarly, the other strong components are $S_2 = \langle v_2 v_3 v_5 \rangle$ and $S_3 = \langle v_4 \rangle$. Note that the sum of the ith row (or column) of $R \times R'$ gives the number of points in the strong component containing v_i.

After we have found the strong components of a digraph D, we may then construct its condensation D^* in accordance with the following general method. The rows and columns of A^* are, of course, the strong components of D, and the entries on the main diagonal of A^* are all 0's. To obtain the remaining entries of A^*, let S_i and S_j be any two strong components of D. Then S_i is adjacent to S_j in D^* if and only if there are two points v_i in S_i and v_j in S_j such that $a_{ij} = 1$. Thus to construct A^*, two steps are required: (a) find the strong components of D to get the points of D^*, (b) determine the lines of D^* by means of the entries of 1 in A.

To illustrate this procedure, we return to the digraph D shown in Figure 5.6.

As noted above, D contains three strong components: $S_1 = \langle v_1 v_6 \rangle$, $S_2 = \langle v_2 v_3 v_5 \rangle$, $S_3 = \langle v_4 \rangle$. Thus, A^* is a 3×3 matrix and has 0's on its main diagonal. To obtain the remaining entries of A^*, we note that the only 1's in the first or sixth columns of A lie on the first or sixth rows. Thus the first column of A^* has all 0's. To find the entries in the second column of A^*, we look for 1's in the second, third, and fifth columns of A. Here we find $a_{12} = 1$, yielding $a_{12}^* = 1$. Similarly, $a_{43} = 1$, giving $a_{32}^* = 1$. Finally, we see that there are no 1's in the fourth column of A. Hence, the third column of A^* has all 0's. The obtained matrix A^* shown below is clearly the adjacency matrix of the condensed digraph D^* of Figure 5.6.

$$A^* = \begin{array}{c} \\ S_1 \\ S_2 \\ S_3 \end{array} \begin{array}{ccc} S_1 & S_2 & S_3 \\ \left[\begin{array}{ccc} 0 & 1 & 0 \\ 0 & 0 & 0 \\ 0 & 1 & 0 \end{array} \right] \end{array}$$

Another useful matrix can be obtained from R. When we square R, we find that

$$r_{ij}^{(2)} = r_{i1}r_{1j} + r_{i2}r_{2j} + \ldots + r_{ip}r_{pj},$$

where p is the number of points in D. Obviously, $r_{i1}r_{1j}$ is 0 or 1. It is 1 if there is a sequence from v_i to v_j containing v_1 and is 0 otherwise. Thus, $r_{ij}^{(2)} = \sum_{k=1}^{p} r_{ik}r_{kj}$ is the total number of points of D which lie on at least one sequence from v_i to v_j. This property of R^2 makes it possible to derive the next two theorems.

Theorem 5.9. Let R be the reachability matrix of D. Then $r_{ii}^{(2)}$ is the number of points in the strong component $S(v_i)$.

Since, as noted above, $r_{ij}^{(2)}$ is the number of points of D lying on at least one sequence from v_i to v_j, it follows at once that $r_{ii}^{(2)}$ is the number of points lying on at least one closed sequence containing v_i. These points thus generate the strong component $S(v_i)$.

Theorem 5.10. A point v_j of D is in the strong component $S(v_i)$ if and only if $r_{ij}^{(2)} = r_{ii}^{(2)}$.

To prove this theorem, we first take as given that $r_{ij}^{(2)} = r_{ii}^{(2)}$. This equation asserts that the number of points that lie on at least one sequence from v_i to v_j equals the number of points in the strong component $S(v_i)$. Moreover, these points are the points in $S(v_i)$. Hence v_j itself is in $S(v_i)$.

Next, we take as given that v_j is in $S(v_i)$. Since every point in $S(v_i)$ is on at least one sequence from v_i to v_j, it follows that $r_{ij}^{(2)} \geq r_{ii}^{(2)}$. We can see, however, that $r_{ij}^{(2)} \leq r_{ii}^{(2)}$, for otherwise there would be a point v_k not in $S(v_i)$ lying on a sequence from v_i to v_j. But there can be no such point, since there is a sequence from v_j to v_i, and thus there would be a closed sequence containing v_i, v_k, and v_j, making v_k an element of $S(v_i)$. Therefore, $r_{ij}^{(2)} = r_{ii}^{(2)}$.

This theorem provides an additional way to find the adjacency matrix A^* of D^*. (See Exercise 4 of this chapter, p. 157.)

Point Bases and Fundamental Sets

The next theorem tells us how to find the point basis of D^* from its adjacency matrix A^*.

Theorem 5.11. A point S is in the point basis of D^* if and only if its column sum is 0 in A^*.

This theorem follows immediately from Corollary 4.3a, which states that D^* has a unique point basis consisting of all its points of indegree 0. By means of this theorem, we see that the point basis of D^* in Figure 5.6 is $\{S_1, S_3\}$.

The next theorem provides a method for finding the fundamental sets of D^*.

Theorem 5.12. Let S_i be any point in the point basis of D^*. Then the reachable set $R^*(S_i)$ in D^* is a fundamental set in D^*, and every fundamental set in D^* is determined in this way. The points in the fundamental set $R^*(S_i)$ are all those points of D^* whose entry in the ith row of the matrix R^* is 1.

By Theorem 4.12 we know that every point in a point basis is an origin of a fundamental set, and conversely. Thus, if S_i is in the point basis of D^*, then $R^*(S_i)$ is a fundamental set in D^*. The last statement of Theorem 5.12 follows from the fact that an entry of 1 in the ith row of R^* indicates that the corresponding point is reachable from S_i and is therefore in $R^*(S_i)$.

It can be seen that the matrix R^* of the digraph D^* of Figure 5.6 is

$$R^* = \begin{array}{c} \\ S_1 \\ S_2 \\ S_3 \end{array} \begin{array}{ccc} S_1 & S_2 & S_3 \\ \left[\begin{array}{ccc} 1 & 1 & 0 \\ 0 & 1 & 0 \\ 0 & 1 & 1 \end{array}\right] \end{array}$$

The fundamental sets of D^* are, accordingly, $\{S_1, S_2\}$ and $\{S_2, S_3\}$.

If we have the matrix A^* of a digraph D^* and if we know the points of D which form each strong component in D^*, we can find all point bases of D immediately. By Theorem 5.11, the unique point basis of D^* is the set of points whose column sums are 0 in A^*, and by Theorem 4.4, each point basis of D consists of exactly one point from each strong component in the point basis of D^*. Thus, in Figure 5.6 the point basis of D^* is $\{S_1, S_3\}$ and the point bases of D are $\{v_1, v_4\}$ and $\{v_6, v_4\}$.

The fundamental sets of D can be found from the matrix R^* in an analogous manner.

The next theorem provides another, closely related, method of finding the origins, fundamental sets, and point bases of a digraph D.

Theorem 5.13. A point v of a digraph D is an origin of a fundamental set if and only if the number of points in the same strong component as v is equal to the number of points from which v is reachable.

Clearly, the two sets $S(v)$ and $Q(v)$ are equal if and only if they contain the same number of points. Therefore, it is sufficient to show that v is an origin if and only if $S(v) = Q(v)$. By Theorem 4.5, $R(v) \cap Q(v)$ generates the strong component $S(v)$. Thus, the set of points in $S(v)$ is always a subset of $Q(v)$. If these two sets are equal, then v must be an origin, for otherwise the set of points in $S(v)$ would be a proper subset of $Q(v)$. Conversely, if v is an origin, then the only points from which v is reachable lie in $S(v)$.

This theorem can easily be translated into terms of the reachability matrix. The number of points in $S(v_i)$ is the sum of the ith row (or column) of $R \times R'$. On the other hand, the sum of the ith column of matrix R gives the number of points in $Q(v_i)$. If these two numbers are equal when compared then v_i is an origin by Theorem 5.13. (By Theorem 5.9, the number of points in $S(v_i)$ can also be obtained from $r_{ii}^{(2)}$.)

This procedure gives a criterion to test each point to see whether it is an origin. The fundamental sets are then immediately available by inspection of the reachability matrix R. For if the point v is already known to be an origin as tested by the preceding theorem, then a fundamental set is given by the collection of all points in the set $R(v)$. We may therefore state the following corollary.

Corollary 5.13a. Let the point v_i be an origin of D. Then the fundamental set $R(v_i)$ consists of all those points of D whose entry in the ith row of the matrix R is 1.

Since, by Theorem 4.12, every point basis of D consists of exactly one origin from each fundamental set, this procedure also gives us the point bases of D. Consider Figure 5.6 again. The sum of the first column of $R \times R'$ is 2, which means that $S(v_1)$ contains two points. And the sum of column 1 of R is also 2. Thus, we know that v_1 is an origin of D. A similar calculation for all points of D shows that v_4 and v_6 are the only other origins of D. By inspecting the rows of R, we see that v_1 and v_6 are in the same fundamental set but that v_4 is not. We conclude, therefore, that there are two point bases, namely, $\{v_1, v_4\}$ and $\{v_6, v_4\}$.

The matrix R also reveals whether D has any sources. Since v is a source if and only if $R(v) = V$, we immediately obtain the next corollary.

Corollary 5.13b. The point v_i is a source of D if and only if the ith row of the matrix R consists entirely of 1's.

A simple application of the directional duality principle to Theorem 5.13 and its corollaries tells us how to find a terminus, contrafundamental set, and sink from the reachability matrix of a digraph.

Kinds of Connectedness

We now consider how the kinds of connectedness of a digraph may be determined by means of its reachability matrix. Recall that if A is the adjacency matrix of D, then A' is the adjacency matrix of D', the converse digraph. Thus, $(A + A')\#$ is the adjacency matrix of D^s, the symmetrized digraph of D. By Theorem 3.11, the digraph D is weak if and only if D^s is strong. Hence if we find a matrix criterion for D to be strong, we may then characterize weak digraphs by applying this criterion to D^s. And, as a matter of fact, such a criterion is readily available. For the defining condition of a strong digraph is that any two of its points are mutually reachable. Stated in matrix terms, we have the following theorem.[2]

Theorem 5.14. A digraph D is strong if and only if its reachability matrix is universal, that is, $R = J$.

Theorem 5.15. A digraph D is weak if and only if the reachability matrix of its symmetrized digraph is universal; symbolically, D is weak if and only if $(I + A + A')^{p-1}\# = J$.

[2] The next three theorems are due to Ross and Harary (1959).

The theorem follows from an application of Theorem 5.14 to Theorem 3.11. The symbolic statement is derived by replacing A in the equation, $R = (I + A)^{p-1}\#$, of Corollary 5.7a by $A(D^s) = (A + A')\#$.

Corollary 5.15a. Let v_i be a point of a digraph D. Then, the weak component of D containing v_i is given by the entries of 1 in the ith row (or column) of the reachability matrix of its symmetrized digraph.

This statement follows from the fact that an entry of 1 in the i, j location of $A(D^s)$ means that the points v_i and v_j lie in the same weak component of D; this, in turn, follows at once from Theorem 5.15.

In Figure 5.7 is shown a digraph D and its matrices A and A'. Also shown is its symmetrized digraph D^s. It can readily be seen that the matrix $(A + A')\#$ is the adjacency matrix of D^s. In order to calculate the matrix $R(D^s)$, we need only to find $(I + A + A')^2\#$, since clearly for this digraph $(I + A + A')^2\# = (I + A + A')^3\#$. By Corollary 5.15a we see that the weak component of D containing v_1 is $\langle v_1 v_2 v_3 \rangle$, since these points correspond to the only 1's in the first row of $R(D^s)$. Similarly, the weak component of D containing v_4 is $\langle v_4 v_5 \rangle$. Moreover, the weak subgraph of D generated by the points v_1, v_2, and v_3 corresponds to the universal submatrix of $R(D^s)$, illustrating Theorem 5.15. Since these same points generate a strong subgraph of D^s, they also illustrate Theorem 5.14.

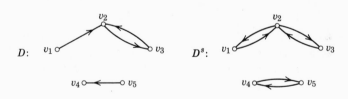

$$
A = \begin{array}{c} \\ v_1 \\ v_2 \\ v_3 \\ v_4 \\ v_5 \end{array}
\begin{array}{ccccc}
v_1 & v_2 & v_3 & v_4 & v_5 \\
\begin{bmatrix} 0 & 1 & 0 & 0 & 0 \\ 0 & 0 & 1 & 0 & 0 \\ 0 & 1 & 0 & 0 & 0 \\ 0 & 0 & 0 & 0 & 0 \\ 0 & 0 & 0 & 1 & 0 \end{bmatrix}
\end{array}
\qquad
A' = \begin{array}{c} \\ v_1 \\ v_2 \\ v_3 \\ v_4 \\ v_5 \end{array}
\begin{array}{ccccc}
v_1 & v_2 & v_3 & v_4 & v_5 \\
\begin{bmatrix} 0 & 0 & 0 & 0 & 0 \\ 1 & 0 & 1 & 0 & 0 \\ 0 & 1 & 0 & 0 & 0 \\ 0 & 0 & 0 & 0 & 1 \\ 0 & 0 & 0 & 0 & 0 \end{bmatrix}
\end{array}
$$

FIGURE 5.7

$$
(I + A + A')\# =
\begin{array}{c}
 \\
v_1 \\
v_2 \\
v_3 \\
v_4 \\
v_5
\end{array}
\begin{array}{ccccc}
v_1 & v_2 & v_3 & v_4 & v_5 \\
\left[\begin{array}{ccccc}
1 & 1 & 0 & 0 & 0 \\
1 & 1 & 1 & 0 & 0 \\
0 & 1 & 1 & 0 & 0 \\
0 & 0 & 0 & 1 & 1 \\
0 & 0 & 0 & 1 & 1
\end{array}\right]
\end{array}
$$

$$
(I + A + A')^2\# =
\begin{array}{c}
 \\
v_1 \\
v_2 \\
v_3 \\
v_4 \\
v_5
\end{array}
\begin{array}{ccccc}
v_1 & v_2 & v_3 & v_4 & v_5 \\
\left[\begin{array}{ccccc}
1 & 1 & 1 & 0 & 0 \\
1 & 1 & 1 & 0 & 0 \\
1 & 1 & 1 & 0 & 0 \\
0 & 0 & 0 & 1 & 1 \\
0 & 0 & 0 & 1 & 1
\end{array}\right]
\end{array} = R(D^s)
$$

FIGURE 5.7 (continued)

We now give a matrix criterion for a digraph D to be unilateral.

Theorem 5.16. A digraph D is unilateral if and only if $(R + R')\# = J$.

By definition, for every two points v_i and v_j of a unilateral digraph D, v_i is in $R(v_j)$ or v_j is in $R(v_i)$. Hence in the matrix R, $r_{ij} = 1$ or $r_{ji} = 1$, so that $(r_{ij} + r_{ji})\# = 1$ always.

By applying this theorem to the digraph of Figure 5.8, we find that it is unilateral because $(R + R')\# = J$, but it is not strong because $R \neq J$.

D:

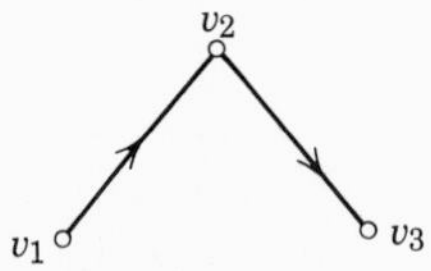

$$
A = \begin{bmatrix} 0 & 1 & 0 \\ 0 & 0 & 1 \\ 0 & 0 & 0 \end{bmatrix}
$$

$$
R = \begin{bmatrix} 1 & 1 & 1 \\ 0 & 1 & 1 \\ 0 & 0 & 1 \end{bmatrix}
\qquad
R' = \begin{bmatrix} 1 & 0 & 0 \\ 1 & 1 & 0 \\ 1 & 1 & 1 \end{bmatrix}
$$

FIGURE 5.8

$$(R + R')\# = \begin{bmatrix} 1 & 1 & 1 \\ 1 & 1 & 1 \\ 1 & 1 & 1 \end{bmatrix} = J$$

FIGURE 5.8 (continued)

Disconnected digraphs can also be characterized in terms of the reachability matrix. Figure 5.9 shows a digraph D and its reachability matrix R, which is partitioned by dashed lines, in a manner suggested by the weak components of D. The fact that D is disconnected is demonstrated in R by its submatrices of zeros in the upper right and lower left, indicating that there are no lines joining pairs of points in different weak components.

D:

$$R = \left[\begin{array}{ccc|cc} 1 & 1 & 1 & 0 & 0 \\ 0 & 1 & 1 & 0 & 0 \\ 0 & 0 & 1 & 0 & 0 \\ \hline 0 & 0 & 0 & 1 & 1 \\ 0 & 0 & 0 & 1 & 1 \end{array}\right]$$

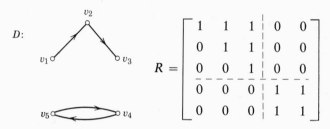

FIGURE 5.9

In order to characterize disconnected digraphs we need to look a bit more closely into the partitioning of matrices. Given a matrix M, we separate its set of rows into two subsets, the first r rows and the rest. We also separate its columns into the first s columns and the rest. Thus, we can regard M as partitioned into submatrices

$$M = \begin{bmatrix} M_{11} & M_{12} \\ M_{21} & M_{22} \end{bmatrix}$$

If M is an $m \times n$ matrix, then M_{11} is $r \times s$, M_{12} is $r \times (n - s)$, and so on.

Now if M is square and can be partitioned into submatrices such that M_{11} and M_{22} are square and M_{12} and M_{21} consist entirely of zeros, then M is said to be *decomposed* by the partition. Thus the partitioned matrix shown in Figure 5.9 is decomposed. Sometimes a matrix M is not already in this form, but after reordering the rows and columns it can then be decomposed; in this case we say that M is *decomposable*. It is possible, of course, that the submatrices M_{11} and M_{22} in a decomposed matrix may themselves be decomposable.

Theorem 5.17. The following conditions are equivalent:
(1) The digraph D is disconnected.
(2) Its adjacency matrix A is decomposable.
(3) Its reachability matrix R is decomposable.

By criterion (3) of Theorem 3.11, D is disconnected if and only if there is a partition of V into two subsets V_1 and V_2 such that no line of D joins a point of V_1 with a point of V_2. Let D_1 and D_2 be the subgraphs of D generated by V_1 and V_2, and let A_1 and A_2 be their respective adjacency matrices. Let the points of D be numbered first using the points in V_1 and then those in V_2. Then this condition of Theorem 3.11 implies that D is disconnected if and only if

$$A = \begin{bmatrix} A_1 & 0 \\ 0 & A_2 \end{bmatrix}$$

where by an abuse of notation the symbol 0 denotes a matrix in which every entry is 0. In this form, A is decomposed. It is then easy to verify that R is decomposable if and only if A is.

The Connectedness Matrix

In Chapter 3 we defined four categories of connectedness for pairs of points of a digraph. This information can be presented conveniently in matrix form. The *connectedness matrix* $C(D)$ has the number $n = 0$, 1, 2, or 3 in its i, j location whenever the points v_i and v_j are n-connected in the digraph D. Clearly, $C(D)$ is a symmetric matrix.

The connectedness matrix $C(D)$ of a digraph D can be constructed from the reachability matrix $R(D)$. In order to do this, we need first to find the weak components of D. Obviously, if D is weak, it consists of one weak component. If, however, D is disconnected, its weak components $D_1, D_2, \ldots, D_n$ can be found by means of Corollary 5.15a (or in simple digraphs by inspection). By a suitable ordering of the points of D, $C(D)$ can be written in the partitioned form:

$$C(D) = \begin{bmatrix} C(D_1) & 0 & \cdot & \cdot & 0 \\ 0 & C(D_2) & \cdot & \cdot & 0 \\ \cdot & \cdot & \cdot & \cdot & \cdot \\ \cdot & \cdot & \cdot & \cdot & \cdot \\ 0 & 0 & \cdot & \cdot & C(D_n) \end{bmatrix}$$

To obtain the entries c_{ij} for the connectedness matrix $C(D)$ we use the following theorem.

Theorem 5.18. For any digraph D, the connectedness matrix $C = [c_{ij}]$ is obtained from the reachability matrix $R = [r_{ij}]$ as follows:
1. If v_i and v_j are in the same weak component,

$$c_{ij} = r_{ij} + r_{ji} + 1.$$

2. Otherwise, $c_{ij} = 0$.

To prove this theorem we note first that if v_i and v_j are not in the same weak component, they are not joined by a semipath and are thus 0-connected. If they are in the same weak component, we consider all three possibilities for the pairs r_{ij} and r_{ji}. If both $r_{ij} = 1$ and $r_{ji} = 1$, then there is a path from v_i to v_j and a path from v_j to v_i so that they are 3-connected. If $r_{ij} + r_{ji} = 1$, then exactly one of the entries r_{ij} or r_{ji} is 1. In this case, v_i and v_j are joined by a path in only one direction and are therefore 2-connected. Finally, when $r_{ij} + r_{ji} = 0$, there is no path joining v_i and v_j. But since they are in the same weak component, they must be joined by a strict semipath and hence are 1-connected. Thus in all three cases $c_{ij} = r_{ij} + r_{ji} + 1$, and the theorem is proved.

Corollary 5.18a. If D is a weak digraph with connectedness matrix C and reachability matrix R, then

$$C = R + R' + J.$$

We now use Theorem 5.18 to obtain the entries for the connectedness matrix of the digraph shown in Figure 5.9. First, from the matrix R, which is partitioned according to its weak components, we construct R',

$$
R' = \begin{array}{c} \\ v_1 \\ v_2 \\ v_3 \\ v_4 \\ v_5 \end{array}
\begin{array}{ccccc} v_1 & v_2 & v_3 & v_4 & v_5 \\ \left[\begin{array}{ccc|cc} 1 & 0 & 0 & 0 & 0 \\ 1 & 1 & 0 & 0 & 0 \\ 1 & 1 & 1 & 0 & 0 \\ \hline 0 & 0 & 0 & 1 & 1 \\ 0 & 0 & 0 & 1 & 1 \end{array}\right] \end{array}
$$

We then obtain

$$
R + R' = \begin{array}{c} \\ v_1 \\ v_2 \\ v_3 \\ v_4 \\ v_5 \end{array}
\begin{array}{ccccc} v_1 & v_2 & v_3 & v_4 & v_5 \\ \left[\begin{array}{ccc|cc} 2 & 1 & 1 & 0 & 0 \\ 1 & 2 & 1 & 0 & 0 \\ 1 & 1 & 2 & 0 & 0 \\ \hline 0 & 0 & 0 & 2 & 2 \\ 0 & 0 & 0 & 2 & 2 \end{array}\right] \end{array}
$$

By Theorem 5.18, we obtain C by adding 1 to each nonzero entry of $R + R'$ and by transferring from $R + R'$ to C all the 0's. This procedure gives the following matrix C, whose values can be checked by inspection of the digraph of Figure 5.9:

$$
C = \begin{array}{c} \\ v_1 \\ v_2 \\ v_3 \\ v_4 \\ v_5 \end{array}
\begin{array}{ccccc}
v_1 & v_2 & v_3 & v_4 & v_5 \\
\left[\begin{array}{ccc|cc}
3 & 2 & 2 & 0 & 0 \\
2 & 3 & 2 & 0 & 0 \\
2 & 2 & 3 & 0 & 0 \\
\hline
0 & 0 & 0 & 3 & 3 \\
0 & 0 & 0 & 3 & 3
\end{array}\right]
\end{array}
$$

Certain properties of the connectedness matrix C of any digraph may be noted. First, the minimum entry in the matrix $C(D)$ gives the category of the entire digraph D. Second, the strong component of D containing v_i is given by the 3's in the ith row of $C(D)$. Third, the weak component of D containing v_i is given by the nonzero entries in the ith row of $C(D)$. Thus, in the example just considered, D is in C_0; the strong components are $\langle v_1 \rangle$, $\langle v_2 \rangle$, $\langle v_3 \rangle$, and $\langle v_4 v_5 \rangle$; and the weak components are $\langle v_1 v_2 v_3 \rangle$ and $\langle v_4 v_5 \rangle$.

THE DISTANCE MATRIX

In analyzing various structural properties of a digraph it is necessary to know the distance from each point of the digraph to every other point. We now show how this information can be presented in the form of a matrix, known as the distance matrix of a digraph, and how this matrix can be obtained from the adjacency matrix by matrix operations.

Let us denote by d_{ji} the distance $d(v_j, v_i)$ from v_j to v_i. Then, the *distance matrix* of D, denoted $N(D)$, is the square matrix of order p whose entries are the distances d_{ij}. Recall that $d_{ij} = \infty$ if there is no path from v_i to v_j, that is, $r_{ij} = 0$. The distances in the simple digraph of Figure 5.10 can be determined by inspection and are displayed in the matrix $N(D)$.

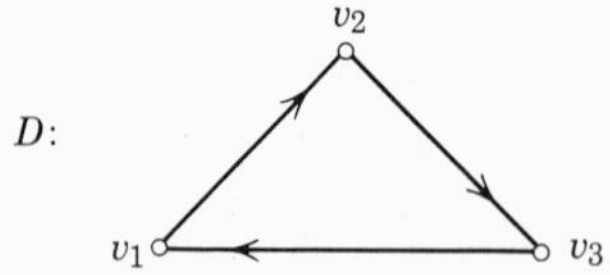

$$
N(D) = \begin{array}{c} \\ v_1 \\ v_2 \\ v_3 \end{array}
\begin{array}{ccc}
v_1 & v_2 & v_3 \\
\left[\begin{array}{ccc}
0 & 1 & 2 \\
2 & 0 & 1 \\
1 & 2 & 0
\end{array}\right]
\end{array}
$$

FIGURE 5.10

It should be noted that the only entries of 0 in $N(D)$ are on the main diagonal, since the distance from every point to itself is 0, and conversely. It can be seen immediately from the matrix $N(D)$ that the digraph of Figure 5.10 is strong, for every entry is finite. However, in the digraph D of Figure 5.11, the point v_4 is a transmitter and is therefore not reachable from any other point. The corresponding entries in $N(D)$ are ∞.

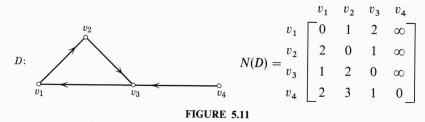

$$N(D) = \begin{array}{c c} & \begin{array}{cccc} v_1 & v_2 & v_3 & v_4 \end{array} \\ \begin{array}{c} v_1 \\ v_2 \\ v_3 \\ v_4 \end{array} & \left[\begin{array}{cccc} 0 & 1 & 2 & \infty \\ 2 & 0 & 1 & \infty \\ 1 & 2 & 0 & \infty \\ 2 & 3 & 1 & 0 \end{array} \right] \end{array}$$

FIGURE 5.11

Obviously, there is an entry of 1 in the distance matrix in exactly those places where there is an entry of 1 in the adjacency matrix of the digraph, since a line v_iv_j constitutes a path of length 1 and is the shortest possible path from v_i to v_j.

These observations concerning the distance matrix are included in the following statements.

Theorem 5.19. Let $N(D) = [d_{ij}]$ be the distance matrix of a given digraph D. Then,

1. Every diagonal entry d_{ii} is 0,
2. $d_{ij} = \infty$ if $r_{ij} = 0$, and
3. Otherwise, d_{ij} is the smallest power n to which A must be raised so that $a_{ij}^{(n)} > 0$, that is, so that the i, j entry of $A^n \#$ is 1.

The last statement requires justification. By Theorem 5.1, $a_{ij}^{(n)}$ is the number of sequences in D of length n from v_i to v_j. The distance from v_i to v_j is the length of a shortest path (and hence sequence). Thus, it is the least n such that $a_{ij}^{(n)} > 0$. But by definition, $a_{ij}^{(n)} > 0$ is equivalent to $a_{ij}^{(n)} \# = 1$.

The procedure for constructing the distance matrix $N(D)$ from the adjacency matrix is illustrated for the digraph of Figure 5.12. First of all, enter 0's on the diagonal of $N(D)$, showing $d_{ii} = 0$. Next, enter 1 in $N(D)$ whenever $a_{ij} = 1$, thus showing the distance $d_{ij} = 1$. Taking higher powers of A, wherever $a_{ij}^{(n)} \# = 1$ and there is no prior i, j entry in $N(D)$, enter an n to show where $d_{ij} = n$. Finally, note that in $A^4 \#$ every 1 occurs where there is already an entry in $N(D)$. Hence, we enter ∞ in all remaining open locations, indicating all ordered pairs (v_i, v_j) for which there is no path from v_i to v_j in D.

$$D: \quad v_5 \quad \begin{array}{c} v_1 \\ \\ \\ v_4 \quad v_3 \end{array} \quad v_2$$

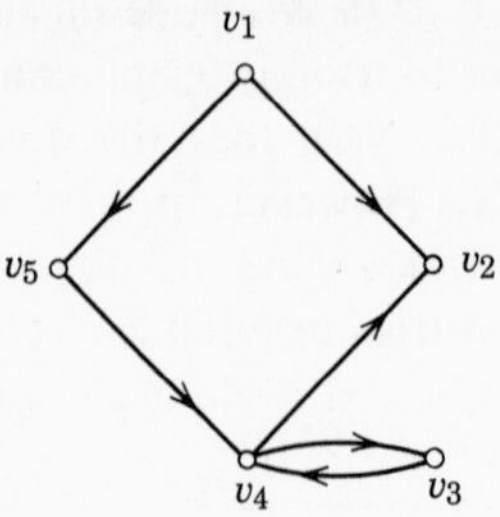

$$A = \begin{array}{c} \\ v_1 \\ v_2 \\ v_3 \\ v_4 \\ v_5 \end{array} \begin{array}{ccccc} v_1 & v_2 & v_3 & v_4 & v_5 \\ \left[\begin{array}{ccccc} 0 & 1 & 0 & 0 & 1 \\ 0 & 0 & 0 & 0 & 0 \\ 0 & 0 & 0 & 1 & 0 \\ 0 & 1 & 1 & 0 & 0 \\ 0 & 0 & 0 & 1 & 0 \end{array}\right] \end{array}$$

$$A^2 \# = \begin{array}{c} \\ v_1 \\ v_2 \\ v_3 \\ v_4 \\ v_5 \end{array} \begin{array}{ccccc} v_1 & v_2 & v_3 & v_4 & v_5 \\ \left[\begin{array}{ccccc} 0 & 0 & 0 & 1 & 0 \\ 0 & 0 & 0 & 0 & 0 \\ 0 & 1 & 1 & 0 & 0 \\ 0 & 0 & 0 & 1 & 0 \\ 0 & 1 & 1 & 0 & 0 \end{array}\right] \end{array}$$

$$A^3 \# = \begin{array}{c} \\ v_1 \\ v_2 \\ v_3 \\ v_4 \\ v_5 \end{array} \begin{array}{ccccc} v_1 & v_2 & v_3 & v_4 & v_5 \\ \left[\begin{array}{ccccc} 0 & 1 & 1 & 0 & 0 \\ 0 & 0 & 0 & 0 & 0 \\ 0 & 0 & 0 & 1 & 0 \\ 0 & 1 & 1 & 0 & 0 \\ 0 & 0 & 0 & 1 & 0 \end{array}\right] \end{array}$$

$$A^4 \# = \begin{array}{c} \\ v_1 \\ v_2 \\ v_3 \\ v_4 \\ v_5 \end{array} \begin{array}{ccccc} v_1 & v_2 & v_3 & v_4 & v_5 \\ \left[\begin{array}{ccccc} 0 & 0 & 0 & 1 & 0 \\ 0 & 0 & 0 & 0 & 0 \\ 0 & 1 & 1 & 0 & 0 \\ 0 & 0 & 0 & 1 & 0 \\ 0 & 1 & 1 & 0 & 0 \end{array}\right] \end{array}$$

$$N(D) = \begin{array}{c} \\ v_1 \\ v_2 \\ v_3 \\ v_4 \\ v_5 \end{array} \begin{array}{ccccc} v_1 & v_2 & v_3 & v_4 & v_5 \\ \left[\begin{array}{ccccc} 0 & 1 & 3 & 2 & 1 \\ \infty & 0 & \infty & \infty & \infty \\ \infty & 2 & 0 & 1 & \infty \\ \infty & 1 & 1 & 0 & \infty \\ \infty & 2 & 2 & 1 & 0 \end{array}\right] \end{array}$$

FIGURE 5.12

Corollary 5.19a. The reachability matrix $R(D)$ is obtained from the distance matrix $N(D)$ by replacing each ∞ by 0 and each other entry by 1.

Corollary 5.19b. D is strong if and only if every entry of $N(D)$ is finite.

This theorem and its corollaries are illustrated by Figure 5.13, which shows a digraph D and its adjacency, distance, and reachability matrices.

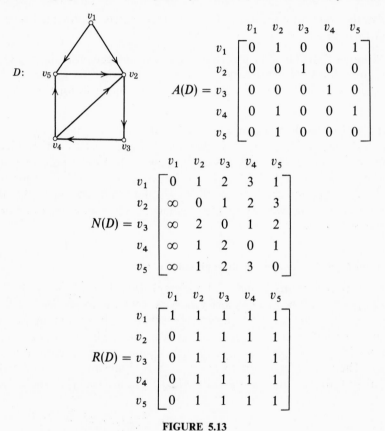

$$A(D) = \begin{array}{c} \\ v_1 \\ v_2 \\ v_3 \\ v_4 \\ v_5 \end{array} \begin{array}{ccccc} v_1 & v_2 & v_3 & v_4 & v_5 \\ \begin{bmatrix} 0 & 1 & 0 & 0 & 1 \\ 0 & 0 & 1 & 0 & 0 \\ 0 & 0 & 0 & 1 & 0 \\ 0 & 1 & 0 & 0 & 1 \\ 0 & 1 & 0 & 0 & 0 \end{bmatrix} \end{array}$$

$$N(D) = \begin{array}{c} \\ v_1 \\ v_2 \\ v_3 \\ v_4 \\ v_5 \end{array} \begin{array}{ccccc} v_1 & v_2 & v_3 & v_4 & v_5 \\ \begin{bmatrix} 0 & 1 & 2 & 3 & 1 \\ \infty & 0 & 1 & 2 & 3 \\ \infty & 2 & 0 & 1 & 2 \\ \infty & 1 & 2 & 0 & 1 \\ \infty & 1 & 2 & 3 & 0 \end{bmatrix} \end{array}$$

$$R(D) = \begin{array}{c} \\ v_1 \\ v_2 \\ v_3 \\ v_4 \\ v_5 \end{array} \begin{array}{ccccc} v_1 & v_2 & v_3 & v_4 & v_5 \\ \begin{bmatrix} 1 & 1 & 1 & 1 & 1 \\ 0 & 1 & 1 & 1 & 1 \\ 0 & 1 & 1 & 1 & 1 \\ 0 & 1 & 1 & 1 & 1 \\ 0 & 1 & 1 & 1 & 1 \end{bmatrix} \end{array}$$

FIGURE 5.13

The distance matrix $N(D)$ can be developed from R in another way. First we form a matrix R_∞ from R by replacing each entry 0 by ∞.

Theorem 5.20. Let k be the smallest integer such that $R_k = R$. Then the distance matrix of D is given by

$$N(D) = kR_\infty - (R_0 + R_1 + \cdots + R_{k-1})$$

Let M denote the matrix defined by the right side of this equation. To verify the theorem we need only show that the i, j entry of M is the distance from v_i to v_j. This distance is ∞ if and only if the i, j entry of R_∞ and hence of M is ∞. And if this distance is d, then the i, j entry of each of the matrices $R_d, R_{d+1}, \ldots, R_{k-1}$ is 1, and is 0 in $R_0, \ldots, R_{d-1}$. There are $k - d$ matrices in which it is 1, and thus in M the i, j entry is $k - (k - d) = d$.

Another interesting feature of the distance matrix is presented in the next theorem.

Theorem 5.21. If k is the largest positive integer entry in a given row (or column) of the distance matrix $N(D)$ of a digraph D, then every integer $0, 1, 2, \ldots, k - 1$ is also an entry in the same row (or column) of $N(D)$.

To prove the theorem, let k be the greatest finite distance d_{ij} in the ith row of $N(D)$. Since $d_{ij} = k$, there is a shortest path L of length k from v_i to v_j in D. This path passes through $k - 1$ distinct points whose distances from v_i are $1, 2, 3, \ldots, k - 1$, respectively. Since L is a shortest path and its points are distinct, all these values must appear in the ith row of $N(D)$. The validity of the statement for columns follows from directional duality.

How to Find the Geodetic Subgraph from v_i to v_j

For any two points v_i and v_j of a digraph D such that v_j is reachable from v_i, there will be one or more geodesics from u to v. By the *geodetic subgraph D_g from v_i to v_j* is meant the subgraph of D containing the points and lines of D that lie on at least one geodesic from v_i to v_j. Thus the geodetic subgraph from v_i to v_j is the union of all geodesics from v_i to v_j. The next three theorems are utilized by Flament (1963) to derive an algorithm for finding the geodetic subgraph from one point to another.

Theorem 5.22. Every subpath of a geodesic is a geodesic.

Let L be a geodesic from v_i to v_j and let L_1 be a subpath of L from u to u'. If L_1 is not a geodesic from u to u', there is a path L_2 from u to u' of shorter length. If in L we replace the subpath L_1 by L_2, the resulting sequence (which may be a path) from v_i to v_j is shorter than L, contrary to the hypothesis that L is a geodesic.

The next two theorems tell in terms of the distance matrix when a given point or line is on a geodesic from one point to another.

Theorem 5.23. A point v_k is on a geodesic from v_i to v_j if and only if $d_{ik} + d_{kj} = d_{ij}$.

First we show that if v_k is on a geodesic L from v_i to v_j, the stated equation holds. Now L is the union of two subpaths L_1 and L_2 from v_i to v_k and from v_k to v_j, respectively. By the preceding theorem each of these is itself a geodesic. Hence their lengths are d_{ik} and d_{kj} respectively, and the length of L is d_{ij}.

To prove the converse, let L_1 be a geodesic from v_i to v_k and let L_2 be a geodesic from v_k to v_j. Call L_3 the union of these two paths. Then the length of L_3 is $d_{ik} + d_{kj} = d_{ij}$. Therefore, L_3 must be a geodesic from v_i to v_j. Hence v_k is on a geodesic from v_i to v_j, completing the proof.

Theorem 5.24. Let v_r and v_s be two points on a geodesic L from v_i to v_j and let D contain the line $v_r v_s$. Then $v_r v_s$ is on L, and hence in the geodetic subgraph from v_i to v_j, if and only if $d_{ir} + 1 = d_{is}$.

We first take as the hypothesis that the line $v_r v_s$ is on L. By Theorem 5.22, the subpath of L from v_i to v_s is a geodesic. Since the point v_r is in this subpath, it follows from Theorem 5.23 that $d_{ir} + 1 = d_{is}$.

Conversely, we take as given the equation $d_{ir} + 1 = d_{is}$. Since $v_r v_s$ is a line of D, $d_{rs} = 1$. Therefore by Theorem 5.23, v_r is on a geodesic L_1 from v_i to v_s. Since the line $v_r v_s$ is the only geodesic from v_r to v_s, it must be on L_1 by Theorem 5.22. Similarly, the line $v_r v_s$ must be on L itself since the subpath of L from v_i to v_s is a geodesic.

The results are now available to state an algorithm for finding any geodetic subgraph of D.

Theorem 5.25. Let v_j be reachable from v_i in D. The geodetic subgraph D_g from v_i to v_j consists of all the points v_k such that $d_{ik} + d_{kj} = d_{ij}$ and all the lines $v_r v_s$ of D such that v_r and v_s are in D and $d_{ir} + 1 = d_{is}$.

This algorithm is a combined corollary of Theorems 5.23 and 5.24, the first giving a criterion for a point of D to be in D_g and the second telling when a line of D is in D_g. We illustrate this algorithm using the same strong digraph as used by Flament (1963, p. 31). The digraph and its distance matrix are shown in Figure 5.14.

Let us find the geodetic subgraph D_g from v_3 to v_8. In order to locate all the points v_k of D such that $d_{3k} + d_{k8} = d_{38}$, we write the third row of the distance matrix $N(D)$ and then write under it the eighth column of $N(D)$ as shown in Figure 5.15. Since $d_{38} = 4$, every point v_k of D for which $d_{3k} + d_{k8} = 4$ must be in D_g. Clearly, every point of D except v_2 is in D_g.

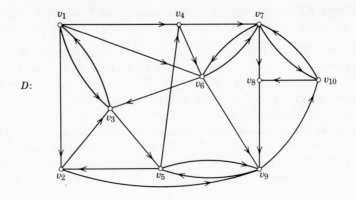

$$
N(D) = \begin{array}{c} \\ v_1 \\ v_2 \\ v_3 \\ v_4 \\ v_5 \\ v_6 \\ v_7 \\ v_8 \\ v_9 \\ v_{10} \end{array}
\begin{array}{c}
\begin{array}{cccccccccc} v_1 & v_2 & v_3 & v_4 & v_5 & v_6 & v_7 & v_8 & v_9 & v_{10} \end{array} \\
\left[\begin{array}{cccccccccc}
0 & 1 & 1 & 1 & 2 & 1 & 2 & 3 & 2 & 3 \\
2 & 0 & 1 & 3 & 2 & 3 & 3 & 3 & 1 & 2 \\
1 & 2 & 0 & 2 & 1 & 2 & 3 & 4 & 2 & 3 \\
3 & 4 & 2 & 0 & 3 & 1 & 1 & 2 & 2 & 2 \\
3 & 1 & 2 & 1 & 0 & 2 & 2 & 3 & 1 & 2 \\
2 & 3 & 1 & 3 & 2 & 0 & 1 & 2 & 1 & 2 \\
3 & 4 & 2 & 4 & 3 & 1 & 0 & 1 & 2 & 1 \\
5 & 3 & 4 & 3 & 2 & 4 & 3 & 0 & 1 & 2 \\
4 & 2 & 3 & 2 & 1 & 3 & 2 & 2 & 0 & 1 \\
4 & 4 & 3 & 4 & 3 & 2 & 1 & 1 & 2 & 0
\end{array} \right]
\end{array}
$$

FIGURE 5.14

k	1	2	3	4	5	6	7	8	9	10
d_{3k}	1	2	0	2	1	2	3	4	2	3
d_{k8}	3	3	4	2	3	2	1	0	2	1
$d_{3k} + d_{k8}$	4	5	4	4	4	4	4	4	4	4

FIGURE 5.15

We now show how to use $N(D)$ to find which lines of D lie in D_g. First, we draw, as in Figure 5.16, all the points v_k of D_g from left to right with their distance d_{3k} from v_3 as in Figure 5.14.

$d_{3k} = 0$	1	2	3	4
	v_1	v_6	v_7	
v_3		v_4		v_8
	v_5	v_9	v_{10}	

FIGURE 5.16

We now add lines to Figure 5.16 to obtain D_g. We add a line from each point to its neighbor immediately on the right if the line is in D, that is, if the distance from the point to its right-hand neighbor is 1. Thus, for example, we add v_3v_1 and v_3v_5 since $d_{31} = d_{35} = 1$, and we add v_1v_4 and v_1v_6 since $d_{14} = d_{16} = 1$. The result is the geodetic subgraph D_g from v_3 to v_8 shown in Figure 5.17. Clearly, there are exactly four geodesics from v_3 to v_8.

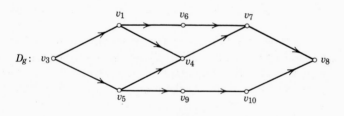

D_g:

FIGURE 5.17

THE NUMBER OF PATHS OF GIVEN LENGTH

For any digraph D with adjacency matrix A, we have already seen in Theorem 5.1 that the i, j entry of A^n gives the number of sequences of length n from v_i to v_j. In general, not all of these sequences will be paths, since it often happens that the same point may be encountered more than once. The question posed by these observations is to determine the number of paths of length n from v_i to v_j and to assemble this formation in matrix form. For brevity in this section we will speak of an *n-sequence* as a sequence of length n and will similarly refer to an *n-path*. By a *redundant sequence* is meant a sequence which is not a path. Let P_n be the matrix whose i, j entry is the number of n-paths from v_i to v_j.

The first formula found for path matrices was due to Luce and Perry (1949), who obtained an expression for P_3 in terms of A. Ross and Harary (1952) extended the solution to $n = 4, 5, 6$ and also presented an algorithm from which P_n could eventually be obtained for any n. Only very recently Parthasarathy (1964) found a general solution for P_n, the matrix of n-paths in D, in terms of matrices of $(n - 1)$-paths of certain submatrices of D which we now describe.

For a given digraph D with adjacency matrix $A = [a_{ij}]$ we define a subgraph D_j by specifying its adjacency matrix: it is obtained from A by replacing every entry in the jth row and jth column of A by 0. Thus D_j is a spanning subgraph of D, that is, it contains all p points of D. Let $P_n(D_j)$ be the matrix of n-paths in D_j.

Theorem 5.26. The matrix P_n of n-paths of digraph D may be expressed in terms of the matrices of $(n - 1)$-paths of each of its subgraphs D_j by specifying its columns: the jth column of P_n is the same as the jth column of the product $P_{n-1}(D_j) \cdot A$ for $j = 1, 2, \ldots, p$.

To prove this theorem, we must verify that the i, j entry of P_n equals the i, j entry of the product $P_{n-1}(D_j) \cdot A$, for all $i = 1, 2, \ldots, p$. For brevity, we denote this product matrix by B_j. There are two possibilities: $i = j$ or $i \neq j$.

Case 1: $i = j$. To verify this case, we need to show that the j, j entry of P_n is the same as the j, j entry of B_j. Since any nontrivial sequence in D from v_j to v_j is necessarily redundant, the j, j entry of P_n is 0. On the other hand, by construction of D_j, there are no sequences in that subgraph from v_j to any other point v_k, so that for all values of k, the j, k entry of $P_{n-1}(D_j)$ is 0. Hence by definition of matrix multiplication, the j, j entry of B_j is also 0.

Case 2: $i \neq j$. Let L be any n-sequence from v_i to v_j and denote it $L = v_i \ldots v_k v_j$. Then L is a path if and only if its subsequence $L' = v_i \ldots v_k$ is a path in which v_j does not occur. Now all paths of D which do not contain v_j appear in the subgraph D_j. Hence the matrix of all $(n - 1)$-paths not containing v_j is given by $P_{n-1}(D_j)$. Since $v_k v_j$ is a line of D, $a_{kj} = 1$. For each $(n - 1)$-path from v_i to v_k, there exists a unique n-path from v_i to v_j. Therefore, the number of n-paths from v_i to v_j is the i, j entry of B_j, completing the proof of the theorem.

We illustrate this theorem using the digraph D with five points shown in Figure 5.18.

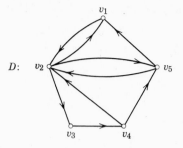

FIGURE 5.18

We can readily verify that the matrices of 2-paths, $P_2(D_j)$, are as follows:

$$A = \begin{bmatrix} 0 & 1 & 0 & 0 & 0 \\ 1 & 0 & 1 & 0 & 1 \\ 0 & 0 & 0 & 1 & 0 \\ 0 & 1 & 0 & 0 & 1 \\ 1 & 1 & 0 & 0 & 0 \end{bmatrix} \qquad P_2(D_1) = \begin{bmatrix} 0 & 0 & 0 & 0 & 0 \\ 0 & 0 & 0 & 1 & 0 \\ 0 & 1 & 0 & 0 & 1 \\ 0 & 1 & 1 & 0 & 1 \\ 0 & 0 & 1 & 0 & 0 \end{bmatrix}$$

$$P_2(D_2) = \begin{bmatrix} 0 & 0 & 0 & 0 & 0 \\ 0 & 0 & 0 & 0 & 0 \\ 0 & 0 & 0 & 0 & 1 \\ 1 & 0 & 0 & 0 & 0 \\ 0 & 0 & 0 & 0 & 0 \end{bmatrix} \qquad P_2(D_3) = \begin{bmatrix} 0 & 0 & 0 & 0 & 1 \\ 1 & 0 & 0 & 0 & 0 \\ 0 & 0 & 0 & 0 & 0 \\ 2 & 1 & 0 & 0 & 1 \\ 1 & 1 & 0 & 0 & 0 \end{bmatrix}$$

$$P_2(D_4) = \begin{bmatrix} 0 & 0 & 1 & 0 & 1 \\ 1 & 0 & 0 & 0 & 0 \\ 0 & 0 & 0 & 0 & 0 \\ 0 & 0 & 0 & 0 & 0 \\ 1 & 1 & 1 & 0 & 0 \end{bmatrix} \qquad P_2(D_5) = \begin{bmatrix} 0 & 0 & 1 & 0 & 0 \\ 0 & 0 & 0 & 1 & 0 \\ 0 & 1 & 0 & 0 & 0 \\ 1 & 0 & 1 & 0 & 0 \\ 0 & 0 & 0 & 0 & 0 \end{bmatrix}$$

Calculating only the jth column of the product $P_2(D_i) \cdot A$ for each $j = 1, \ldots, 5$, we find that the matrix of 3-paths of D is, by Theorem 5.26,

$$P_3(D) = \begin{bmatrix} 0 & 0 & 0 & 1 & 0 \\ 0 & 0 & 0 & 0 & 1 \\ 2 & 1 & 0 & 0 & 1 \\ 2 & 1 & 1 & 0 & 0 \\ 0 & 0 & 1 & 1 & 0 \end{bmatrix}$$

Thus, for example, the 3, 1 entry of $P_3(D)$ tells us that D has two paths of length 3 from v_3 to v_1. By inspecting Figure 5.18, we find these paths to be $v_3v_4v_5v_1$ and $v_3v_4v_2v_1$. Although the procedure given by Theorem 5.26 involves a great deal of calculation, it can be programmed for the computer.

The path matrix P_n of a digraph D may be employed to construct another useful matrix, the detour matrix of D. *A detour from v_i to v_j* is a path of maximum length from v_i to v_j. The *detour matrix* is the square matrix $E(D) = E = [e_{ij}]$, where $e_{ij} = \infty$ if there is no path from v_i to v_j and otherwise e_{ij} is the length of a detour from v_i to v_j. Thus, a detour is a natural opposite of a geodesic and the detour matrix $E(D)$ is similarly related to the distance matrix $N(D)$. The detour matrix $E(D)$ can be expressed in terms of the path matrices $P_n(D)$ by means of the following observation.

Theorem 5.27. If there is no path from v_i to v_j, then $e_{ij} = \infty$. Otherwise, the entry e_{ij} of the detour matrix of a digraph is the maximum integer n such that the i, j entry of the path matrix P_n is positive.

This statement is an immediate consequence of the definitions of the path matrix and detour matrix. For certainly the length of a longest path from v_i to v_j is the largest integer n such that there is at least one n-path from v_i to v_j.

One can verify that, in accordance with Theorem 5.27, the detour matrix E of the digraph D of Figure 5.18 is

$$\begin{bmatrix} 0 & 1 & 2 & 3 & 4 \\ 4 & 0 & 1 & 2 & 3 \\ 4 & 4 & 0 & 1 & 3 \\ 3 & 3 & 4 & 0 & 2 \\ 2 & 2 & 3 & 4 & 0 \end{bmatrix}$$

SOME EXAMPLES

We now illustrate the use of matrices to determine certain properties of digraphs. In order to gain experience in working with matrices, the reader is urged to carry out for himself the calculations indicated at each step in the following examples.

Matrix operations will be used to find the following properties of a digraph D: (a) the distance from each point to every other point, (b) the category of connectedness of every pair of points, and hence the category of D, (c) the condensed digraph D^*, (d) point bases and point contrabases, (e) fundamental sets, (f) strong components, and (g) weak components.

To find the distance matrix we calculate R_n for $n = 1$ to k, where k is the minimum value of n such that $R_n = R_{n+1}$. This will also give us the reachability matrix R, since $R_k = R$. Then to find the adjacency matrix A^* of D^* we construct R'. If D is weak, we can obtain all needed information from these matrices. If D is not weak we must find its weak components by means of the matrix $(A + A')\#$.

EXAMPLE 1

Figure 5.19 shows a digraph D for which the desired properties will be ascertained by matrix methods.

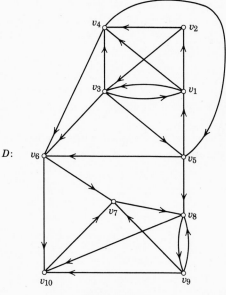

FIGURE 5.19

We first construct its adjacency matrix A.

$$A = \begin{bmatrix}
0 & 1 & 1 & 1 & 0 & 0 & 0 & 0 & 0 & 0 \\
0 & 0 & 1 & 1 & 0 & 0 & 0 & 0 & 0 & 0 \\
1 & 0 & 0 & 1 & 1 & 1 & 0 & 0 & 0 & 0 \\
0 & 0 & 0 & 0 & 1 & 1 & 0 & 0 & 0 & 0 \\
1 & 0 & 0 & 0 & 0 & 1 & 0 & 1 & 0 & 0 \\
0 & 0 & 0 & 0 & 0 & 0 & 1 & 0 & 0 & 1 \\
0 & 0 & 0 & 0 & 0 & 0 & 0 & 1 & 0 & 0 \\
0 & 0 & 0 & 0 & 0 & 0 & 0 & 0 & 1 & 1 \\
0 & 0 & 0 & 0 & 0 & 0 & 1 & 1 & 0 & 1 \\
0 & 0 & 0 & 0 & 0 & 0 & 1 & 0 & 0 & 0
\end{bmatrix}$$

To construct the matrix R_1, we calculate $I + A$, with the following result:

$$R_1 = \begin{bmatrix}
1 & 1 & 1 & 1 & 0 & 0 & 0 & 0 & 0 & 0 \\
0 & 1 & 1 & 1 & 0 & 0 & 0 & 0 & 0 & 0 \\
1 & 0 & 1 & 1 & 1 & 1 & 0 & 0 & 0 & 0 \\
0 & 0 & 0 & 1 & 1 & 1 & 0 & 0 & 0 & 0 \\
1 & 0 & 0 & 0 & 1 & 1 & 0 & 1 & 0 & 0 \\
0 & 0 & 0 & 0 & 0 & 1 & 1 & 0 & 0 & 1 \\
0 & 0 & 0 & 0 & 0 & 0 & 1 & 1 & 0 & 0 \\
0 & 0 & 0 & 0 & 0 & 0 & 0 & 1 & 1 & 1 \\
0 & 0 & 0 & 0 & 0 & 0 & 1 & 1 & 1 & 1 \\
0 & 0 & 0 & 0 & 0 & 0 & 1 & 0 & 0 & 1
\end{bmatrix}$$

We next construct the matrix R_2 by calculating $(I + A)^2 \#$.

$$R_2 = \begin{bmatrix}
1 & 1 & 1 & 1 & 1 & 1 & 0 & 0 & 0 & 0 \\
1 & 1 & 1 & 1 & 1 & 1 & 0 & 0 & 0 & 0 \\
1 & 1 & 1 & 1 & 1 & 1 & 1 & 1 & 0 & 1 \\
1 & 0 & 0 & 1 & 1 & 1 & 1 & 1 & 0 & 1 \\
1 & 1 & 1 & 1 & 1 & 1 & 1 & 1 & 1 & 1 \\
0 & 0 & 0 & 0 & 0 & 1 & 1 & 1 & 0 & 1 \\
0 & 0 & 0 & 0 & 0 & 0 & 1 & 1 & 1 & 1 \\
0 & 0 & 0 & 0 & 0 & 0 & 1 & 1 & 1 & 1 \\
0 & 0 & 0 & 0 & 0 & 0 & 1 & 1 & 1 & 1 \\
0 & 0 & 0 & 0 & 0 & 0 & 1 & 1 & 0 & 1
\end{bmatrix}$$

The matrix R_3 is obtained by calculating $(I + A)^3 \#$.

$$R_3 = \begin{bmatrix}
1 & 1 & 1 & 1 & 1 & 1 & 1 & 1 & 0 & 1 \\
1 & 1 & 1 & 1 & 1 & 1 & 1 & 1 & 0 & 1 \\
1 & 1 & 1 & 1 & 1 & 1 & 1 & 1 & 1 & 1 \\
1 & 1 & 1 & 1 & 1 & 1 & 1 & 1 & 1 & 1 \\
1 & 1 & 1 & 1 & 1 & 1 & 1 & 1 & 1 & 1 \\
0 & 0 & 0 & 0 & 0 & 1 & 1 & 1 & 1 & 1 \\
0 & 0 & 0 & 0 & 0 & 0 & 1 & 1 & 1 & 1 \\
0 & 0 & 0 & 0 & 0 & 0 & 1 & 1 & 1 & 1 \\
0 & 0 & 0 & 0 & 0 & 0 & 1 & 1 & 1 & 1 \\
0 & 0 & 0 & 0 & 0 & 0 & 1 & 1 & 1 & 1
\end{bmatrix}$$

Finally, we construct the matrix R_4 by calculating $(I + A)^4 \#$. It can be shown that $R_4 = R_5$. Thus we know that $R_4 = R$, the reachability matrix of D.

$$R_4 = R = \begin{bmatrix} 1 & 1 & 1 & 1 & 1 & 1 & 1 & 1 & 1 & 1 \\ 1 & 1 & 1 & 1 & 1 & 1 & 1 & 1 & 1 & 1 \\ 1 & 1 & 1 & 1 & 1 & 1 & 1 & 1 & 1 & 1 \\ 1 & 1 & 1 & 1 & 1 & 1 & 1 & 1 & 1 & 1 \\ 1 & 1 & 1 & 1 & 1 & 1 & 1 & 1 & 1 & 1 \\ 0 & 0 & 0 & 0 & 0 & 1 & 1 & 1 & 1 & 1 \\ 0 & 0 & 0 & 0 & 0 & 0 & 1 & 1 & 1 & 1 \\ 0 & 0 & 0 & 0 & 0 & 0 & 1 & 1 & 1 & 1 \\ 0 & 0 & 0 & 0 & 0 & 0 & 1 & 1 & 1 & 1 \\ 0 & 0 & 0 & 0 & 0 & 0 & 1 & 1 & 1 & 1 \end{bmatrix}$$

These matrices provide all the information needed to construct the distance matrix N. We begin by placing 0's on the diagonal of N. Then we transfer the 1's from R_1 to N. Next, we enter 2's in all empty locations of N whenever there is a 1 in R_2. The next step is to enter 3's in all empty locations of N whenever there is 1 in R_3. Finally, we enter ∞ in N whenever there is 0 in $R_4 = R$ and enter 4's in all remaining locations. The resulting matrix N is as follows:

$$N = \begin{bmatrix} 0 & 1 & 1 & 1 & 2 & 2 & 3 & 3 & 4 & 3 \\ 2 & 0 & 1 & 1 & 2 & 2 & 3 & 3 & 4 & 3 \\ 1 & 2 & 0 & 1 & 1 & 1 & 2 & 2 & 3 & 2 \\ 2 & 3 & 3 & 0 & 1 & 1 & 2 & 2 & 3 & 2 \\ 1 & 2 & 2 & 2 & 0 & 1 & 2 & 1 & 2 & 2 \\ \infty & \infty & \infty & \infty & \infty & 0 & 1 & 2 & 3 & 1 \\ \infty & \infty & \infty & \infty & \infty & \infty & 0 & 1 & 2 & 2 \\ \infty & \infty & \infty & \infty & \infty & \infty & 2 & 0 & 1 & 1 \\ \infty & \infty & \infty & \infty & \infty & \infty & 1 & 1 & 0 & 1 \\ \infty & \infty & \infty & \infty & \infty & \infty & 1 & 2 & 3 & 0 \end{bmatrix}$$

Inspection of the reachability matrix shows that D is weak, for it has a row containing all 1's. We may, therefore, employ Corollary 5.18a to construct the connectedness matrix C. To do so, we require the matrix R', which may be obtained immediately from R. We then calculate $R + R' + J = C$.

$$
C = \begin{bmatrix}
3 & 3 & 3 & 3 & 3 & 2 & 2 & 2 & 2 & 2 \\
3 & 3 & 3 & 3 & 3 & 2 & 2 & 2 & 2 & 2 \\
3 & 3 & 3 & 3 & 3 & 2 & 2 & 2 & 2 & 2 \\
3 & 3 & 3 & 3 & 3 & 2 & 2 & 2 & 2 & 2 \\
3 & 3 & 3 & 3 & 3 & 2 & 2 & 2 & 2 & 2 \\
2 & 2 & 2 & 2 & 2 & 3 & 2 & 2 & 2 & 2 \\
2 & 2 & 2 & 2 & 2 & 2 & 3 & 3 & 3 & 3 \\
2 & 2 & 2 & 2 & 2 & 2 & 3 & 3 & 3 & 3 \\
2 & 2 & 2 & 2 & 2 & 2 & 3 & 3 & 3 & 3 \\
2 & 2 & 2 & 2 & 2 & 2 & 3 & 3 & 3 & 3
\end{bmatrix}
$$

To construct the adjacency matrix A^* of the condensed digraph D^*, we must first find the strong components of D. This information is readily obtained from the matrix C, for all points that are 3-connected lie in the same strong component. Thus, $S_1 = \langle v_1 v_2 v_3 v_4 v_5 \rangle$; $S_2 = \langle v_6 \rangle$; and $S_3 = \langle v_7 v_8 v_9 v_{10} \rangle$. We know, then, that A^* is a 3×3 matrix and, of course, it has 0's on its main diagonal. To find the remaining entries of A^*, we reexamine A noting its strong components.

$$
A = \begin{array}{c}
\\
S_1 \left\{ \begin{array}{c} \\ \\ \\ \\ \\ \end{array} \right. \\
S_2 \left\{ \begin{array}{c} \\ \end{array} \right. \\
S_3 \left\{ \begin{array}{c} \\ \\ \\ \\ \end{array} \right.
\end{array}
\overbrace{}^{S_1} \overbrace{}^{S_2} \overbrace{}^{S_3}
\begin{bmatrix}
0 & 1 & 1 & 1 & 0 & 0 & 0 & 0 & 0 & 0 \\
0 & 0 & 1 & 1 & 0 & 0 & 0 & 0 & 0 & 0 \\
1 & 0 & 0 & 1 & 1 & 1 & 0 & 0 & 0 & 0 \\
0 & 0 & 0 & 0 & 1 & 1 & 0 & 0 & 0 & 0 \\
1 & 0 & 0 & 0 & 0 & 1 & 0 & 1 & 0 & 0 \\
0 & 0 & 0 & 0 & 0 & 0 & 1 & 0 & 0 & 1 \\
0 & 0 & 0 & 0 & 0 & 0 & 0 & 1 & 0 & 0 \\
0 & 0 & 0 & 0 & 0 & 0 & 0 & 0 & 1 & 1 \\
0 & 0 & 0 & 0 & 0 & 0 & 1 & 1 & 0 & 1 \\
0 & 0 & 0 & 0 & 0 & 0 & 1 & 0 & 0 & 0
\end{bmatrix}
$$

The strong components of D are indicated by the dashed lines in this matrix. It will be noted that because of the ordering of the rows and columns of A, the strong components correspond to submatrices lying on its main diagonal. We need, therefore, to look only for 1's in the off-diagonal submatrices, and we find that none of these lie in submatrices below the main diagonal. We conclude that A^* has all 0's below its main diagonal. The remaining entries of A^* are found readily: since $a_{56} = 1$, $a_{12}^* = 1$; since $a_{58} = 1$, $a_{13}^* = 1$; and since $a_{67} = 1$, $a_{23}^* = 1$. Thus, we obtain the matrix A^* and the digraph D^* as shown in Figure 5.20.

$$A^* = \begin{array}{c} \\ S_1 \\ S_2 \\ S_3 \end{array} \begin{array}{ccc} S_1 & S_2 & S_3 \\ \left[\begin{array}{ccc} 0 & 1 & 1 \\ 0 & 0 & 1 \\ 0 & 0 & 0 \end{array}\right] \end{array}$$

D^*:

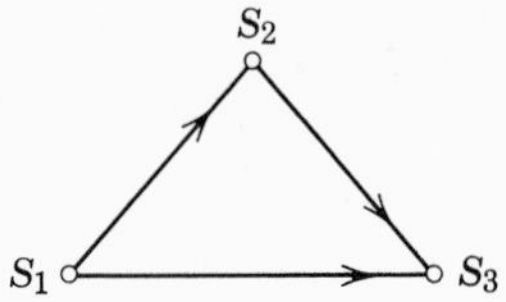

FIGURE 5.20

We now summarize our findings concerning the digraph D of Figure 5.19.

(1) The distance from each point to every other point can be read from the matrix N. For example, the greatest finite distance in D is 4, and no point is at a distance greater than 2 from v_5.

(2) The category of connectedness of every pair of points is given by the matrix C. The minimum entry of this matrix gives the category of D. Hence, D is in C_2. The same conclusion can, of course, also be reached quite readily from inspection of D^* or A^*.

(3) The condensed digraph D^* is shown in Figure 5.20.

(4) Point bases and point contrabases may be found using Theorem 5.11. We know that S_1 is the source of D^*, for it is the only point whose column sum is 0 in A^*. It follows that D has a source consisting of any one of the points v_1, v_2, v_3, v_4, v_5. The same reasoning through use of the directional duality principle shows that D has a sink consisting of any one of the points v_7, v_8, v_9, v_{10}. These same conclusions can be reached directly from the reachability matrix R with the aid of Corollary 5.13b, for the first five rows of R contain all 1's, as do the last four columns.

(5) Since D has a source, it follows that all the points of D constitute a fundamental set.

(6) Strong components can be found by constructing A^* from the matrix C. They could also have been found, by Theorem 5.8, from the matrix $R \times R'$ or, by Theorem 5.10, from the matrix R^2.

(7) Weak components. Since D has a source, all points lie in the same weak component.

EXAMPLE 2

In using matrices to find properties of a digraph it is not necessary, of course, to have a geometric representation of the digraph.[3] For our second example, then, we begin simply with the adjacency matrix of a digraph D. We shall seek the same information as in Example 1, but we shall proceed in a somewhat different way. Our first step will be to find the weak components of the digraph. To do this we need the reachability matrix of the symmetrized digraph D^s.

$$
A(D) = \begin{bmatrix}
0 & 0 & 0 & 1 & 0 & 0 & 0 & 0 & 0 & 0 \\
0 & 0 & 0 & 0 & 0 & 1 & 0 & 0 & 1 & 0 \\
0 & 0 & 0 & 0 & 0 & 0 & 1 & 1 & 0 & 0 \\
1 & 0 & 0 & 0 & 1 & 0 & 0 & 0 & 0 & 1 \\
0 & 0 & 0 & 0 & 0 & 0 & 0 & 0 & 0 & 0 \\
0 & 1 & 0 & 0 & 0 & 0 & 0 & 0 & 1 & 0 \\
0 & 0 & 1 & 0 & 0 & 0 & 0 & 1 & 0 & 0 \\
0 & 0 & 0 & 0 & 0 & 0 & 1 & 0 & 0 & 0 \\
0 & 0 & 0 & 0 & 0 & 0 & 0 & 0 & 0 & 0 \\
0 & 0 & 0 & 0 & 0 & 0 & 0 & 0 & 0 & 0
\end{bmatrix}
$$

[3] Bertrand Russell has asserted that in the best books there are no figures.

Clearly, the matrix $A'(D)$ is the following:

$$
A'(D) = \begin{bmatrix}
0 & 0 & 0 & 1 & 0 & 0 & 0 & 0 & 0 & 0 \\
0 & 0 & 0 & 0 & 0 & 1 & 0 & 0 & 0 & 0 \\
0 & 0 & 0 & 0 & 0 & 0 & 1 & 0 & 0 & 0 \\
1 & 0 & 0 & 0 & 0 & 0 & 0 & 0 & 0 & 0 \\
0 & 0 & 0 & 1 & 0 & 0 & 0 & 0 & 0 & 0 \\
0 & 1 & 0 & 0 & 0 & 0 & 0 & 0 & 0 & 0 \\
0 & 0 & 1 & 0 & 0 & 0 & 0 & 1 & 0 & 0 \\
0 & 0 & 1 & 0 & 0 & 0 & 1 & 0 & 0 & 0 \\
0 & 1 & 0 & 0 & 0 & 1 & 0 & 0 & 0 & 0 \\
0 & 0 & 0 & 1 & 0 & 0 & 0 & 0 & 0 & 0
\end{bmatrix}
$$

To obtain $R_1(D^s)$, we calculate $(I + A + A')\#$, with the following result:

$$
R_1(D^s) = \begin{bmatrix}
1 & 0 & 0 & 1 & 0 & 0 & 0 & 0 & 0 & 0 \\
0 & 1 & 0 & 0 & 0 & 1 & 0 & 0 & 1 & 0 \\
0 & 0 & 1 & 0 & 0 & 0 & 1 & 1 & 0 & 0 \\
1 & 0 & 0 & 1 & 1 & 0 & 0 & 0 & 0 & 1 \\
0 & 0 & 0 & 1 & 1 & 0 & 0 & 0 & 0 & 0 \\
0 & 1 & 0 & 0 & 0 & 1 & 0 & 0 & 1 & 0 \\
0 & 0 & 1 & 0 & 0 & 0 & 1 & 1 & 0 & 0 \\
0 & 0 & 1 & 0 & 0 & 0 & 1 & 1 & 0 & 0 \\
0 & 1 & 0 & 0 & 0 & 1 & 0 & 0 & 1 & 0 \\
0 & 0 & 0 & 1 & 0 & 0 & 0 & 0 & 0 & 1
\end{bmatrix}
$$

The matrix $R_2(D^s)$ is obtained by calculating $(I + A + A')^2 \#$ as follows:

$$R_2(D^s) = \begin{bmatrix} 1 & 0 & 0 & 1 & 1 & 0 & 0 & 0 & 0 & 1 \\ 0 & 1 & 0 & 0 & 0 & 1 & 0 & 0 & 1 & 0 \\ 0 & 0 & 1 & 0 & 0 & 0 & 1 & 1 & 0 & 0 \\ 1 & 0 & 0 & 1 & 1 & 0 & 0 & 0 & 0 & 1 \\ 1 & 0 & 0 & 1 & 1 & 0 & 0 & 0 & 0 & 1 \\ 0 & 1 & 0 & 0 & 0 & 1 & 0 & 0 & 1 & 0 \\ 0 & 0 & 1 & 0 & 0 & 0 & 1 & 1 & 0 & 0 \\ 0 & 0 & 1 & 0 & 0 & 0 & 1 & 1 & 0 & 0 \\ 0 & 1 & 0 & 0 & 0 & 1 & 0 & 0 & 1 & 0 \\ 1 & 0 & 0 & 1 & 1 & 0 & 0 & 0 & 0 & 1 \end{bmatrix}$$

It can be shown that $R_2(D^s) = R_3(D^s)$. Hence, $R_2(D^s) = R(D^s)$, the reachability matrix of D^s. The weak components of D can now be obtained from inspection of $R(D^s)$. The weak component containing the point v_i is given by the 1's in the ith row of $R(D^s)$. Thus, we see that the digraph D has the following weak components: $W_1 = \langle v_1 v_4 v_5 v_{10} \rangle$, $W_2 = \langle v_2 v_6 v_9 \rangle$, $W_3 = \langle v_3 v_7 v_8 \rangle$. In subsequent matrices, the points will be reordered so that the matrices are partitioned by the weak components of D.

We now proceed to construct the reachability matrix of the digraph D. The first step is to obtain the matrix $R_1(D)$ by calculating $I + A$.

$$R_1(D) = \begin{array}{c} \\ v_1 \\ v_4 \\ v_5 \\ v_{10} \\ v_2 \\ v_6 \\ v_9 \\ v_3 \\ v_7 \\ v_8 \end{array} \begin{array}{cccccccccc} v_1 & v_4 & v_5 & v_{10} & v_2 & v_6 & v_9 & v_3 & v_7 & v_8 \\ \left[\begin{array}{cccc|ccc|ccc} 1 & 1 & 0 & 0 & 0 & 0 & 0 & 0 & 0 & 0 \\ 1 & 1 & 1 & 1 & 0 & 0 & 0 & 0 & 0 & 0 \\ 0 & 0 & 1 & 0 & 0 & 0 & 0 & 0 & 0 & 0 \\ 0 & 0 & 0 & 1 & 0 & 0 & 0 & 0 & 0 & 0 \\ \hline 0 & 0 & 0 & 0 & 1 & 1 & 1 & 0 & 0 & 0 \\ 0 & 0 & 0 & 0 & 1 & 1 & 1 & 0 & 0 & 0 \\ 0 & 0 & 0 & 0 & 0 & 0 & 1 & 0 & 0 & 0 \\ \hline 0 & 0 & 0 & 0 & 0 & 0 & 0 & 1 & 1 & 1 \\ 0 & 0 & 0 & 0 & 0 & 0 & 0 & 1 & 1 & 1 \\ 0 & 0 & 0 & 0 & 0 & 0 & 0 & 0 & 1 & 1 \end{array}\right] \end{array}$$

We next calculate $(I + A)^2 \#$ to obtain $R_2(D)$. This matrix is also the reachability matrix $R(D)$, since it can be shown that $R_2(D) = R_3(D)$.

$$R_2(D) = R =
\begin{array}{c c}
 & \begin{array}{c c c c c c c c c c} v_1 & v_4 & v_5 & v_{10} & v_2 & v_6 & v_9 & v_3 & v_7 & v_8 \end{array} \\
\begin{array}{c} v_1 \\ v_4 \\ v_5 \\ v_{10} \\ v_2 \\ v_6 \\ v_9 \\ v_3 \\ v_7 \\ v_8 \end{array} &
\left[\begin{array}{c c c c | c c c | c c c}
1 & 1 & 1 & 1 & 0 & 0 & 0 & 0 & 0 & 0 \\
1 & 1 & 1 & 1 & 0 & 0 & 0 & 0 & 0 & 0 \\
0 & 0 & 1 & 0 & 0 & 0 & 0 & 0 & 0 & 0 \\
0 & 0 & 0 & 1 & 0 & 0 & 0 & 0 & 0 & 0 \\ \hline
0 & 0 & 0 & 0 & 1 & 1 & 1 & 0 & 0 & 0 \\
0 & 0 & 0 & 0 & 1 & 1 & 1 & 0 & 0 & 0 \\
0 & 0 & 0 & 0 & 0 & 0 & 1 & 0 & 0 & 0 \\ \hline
0 & 0 & 0 & 0 & 0 & 0 & 0 & 1 & 1 & 1 \\
0 & 0 & 0 & 0 & 0 & 0 & 0 & 1 & 1 & 1 \\
0 & 0 & 0 & 0 & 0 & 0 & 0 & 1 & 1 & 1
\end{array} \right]
\end{array}$$

Since the reachability matrix R is partitioned by its weak components and since these are relatively small, we can readily see that in D one of these is strong, one is strictly unilateral, and one is strictly weak.

To construct the connectedness matrix C we calculate the values within each weak component by the formula

$$c_{ij} = r_{ij} + r_{ji} + 1.$$

All remaining entries of C are 0. The resulting matrix is as follows.

$$C =
\begin{array}{c c}
 & \begin{array}{c c c c c c c c c c} v_1 & v_4 & v_5 & v_{10} & v_2 & v_6 & v_9 & v_3 & v_7 & v_8 \end{array} \\
\begin{array}{c} v_1 \\ v_4 \\ v_5 \\ v_{10} \\ v_2 \\ v_6 \\ v_9 \\ v_3 \\ v_7 \\ v_8 \end{array} &
\left[\begin{array}{c c c c | c c c | c c c}
3 & 3 & 2 & 2 & 0 & 0 & 0 & 0 & 0 & 0 \\
3 & 3 & 2 & 2 & 0 & 0 & 0 & 0 & 0 & 0 \\
2 & 2 & 3 & 1 & 0 & 0 & 0 & 0 & 0 & 0 \\
2 & 2 & 1 & 3 & 0 & 0 & 0 & 0 & 0 & 0 \\ \hline
0 & 0 & 0 & 0 & 3 & 3 & 2 & 0 & 0 & 0 \\
0 & 0 & 0 & 0 & 3 & 3 & 2 & 0 & 0 & 0 \\
0 & 0 & 0 & 0 & 2 & 2 & 3 & 0 & 0 & 0 \\ \hline
0 & 0 & 0 & 0 & 0 & 0 & 0 & 3 & 3 & 3 \\
0 & 0 & 0 & 0 & 0 & 0 & 0 & 3 & 3 & 3 \\
0 & 0 & 0 & 0 & 0 & 0 & 0 & 3 & 3 & 3
\end{array} \right]
\end{array}$$

The strong components of D are readily obtained by noting the entries of 3 in each row of the connectedness matrix C. We denote these as follows $S_1 = \langle v_1 v_4 \rangle$, $S_2 = \langle v_5 \rangle$, $S_3 = \langle v_{10} \rangle$, $S_4 = \langle v_2 v_6 \rangle$, $S_5 = \langle v_9 \rangle$, $S_6 = \langle v_3 v_7 v_8 \rangle$. With the aid of the adjacency matrix, we then construct the matrix A^* with the following result.

$$
A^* = \begin{array}{c} \\ S_1 \\ S_2 \\ S_3 \\ S_4 \\ S_5 \\ S_6 \end{array}
\begin{array}{c}
\begin{array}{cccccc} S_1 & S_2 & S_3 & S_4 & S_5 & S_6 \end{array} \\
\left[\begin{array}{cccccc}
0 & 1 & 1 & 0 & 0 & 0 \\
0 & 0 & 0 & 0 & 0 & 0 \\
0 & 0 & 0 & 0 & 0 & 0 \\
0 & 0 & 0 & 0 & 1 & 0 \\
0 & 0 & 0 & 0 & 0 & 0 \\
0 & 0 & 0 & 0 & 0 & 0
\end{array} \right]
\end{array}
$$

The distance matrix $N(D)$ is easily obtained from matrices $R_1(D)$ and $R_2(D)$ with the following result.

$$
N = \begin{array}{c} \\ v_1 \\ v_4 \\ v_5 \\ v_{10} \\ v_2 \\ v_6 \\ v_9 \\ v_3 \\ v_7 \\ v_8 \end{array}
\begin{array}{c}
\begin{array}{cccccccccc} v_1 & v_4 & v_5 & v_{10} & v_2 & v_6 & v_9 & v_3 & v_7 & v_8 \end{array} \\
\left[\begin{array}{cccc|ccc|ccc}
0 & 1 & 2 & 2 & \infty & \infty & \infty & \infty & \infty & \infty \\
1 & 0 & 1 & 1 & \infty & \infty & \infty & \infty & \infty & \infty \\
\infty & \infty & 0 & \infty & \infty & \infty & \infty & \infty & \infty & \infty \\
\infty & \infty & \infty & 0 & \infty & \infty & \infty & \infty & \infty & \infty \\ \hline
\infty & \infty & \infty & \infty & 0 & 1 & 1 & \infty & \infty & \infty \\
\infty & \infty & \infty & \infty & 1 & 0 & 1 & \infty & \infty & \infty \\
\infty & \infty & \infty & \infty & \infty & \infty & 0 & \infty & \infty & \infty \\ \hline
\infty & \infty & \infty & \infty & \infty & \infty & \infty & 0 & 1 & 1 \\
\infty & \infty & \infty & \infty & \infty & \infty & \infty & 1 & 0 & 1 \\
\infty & \infty & \infty & \infty & \infty & \infty & \infty & 2 & 1 & 0
\end{array} \right]
\end{array}
$$

The requested properties of the digraph of Example 2 may now be listed.

1. The distance from each point to every point is obtained from the distance matrix $N(D)$.

2. The category of connectedness of every pair of points is given by the matrix $C(D)$. Since D has more than one weak component, D is in C_0.

3. From the adjacency matrix A^* the condensed digraph D^* can be drawn immediately.

4. In A^* there are three columns whose sum is 0: S_1, S_4, S_6. We conclude, therefore, that the digraph D has twelve point bases, each consisting of one point from $\{v_1, v_4\}$, one from $\{v_2, v_6\}$, and one from $\{v_3, v_7, v_8\}$. From inspection of the rows of A^* we find that D has three point contrabases, each consisting of one point from $\{v_3, v_7, v_8\}$, together with v_5, v_9, and v_{10}.

5. Fundamental sets. Knowing the point bases of D, we obtain the fundamental sets from $R(D)$. These are $\{v_1, v_4, v_5, v_{10}\}$, $\{v_2, v_6, v_9\}$, and $\{v_3, v_7, v_8\}$.

6. Strong components. From the connectedness matrix, we find that the strong components are $\langle v_1 v_4 \rangle$, $\langle v_5 \rangle$, $\langle v_{10} \rangle$, $\langle v_2 v_6 \rangle$, $\langle v_9 \rangle$, and $\langle v_3 v_7 v_8 \rangle$.

7. We saw above how the weak components are obtained from the reachability matrix $R(D^s)$: $W_1 = \langle v_1 v_4 v_5 v_{10} \rangle$, $W_2 = \langle v_2 v_6 v_9 \rangle$, and $W_3 = \langle v_3 v_7 v_8 \rangle$.

SUMMARY

Our purpose in this chapter has been to study the interrelations between digraphs and matrices, so as to be able to exploit matrix algebra in working with digraphs. The chapter began with a brief introduction to some of the principal operations on matrices. In the following sections we saw how these operations can be employed to obtain information about a particular digraph D from various matrices associated with D.

The basic matrix associated with any digraph is the adjacency matrix A, first introduced in Chapter 1. By raising this matrix to the nth power, we get a matrix A^n whose entry $a_{ij}^{(n)}$ gives the number of sequences in D of length n from v_i to v_j. We later saw how to obtain a matrix P_n whose entries give the number of paths in D of length n from v_i to v_j. Another very useful matrix, the reachability matrix $R(D)$, can be constructed from $A(D)$ through the use of boolean arithmetic by which we obtain the matrix $A^n \#$ in which $a_{ij}^{(n)} \# = 1$ if and only if there exists in D at least one sequence of length n from v_i to v_j. In the reachability matrix, $r_{ij} = 1$ if and only if v_j is reachable from v_i in D. Another useful matrix, the distance matrix $N(D)$, can be constructed from the adjacency matrix, and this matrix gives the distance from each point of D to every other point. The distance matrix, in turn, can be used to construct the geodetic subgraph D_g from v_i to v_j, which contains all the geodesics in D from v_i to v_j.

The reachability matrix has many uses. Among the more important of these are: (a) to find the strong components of D, (b) to construct the condensed digraph D^* and its adjacency matrix A^*, (c) to find the point bases and point contrabases of D, (d) to identify the fundamental sets and contrafundamental sets, and (e) to construct another matrix, the connectedness matrix $C(D)$, which gives the connectedness category of every pair of points of D and hence the category of D itself.

Some of the uses of the distance matrix will become evident in the next chapter, when we take up the topic of limited reachability in a digraph. In the final chapter, we develop a different method (Corollary 14.4a) for computing the distance matrix of a digraph. This method is shorter but involves more general concepts than those for digraphs.

EXERCISES

1. Let A be the adjacency matrix of D. Show that $A \times A'$ has only 0's and 1's in it. What information about D does an entry of 1 in $A \times A'$ provide?

2. Let M be a matrix of 0's and 1's. What is $(M \times M)\#$? $(M + M)\#$?

3. Let D_1 represent a rumor network of a group of p people, and let D_2 represent a joke-telling network of the same group. Let A_1 and A_2 be the adjacency matrices of these two networks. (a) In terms of the realization, what does an entry of 2 in the matrix $A_1 + A_2$ mean? An entry of 1? An entry of 0? (b) In the matrix $A_1 - A_2$, what does an entry of $+1$ mean? -1? 0?

4. Given the digraph D shown in Figure 5.21, construct the matrix A^* and the digraph D^* from the matrices R and R^2.

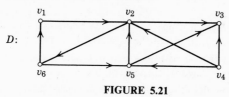

FIGURE 5.21

5. Show for any digraph D that if the diagonal entries of its matrix R^2 are all 1's, then D has a unique point basis consisting of those points that correspond in its adjacency matrix A to columns with sum 0.

6. Show that the digraph D is totally disconnected if and only if $C(D) = 3I$.

7. Prove the following statement: A digraph is disconnected if and only if there is an ordering of its points such that its connectedness matrix may be partitioned into submatrices in such a way that every nondiagonal submatrix is 0. (Hint: Use the weak components to form the partitioning.)

8. Prove the following statement: A digraph is strictly unilateral if and only if for some ordering of its points its connectedness matrix can be partitioned in such a way that every diagonal submatrix is $3J$ and every nondiagonal submatrix is $2J$.

9. Prove the following statement: A digraph has a point duobasis if and only if for some ordering of its points, its connectedness matrix can be partitioned in such a way that every diagonal submatrix is $3J$ and every nondiagonal submatrix is 0.

10. Show that for any strictly weak digraph the connectedness matrix C^* of D^* has 1's, 2's, and 3's in it.

11. For each of the digraphs shown in Figure 5.22, use matrix methods to find (a) the category of the digraph, (b) the condensed digraph, (c) the point bases and point contrabases, (d) the fundamental sets, (e) the weak components, and (f) the distance from each point to every other point.

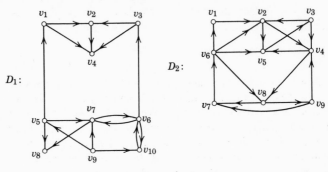

FIGURE 5.22

12. Prove or disprove: If $d_{ik} + 1 = d_{ij}$ and $d_{kj} = 1$, then $v_k v_j$ is on every geodesic from v_i to v_j.

13. Construct a digraph in which v_r and v_s are points on a geodesic from v_i to v_j and the line $v_r v_s$ is in D, but the equation $d_{ir} + 1 = d_{is}$ does not hold.

14. For any digraph D with adjacency matrix A, show that P_2 is obtained from A^2 by replacing its diagonal entries with 0's.

15. Let $d_{ij} > n$. Show that if v_k is the only point such that $d_{ik} = n$, then v_k is on every geodesic from v_i to v_j.

16. Prove the following statements: If $d_{ij} = n$ and there are exactly n entries d_{ik} less than n in the ith row of $N(D)$, there is a unique geodesic from v_i to v_j. In particular, if $d_{ij} = p - 1$, there is a unique geodesic from v_i to v_j.

6 • *Limited Reachability*

> Ill can he rule the great, that cannot
> reach the small.
> EDMUND SPENSER
> *The Faerie Queene*

There are many reasons for wanting to know whether one point of a digraph is reachable from another within a certain distance. For example, person v may be reachable from u in the digraph of a communication network, but there may be a distance beyond which it is not feasible for u to communicate to v because of costs or distortions entailed in each act of transmission. If v does not lie within this critical distance, then he will not receive messages originating with u. It will be useful, in general, to combine considerations of reachability and distance whenever a line of a digraph is associated with a unit of some empirical property such as time, cost, or amount of distortion.

The purpose of this chapter is to study certain features of digraphs which depend upon the relation of "reachability within a certain distance." We begin by associating two numbers with each point v of a digraph: the maximum distance from v and the maximum distance to v. These numbers indicate how "close" v is to a most distant point and how "close" such a point is to v. Thus, the smaller these numbers are, the more "central" is the location of v in the digraph. These numbers are also useful in estimating the "compactness" of a digraph, since the largest of them is the greatest distance between any pair of its points.

It will be recalled that the set $R_n(v)$ consists of those points reachable from v within distance n. If all points of D are in this set, we may say that v "covers" the digraph within distance n. We shall examine this notion in some detail and show how it is related to the concept of point basis.

In the final section of this chapter, we consider some other indexes based upon the sum of the finite distances from (or to) a point v, and indicate how these may be used in research on communication networks and the formal structure of organizations.

ASSOCIATED NUMBER PAIR OF A POINT

The *outnumber* of a point v, denoted o(v), is the largest of the numbers $d(v, u)$ for all u in D. Symbolically, o(v) = $\max_u d(v, u)$. The outnumber of a point v can be found at once from inspection of the distance matrix $N(D)$, since it is the largest entry in the row corresponding to v. The *innumber* of a point v, denoted i(v), is the largest of the numbers $d(u, v)$ for all u in D. Hence, in the distance matrix it is the largest entry in the column corresponding to v. Obviously, o(v) and i(v) are directional duals. The *associated number pair* of a point v is the ordered pair [o(v), i(v)].

Figure 6.1 shows three digraphs and their corresponding distance matrices. The associated number pair of each point is indicated beside the point. It can be verified that for each point v_i the first number is the largest entry in the ith row of the distance matrix while the second number is the largest entry in the ith column.

We recall that v is a source of D if the reachable set $R(v) = V$ and that v is a sink if the antecedent set $Q(v) = V$. We say that v is an *n-source* if $R_n(v) = V$ and that v is an *n-sink* if $Q_n(v) = V$. Thus, if v is an n-source, it can reach within distance n every point of the digraph. The following theorem and corollary follow immediately from these definitions.

Theorem 6.1. The outnumber o(v) is finite if and only if v is a source of D. The innumber i(v) is finite if and only if v is a sink of D.

Corollary 6.1a. If v is a source, then v is an n-source, where $n = $ o(v). By duality, if v is a sink, v is an n-sink where $n = $ i(v).

From the associated number pairs indicated in Figure 6.1 we draw the following conclusions: In D_1, point v_1 is a 2-source but not a sink, v_3 is a 2-sink but not a source, and v_2 and v_4 are neither sources nor sinks; D_2 contains one source v_1, which is a 2-source, but no sinks; and in D_3, points v_1 and v_3 are both 2-sources and 2-sinks, whereas v_2 and v_4 are both 3-sources and 3-sinks. It is evident that D_3 is strong. The next theorem characterizes strong digraphs in terms of the associated numbers of their points.

Theorem 6.2. The following statements are equivalent.
(1) D is strong.
(2) Every point of D has finite outnumber.

(3) Every point of D has finite innumber.

(4) D has a point of both finite outnumber and finite innumber.

The proof of this theorem is not difficult, and the reader may wish to construct it for himself.

D_1: diagram with $v_1[2, \infty]$, $v_4[\infty, \infty]$, $v_2[\infty, \infty]$, $v_3[\infty, 2]$

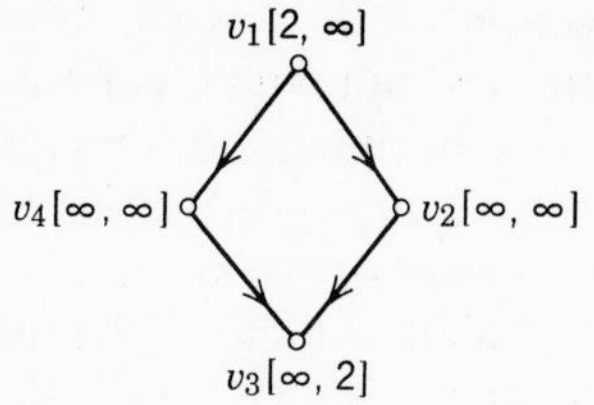

$$N(D_1) = \begin{array}{c} \\ v_1 \\ v_2 \\ v_3 \\ v_4 \\ i(v_i) \end{array} \begin{array}{cccc} v_1 & v_2 & v_3 & v_4 \\ 0 & 1 & 2 & 1 \\ \infty & 0 & 1 & \infty \\ \infty & \infty & 0 & \infty \\ \infty & \infty & 1 & 0 \\ \infty & \infty & 2 & \infty \end{array} \begin{array}{c} o(v_i) \\ 2 \\ \infty \\ \infty \\ \infty \\ \end{array}$$

D_2: diagram with $v_1[2, \infty]$, $v_2[\infty, \infty]$, $v_4[\infty, \infty]$, $v_3[\infty, \infty]$

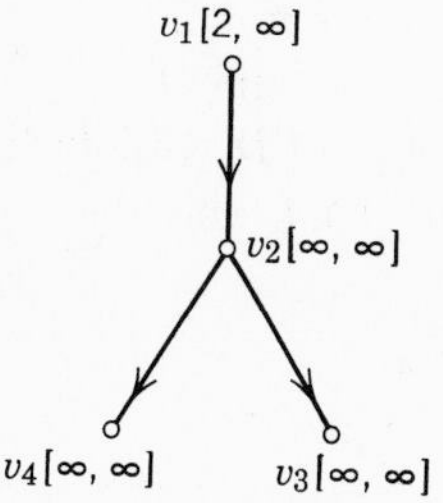

$$N(D_2) = \begin{array}{c} \\ v_1 \\ v_2 \\ v_3 \\ v_4 \\ i(v_i) \end{array} \begin{array}{cccc} v_1 & v_2 & v_3 & v_4 \\ 0 & 1 & 2 & 2 \\ \infty & 0 & 1 & 1 \\ \infty & \infty & 0 & \infty \\ \infty & \infty & \infty & 0 \\ \infty & \infty & \infty & \infty \end{array} \begin{array}{c} o(v_i) \\ 2 \\ \infty \\ \infty \\ \infty \\ \end{array}$$

D_3: diagram with $v_1[2, 2]$, $v_4[3, 3]$, $v_2[3, 3]$, $v_3[2, 2]$

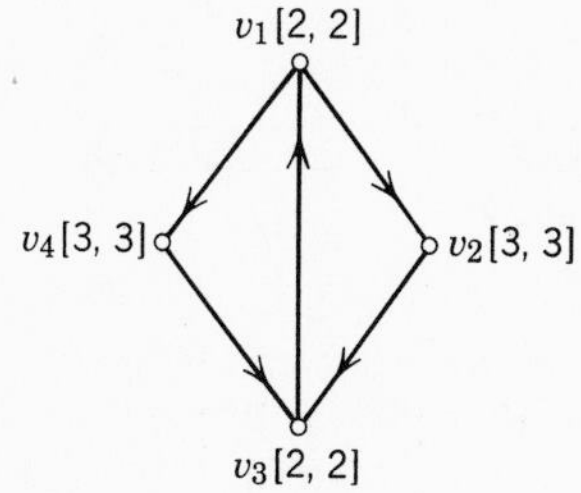

$$N(D_3) = \begin{array}{c} \\ v_1 \\ v_2 \\ v_3 \\ v_4 \\ i(v_i) \end{array} \begin{array}{cccc} v_1 & v_2 & v_3 & v_4 \\ 0 & 1 & 2 & 1 \\ 2 & 0 & 1 & 3 \\ 1 & 2 & 0 & 2 \\ 2 & 3 & 1 & 0 \\ 2 & 3 & 2 & 3 \end{array} \begin{array}{c} o(v_i) \\ 2 \\ 3 \\ 2 \\ 3 \\ \end{array}$$

FIGURE 6.1

RADII AND CENTERS

The associated number pairs of the points of a digraph provide information concerning both the "compactness" of the digraph as a whole and the "centrality" of points within the digraph. Consider the two digraphs shown in Figure 6.2. We see that the minimum outnumber of D_1 is 2 while that of D_2 is 5. Thus, if these digraphs are taken to represent communication networks, we know that a message originating with v_1 or v_6 in D_1 will reach everyone in 2 steps but that a message originating anywhere in D_2 will require 5 steps to reach everyone. We might say, then, that D_1 is more compact than D_2. Moreover, in D_1 we note that v_1 and v_6 have the smallest outnumbers, so that these points are most centrally located. Inspection of D_1 reveals, however, that the minimum outnumber of a digraph need not equal its minimum innumber, for these numbers are 2 and 3. In describing the compactness of digraphs or the centrality of points within a digraph, therefore, it is necessary to consider the outnumbers and innumbers separately.

The *outradius* $r_0(D)$ of a digraph D is the smallest finite outnumber in D. Thus, in Figure 6.2 $r_0(D_1) = 2$ and $r_0(D_2) = 5$. The *inradius* $r_i(D)$ of a digraph D is the smallest finite innumber of D. In Figure 6.2 $r_i(D_1) = 3$, and $r_i(D_2) = 5$. We note that in Figure 6.1 digraph D_2 has no inradius, since its minimum innumber is not finite.

A point with smallest finite outnumber in a digraph D is an *outcentral point*, and the set of such points is the *outcenter* of D. Similarly, a point with smallest finite innumber is an *incentral point*, and the set of such

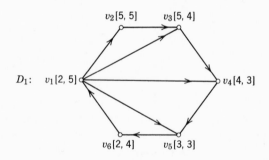

$$D_1: \quad v_1[2, 5]$$

with $v_2[5, 5]$, $v_3[5, 4]$, $v_4[4, 3]$, $v_6[2, 4]$, $v_5[3, 3]$

		v_1	v_2	v_3	v_4	v_5	v_6	$o(v_i)$
	v_1	0	1	1	1	1	2	2
	v_2	5	0	1	2	3	4	5
$N(D_1) =$	v_3	4	5	0	1	2	3	5
	v_4	3	4	4	0	1	2	4
	v_5	2	3	3	3	0	1	3
	v_6	1	2	2	2	2	0	2
$i(v_i)$		5	5	4	3	3	4	

FIGURE 6.2

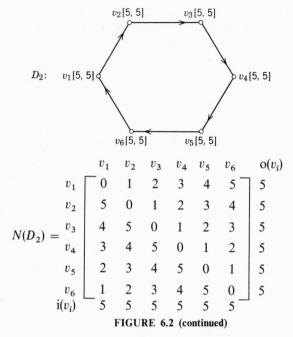

$v_2[5, 5]$ $v_3[5, 5]$

D_2: $v_1[5, 5]$ $v_4[5, 5]$

$v_6[5, 5]$ $v_5[5, 5]$

$$N(D_2) = \begin{array}{c|cccccc|c} & v_1 & v_2 & v_3 & v_4 & v_5 & v_6 & o(v_i) \\ \hline v_1 & 0 & 1 & 2 & 3 & 4 & 5 & 5 \\ v_2 & 5 & 0 & 1 & 2 & 3 & 4 & 5 \\ v_3 & 4 & 5 & 0 & 1 & 2 & 3 & 5 \\ v_4 & 3 & 4 & 5 & 0 & 1 & 2 & 5 \\ v_5 & 2 & 3 & 4 & 5 & 0 & 1 & 5 \\ v_6 & 1 & 2 & 3 & 4 & 5 & 0 & 5 \\ \hline i(v_i) & 5 & 5 & 5 & 5 & 5 & 5 & \end{array}$$

FIGURE 6.2 (continued)

points is the *incenter*. In digraph D_1 of Figure 6.2, the outcenter is $\{v_1, v_6\}$ and the outradius is 2. Clearly, each of these points can reach every point of the digraph in two steps or less, and no other points are so favorably located. The incenter of D_1 is $\{v_4, v_5\}$, and since the inradius is 3 we know that every point of D_1 can reach v_4 and v_5 within 3 steps. In digraph D_2, the situation is quite different, because every point is both outcentral and incentral; no point has a more favorable location than any other. In each of these digraphs we note that the outnumber $o(v)$ of an outcentral point v is the outradius r_0 and that each outcentral point is an n-source, where $n = r_0$. This observation is stated in general form in the next theorem.

Theorem 6.3. Let $r_0(D) = n$. Then v is an outcentral point if and only if v is an n-source.

Theorem 6.3'. Let $r_i(D) = n$. Then v is an incentral point if and only if v is an n-sink.

Corollary 6.3a. Any two outcentral points lie in the same strong component, and by duality any two incentral points lie in the same strong component.

Theorem 6.3 establishes that every outcentral point is an n-source, for some n. Clearly, then, every outcentral point is a source. By Theorem

4.8, all sources lie in the same strong component. It follows, therefore, that all outcentral points lie in the same strong component. The remainder of the corollary follows by directional duality.

In the strictly unilateral digraph shown in Figure 6.3 the outcenter is $\{v_1, v_2, v_3\}$. We see that these points are all contained in the strong component $\langle v_1 v_2 v_3 v_4 \rangle$. It should be noted that v_4 is a source and lies in the same strong component with the outcentral points but is not itself outcentral. In fact, outcentral point v_1 can reach outcentral points v_2 or v_3 only by a path containing v_4. The incenter of this digraph is $\{v_6, v_7\}$, and both of these points lie in the same strong component. It follows from Corollary 6.3a that in a communication network any two outcentral persons and any two incentral persons can engage in two-way communication. But, as noted above, it may be necessary for them to send messages via a person who is not central.

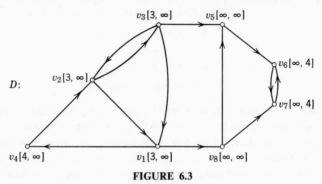

FIGURE 6.3

Corollary 6.3b. If D is unilateral, then D has at least one outcentral point and at least one incentral point.

This corollary is proved by making use of Corollary 4.10a, which asserts that every unilateral digraph has at least one source and at least one sink. The digraph of Figure 6.3 illustrates the corollary. It should be noted that the converse of the corollary is not true in general; for if the line $v_8 v_5$ were removed from the digraph of Figure 6.3 it would become strictly weak but still have an outcenter and an incenter.

CENTRALITY AND PERIPHERALITY IN STRONG DIGRAPHS

In the preceding section, we made use of the minimum outnumber and the minimum innumber of a digraph. We now consider the maximum value of these numbers. The next theorem provides basic information for this discussion.

Theorem 6.4. For any digraph D, the maximum outnumber and the maximum innumber are equal, and each is the largest entry in the distance matrix $N(D)$.

This theorem follows at once from the fact, noted above, that the outnumber and innumber of a point v_i are respectively the maximum in the ith row and in the ith column of $N(D)$. Therefore, the maximum entry in $N(D)$ must be both the maximum outnumber and the maximum innumber.

We see in Figure 6.2 that the maximum outnumber and the maximum innumber of D_1 are both 5. Thus, the greatest distance between any two points of this digraph is 5. It should be apparent that the maximum outnumber (or innumber) is finite if and only if the digraph is strong, for only in a strong digraph are all pairs of points mutually reachable. For this reason, the maximum outnumber and maximum innumber are interesting only for strong digraphs.

The *diameter δ of a strong digraph D* is the largest outnumber (or innumber) in D. In other words, the diameter of a strong digraph is the largest distance between any pair of points. A point with greatest outnumber in a strong digraph D is an *outperipheral point*, and the set of such points is the *outperiphery* of D. Similarly, a point with greatest innumber is an *inperipheral point*, and the set of such points is the *inperiphery*. In Figure 6.2, the diameter of D_1 is 5, its outperiphery is $\{v_2, v_3\}$, and its inperiphery is $\{v_1, v_2\}$. In terms of the communication example, then, we know that it will take five units of time for a message to reach everyone from v_2 or v_3 and that this is the longest time required to reach everyone from a single person. We also know that v_1 and v_2 are the only ones who cannot receive messages from everyone in less than five units of time.

The three strong digraphs shown in Figure 6.4 illustrate some of the many possible combinations of centrality and peripherality. From the associated number pairs we can readily identify the various centers and peripheries. In digraphs D_1 and D_3 the outcenter coincides with the incenter and the outperiphery coincides with the inperiphery. In D_2, however, the outcenter and the incenter are disjoint, as are the outperiphery and the inperiphery. And in this digraph one point is both incentral and outperipheral. It is interesting to note that in D_3 two points are both outcentral and incentral and yet they are as far apart from each other as either is from any point of the digraph. We observe, moreover, that in D_3 the outcenter generates a disconnected subgraph, as do the incenter, the outperiphery, and the inperiphery.

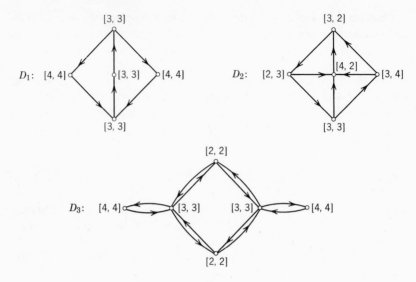

FIGURE 6.4

Finally, we make an observation concerning symmetric digraphs. Since the distance function of a symmetric digraph is symmetric, it follows that for each point the outnumber equals the innumber. Thus, for any symmetric digraph the outcenter and the incenter are identical, as are the outperiphery and the inperiphery. This conclusion is illustrated by the symmetric digraph D_3.

Just as a strong digraph has an outcenter, incenter, outperiphery, and inperiphery, it also has an outradius, inradius, and diameter. The next two theorems specify some necessary relationships among these values.

Theorem 6.5. Let D be a strong digraph with p points, outradius r_0, inradius r_i, and diameter δ. Then,

$$1 \leq r_0 \leq \delta \leq (p - 1)$$

and, by duality,

$$1 \leq r_i \leq \delta \leq (p - 1)$$

It follows directly from the definitions of these terms that the diameter of a digraph is at least as great as its outradius. It is obvious, too, that in a complete symmetric digraph K_p every outnumber is 1, giving the lower bound to both r_0 and δ. Finally, since the longest possible path of any digraph has length $(p - 1)$, both the minimum and the maximum outnumbers are at most $(p - 1)$.

Theorem 6.6. Let D be a strong digraph with p points, outradius r_0, and inradius r_i. Then,

$$r_0 \leq \frac{r_i + (p - 1)}{2}$$

and, by duality,

$$r_i \leq \frac{r_0 + (p - 1)}{2}$$

Since the proof of this theorem is rather complicated, we shall not present it here. Figure 6.5, however, provides an illustration. The only outcentral point of this digraph is v_1, whose outnumber is 3. The incentral points of the digraph are v_2 and v_3, which have innumber 5. Thus, $p = 8$, $r_0 = 3$, and $r_i = 5$. The two inequalities of Theorem 6.6 assert respectively that

$$3 \leq \frac{5 + 7}{2} = 6$$

and

$$5 \leq \frac{3 + 7}{2} = 5$$

both of which we see are true.

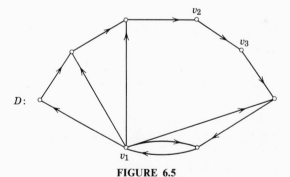

FIGURE 6.5

Since $(p - 1)$ is the length of the longest possible path in a digraph with p points, Theorem 6.6 indicates that the outradius of a digraph is at most the average of the inradius and the longest possible path. Also, the difference between the outradius and the inradius is no greater than the difference between either of them and the longest possible path.

We now present several corollaries of Theorem 6.6 which state its inequalities in different form. We first observe that simply by rearranging the terms of these inequalities, we obtain

$$r_0 \geq 2r_i - (p - 1)$$

and

$$r_i \geq 2r_0 - (p - 1)$$

Combining these inequalities with those of Theorem 6.6, we obtain the first corollary, which expresses both the maximum and minimum possible values of the outradius or the inradius when the other is known.

Corollary 6.6a. Let D be a strong digraph with p points, outradius r_0, and inradius r_i. Then,

$$2r_i - (p - 1) \leq r_0 \leq \frac{r_i + (p - 1)}{2}$$

and, by duality,

$$2r_0 - (p - 1) \leq r_i \leq \frac{r_0 + (p - 1)}{2}$$

To illustrate this corollary, let us suppose that we are interested in a digraph with 12 points and want to fix the outradius at some value, say $r_0 = 7$. By inserting these values for p and r_0 into the appropriate inequality of this corollary, we find that the inradius must satisfy $3 \leq r_i \leq 9$.

These inequalities may now be solved for p to yield the next corollary.

Corollary 6.6b. Let D be a strong digraph with p points, outradius r_0, and inradius r_i. Then,

$$p \geq \max \{2r_0 - r_i + 1, 2r_i - r_0 + 1\}$$

This corollary gives the lower bound on the number of points in a strong digraph for given values of its outradius and inradius. Clearly, if we take specified values for r_0 and r_i, then the minimum number of points among all digraphs having these values is

$$p = \max \{2r_0 - r_i + 1, 2r_i - r_0 + 1\}$$

Thus, suppose that we wish to construct a strong digraph with $r_0 = 5$ and $r_i = 3$. Then Corollary 6.6b tells us that any such digraph must have at least $p = \max\{8, 2\} = 8$ points. Figure 6.5 shows such a digraph.

Theorems 6.5 and 6.6 give upper and lower bounds on the values of r_0, r_i, and δ. We may ask, however, whether there are digraphs for all values falling within these bounds. The answer to this question is affirmative, although its proof is so complicated that we omit it here. The basic idea, however, can be illustrated by showing how, starting with the digraph of Figure 6.6, which has 8 points, outradius 1, and inradius 4, we can add lines to make the inradius 3 or 2. Clearly, the incentral points of this digraph are v_4 and v_5, having innumber 4. We see that there is only one point from which the distance to v_4 is 4, namely v_5. Adding the line v_6v_0 reduces this distance to 3. Thus, the resulting digraph, shown in Figure 6.7, has 8 points, inradius 3, and outradius 1. To reduce the inradius to 2, we can add v_5v_0 and v_1v_4. Clearly, we could start with a digraph having any number of points and proceed similarly. In general, given any two positive integers m and n, there is a strong digraph with outradius m and inradius n.

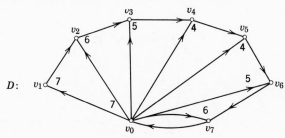

FIGURE 6.6

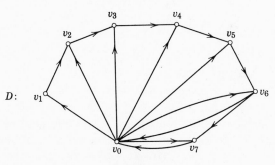

FIGURE 6.7

MINIMAL *n*-COVERS AND *n*-BASES

It was established in Corollary 6.1a that if v is a source of D, then v is an n-source, where $n = o(v)$. Thus, if we know that a point v is a source of D and if we know that $o(v) = n$, we can conclude that every point of D is reachable from v within n steps, that is, $R_n(v) = V$. It will be recalled that a source is a special instance of a point basis, namely, one consisting of a single point. Analogous statements can be made, of course, concerning sinks and point contrabases.

We now consider how concepts of reachability and distance may be combined to produce the concept of an n-basis. To do so, we need the next definition. The *n-reachable set* $R_n(S)$ is the collection of points reachable from a point of S within distance n. Clearly, $R_n(S)$ is a subset of $R(S)$. This concept is illustrated by the digraph shown in Figure 6.8. Suppose that we are interested in the 2-reachable set $R_2(S)$, where $S = \{v_1, v_4\}$. First we find $R_2(v_1)$ and $R_2(v_4)$. These are $R_2(v_1)$ $= \{v_1, v_2, v_3, v_5, v_6\}$ and $R_2(v_4) = \{v_2, v_3, v_4, v_5, v_6\}$. The set $R_2(S)$ is clearly the union of these two sets, which in this case is the set of all points of D; hence $R_2(S) = V$.

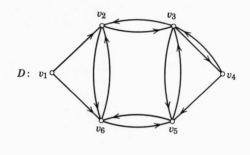

$$N(D) = \begin{array}{c} \\ v_1 \\ v_2 \\ v_3 \\ v_4 \\ v_5 \\ v_6 \end{array} \begin{array}{cccccc} v_1 & v_2 & v_3 & v_4 & v_5 & v_6 \\ \left[\begin{array}{cccccc} 0 & 1 & 2 & 3 & 2 & 1 \\ \infty & 0 & 1 & 2 & 2 & 1 \\ \infty & 1 & 0 & 1 & 1 & 2 \\ \infty & 2 & 1 & 0 & 1 & 2 \\ \infty & 2 & 1 & 2 & 0 & 1 \\ \infty & 1 & 2 & 3 & 1 & 0 \end{array}\right] \end{array}$$

FIGURE 6.8

A set S of points is an *n-cover* for a digraph D if $R_n(S) = V$, that is, every point of D is reachable from a point of an n-cover in no more than n steps. Thus, in Figure 6.8 the set $S = \{v_1, v_4\}$ is a 2-cover. An n-cover S is said to be minimal if no proper subset of S is an n-cover. In our example, the set S is clearly a minimal 2-cover. Obviously, S is also a 3-cover, but we see that it is not a minimal 3-cover, since its proper subset $\{v_1\}$ is a 3-cover.

It will be recalled from Chapter 4 that a point basis B is a minimal collection of points from which all points of D are reachable, that is, a minimal set B such that $R(B) = V$. The definition of a minimal n-cover is analogous to that of point basis. We must note, however, that the analogy is not complete. According to Theorem 4.2, a set B of points is a point basis if and only if it satisfies the following two conditions: (1) $R(B) = V$, and (2) no point of B is reachable from any other. The analogue of the first statement clearly holds for minimal n-covers, but the analogue of the second does not. This fact is illustrated in Figure 6.8 by the set $\{v_1, v_2\}$, which is a minimal 2-cover, but v_2 is reachable from v_1 at a distance 1. Because of these considerations we need a concept satisfying both conditions. An *n-basis* B is a set of points satisfying the following conditions: (1) B is an n-cover, and (2) no point of B is reachable from any other within distance n. In Figure 6.8, $\{v_1, v_4\}$ is a 2-basis, but $\{v_1, v_2\}$ is not. And we see that v_1 is a 3-source. Clearly, v is an n-source if and only if $\{v\}$ is an n-basis.

Our observations concerning the concepts of n-basis and minimal n-cover may be summarized in the following theorem.

Theorem 6.7. Every n-basis is a minimal n-cover (but not conversely).

This result means that any statement giving a sufficient condition for the existence of an n-basis also gives a sufficient condition for the existence of a minimal n-cover.

It is evident that each concept introduced in this section has a directional dual. These are as follows: (1) The *n-antecedent set* $Q_n(S)$ is the collection of points which can reach a point of S within distance n; (2) a set S of points is an *n-contracover* for a digraph D if $Q_n(S) = V$; and (3) an *n-contrabasis* B is an n-contracover such that no point of B is reachable from any other within distance n. In the remainder of this chapter we leave to the reader the task of forming the directional duals of the theorems and corollaries.

The next theorem establishes a relationship between point bases and n-bases of a digraph.

Theorem 6.8. Let r be the greatest finite distance in a digraph D with p points. Then, every point basis of D is an n-basis for each $n \geq r$. In particular, every point basis is a $(p - 1)$-basis.

Since every point of D is reachable from a point of its point basis by a path of length at most r, and since no two points of the point basis are reachable from each other, the first statement of the theorem is proved. The second statement follows at once, since the greatest possible finite distance in D is $p - 1$.

This theorem is illustrated by the digraph of Figure 6.9. It can be seen that the largest finite distance in this digraph is 3. Moreover, there are two point bases: $\{v_1, v_5\}$ and $\{v_2, v_5\}$. In keeping with Theorem 6.8, each of these is a 3-basis. It may be noted in passing that $\{v_2, v_5\}$ is also a 1-basis but $\{v_1, v_5\}$ is not.

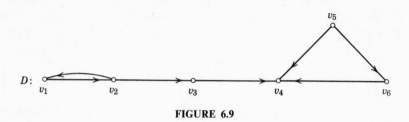

FIGURE 6.9

In the light of Theorem 6.8, one might wonder whether a digraph that has an n-basis must necessarily have an $(n + 1)$-basis. It is easy to see that this is not the case. Digraph D_1 of Figure 6.10 consists of a cycle of length 4 and has a 1-basis but no 2-basis. It is also possible for a digraph to have an n-basis but not an $(n - 1)$-basis. For example, digraph D_2 consisting of a cycle of length 3 has a 2-basis but no 1-basis.

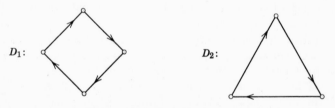

FIGURE 6.10

The fact that for any n less than $p - 1$ there may be a digraph without an n-basis makes the establishment of a criterion for the existence of an n-basis an interesting topic. Unfortunately, no such criterion is known which applies to digraphs in general. However, the next theorem shows that the question of the existence of an n-basis can be settled if the corresponding existence question for 1-bases can be.

In order to state this theorem, we need to construct a new digraph $D^{(n)}$ from a given digraph D. The digraph $D^{(n)}$ has the same point set as D and its lines indicate reachability in D in at most n steps. More specifically, line uv is in $D^{(n)}$ if and only if there is a path in D from u to v of length n or less. Of course $D^{(n)}$ is closely related to the matrix $R_n(D)$ discussed in Chapter 5. Indeed, the adjacency matrix of $D^{(n)}$ is obtainable from $R_n(D)$ by replacing all diagonal elements of this matrix by 0, that is, $A(D^{(n)}) = R_n(D) - I$. And if n is at least as large as the length of the longest path of D, then $D^{(n)} = D^t$, the transitive closure of D. Figure 6.11 shows a digraph D together with $D^{(2)}$ and $D^{(3)}$. It will be noticed that D is the digraph of Figure 6.9.

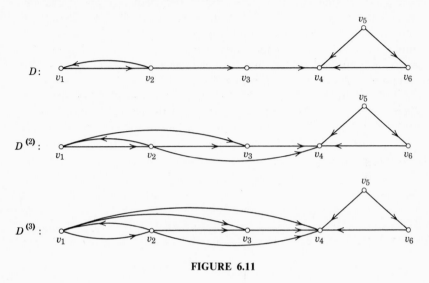

FIGURE 6.11

Theorem 6.9. A set B of points is an n-basis for a digraph D if and only if it is a 1-basis for $D^{(n)}$.

This theorem[1] follows at once from the construction of $D^{(n)}$. Clearly, $R_n(B) = V$ for D if and only if $R_1(B) = V$ for $D^{(n)}$. And a point v is not reachable from u within distance n in D if and only if v is not reachable from u within distance 1 in $D^{(n)}$.

The digraphs shown in Figure 6.11 illustrate Theorem 6.9. As noted in discussing Figure 6.9, both $\{v_1, v_5\}$ and $\{v_2, v_5\}$ are 3-bases for D, and we find that these are the only 1-bases for $D^{(3)}$.

Since the formation of $D^{(n)}$ from D does not change the reachability relation, it follows that D and $D^{(n)}$ have the same reachability matrix. Thus, they are in the same connectedness category. Moreover, if one is acyclic, so is the other. It will be shown later, in Corollary 6.12a, that every acyclic digraph has a unique 1-basis. We may, therefore, use Theorem 6.9 to derive the following theorem.

[1] Theorems 6.9 and 6.12 are due to Harary and Richardson (1959).

Theorem 6.10. Every acyclic digraph has a unique n-basis for every positive integer n.

Example. The staff of a research organization wanted to select a committee to participate in setting personnel and administrative policy. It was hoped that the committee would best represent the needs and viewpoints of the entire staff but still not be too large. How should the committee be chosen? The following unusual election procedure was employed. Each staff member indicated on his ballot the person who, in his opinion, best understood his needs and would best represent his viewpoint. But instead of forming the committee from those receiving the largest number of votes, a structural analysis was made of the votes. Each ballot was signed so that a digraph of the election could be constructed. If person u voted for person v, a line vu was drawn to indicate that "v best represents the viewpoint of u." The obtained digraph is shown in Figure 6.12.

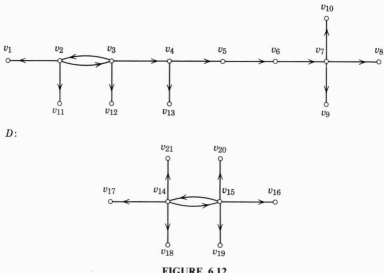

FIGURE 6.12

It is interesting to note, first of all, that had the usual voting procedure been employed the tabulation of votes received (indicated by the out-degree of the points) would have produced the following results: v_{14} and v_{15} received 4 votes each, while v_2, v_3, and v_7 received 3 votes each. It is fairly evident from the digraph of the votes that a committee composed of v_{14}, v_{15}, and one of v_2, v_3, or v_7 would not have been optimally representative of the staff, for the weak component containing

v_{14} and v_{15} would be overly weighted and the remaining weak component would be rather poorly represented.

A little thought about the structural properties of the digraph suggested a better solution. A committee consisting of a 2-cover of the digraph would contain members who were either the direct choice or chosen by the direct choice of every person on the staff. And if the committee were restricted to those consisting of a minimal 2-cover, the committee would be as small as possible and still have this property. And, if a 2-basis could be found, it would produce a committee none of whose members represent any other.

From the distance matrix of the digraph, the following result was obtained:

$$R_2(v_3) = \{v_1, v_2, v_3, v_4, v_5, v_{11}, v_{12}, v_{13}\}$$

$$R_2(v_6) = \{v_6, v_7, v_8, v_9, v_{10}\}$$

$$R_2(v_{14}) = R_2(v_{15}) = \{v_{14}, v_{15}, v_{16}, v_{17}, v_{18}, v_{19}, v_{20}, v_{21}\}$$

It can be seen that $\{v_3, v_6, v_{14}\}$ and $\{v_3, v_6, v_{15}\}$ are both 2-bases of the voting digraph. It can also be established that there are no other 2-bases. Thus, a committee consisting of either of these sets of people would satisfy the requirements for a representative committee. A coin was tossed to select between v_{14} and v_{15}. The resulting committee of v_3, v_6, and v_{14} was quite different from the one that would have been chosen by the usual procedure. Since no comparison was possible between the traditional method and this more structural one, no firm conclusion can be reached as to which produced "better" results, but intuition favors the structural approach as the more representative.

It should be noted that in using this procedure we might obtain a digraph that does not contain a 2-basis. However, it must contain a 2-cover. We could then form the committee from a minimal 2-cover. This committee will have the same properties as that produced by a 2-basis, except that at least one member of the committee will be the direct or indirect choice of one other member.

1-COVERS AND 1-BASES

In this section we investigate the specialized concepts of 1-cover and 1-basis. The concept of 1-basis has particular importance in view of the result given in Theorem 6.9. The reason is that if we can establish that $D^{(n)}$ has a 1-basis for any value of $n \leq \delta$, we know at once that D has an n-basis. Moreover, 1-bases are of interest in their own right, and at the end of this section we shall describe their applicability to the theory of games.

We begin by noting that though every digraph has a 1-cover, it need not have a 1-basis. For example, in a cycle of length 3, any two points constitute a (minimal) 1-cover, but there is no 1-basis. We also observe that two minimal 1-covers or two 1-bases need not have the same number of points, as is shown in the digraph of Figure 6.13, where two 1-bases are indicated respectively by circles and squares.

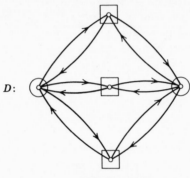

D:

FIGURE 6.13

Obviously every isolate of a digraph is in every 1-basis. The next two theorems show that transmitters play a special role in the formation of 1-bases.

Theorem 6.11. Every transmitter of a digraph is in every 1-cover, and hence in every 1-basis.

This is immediate, since no transmitter is reachable from any other point.

Corollary 6.11a. In a digraph D, every strong component that is a transmitter of D^* contains at least one point in every 1-cover and hence in every 1-basis.

By the digraph $D - R_1(v)$, we mean the subgraph of D which contains all points of D, except the set $R_1(v)$, and all lines of D, except those incident with a point of $R_1(v)$. Figure 6.14 shows a digraph D and the corresponding digraph $D - R_1(v_1)$.

Theorem 6.12. If v is a transmitter of a digraph D, then every 1-basis of D contains v together with a 1-basis of $D - R_1(v)$.

If D has a 1-basis B, then the transmitter v of D is in B by Theorem 6.11. Clearly v is the only point of $R_1(v)$ which is in B. By definition of a 1-basis, it follows that $B - \{v\}$ is a 1-basis of $D - R_1(v)$, proving the theorem.

Of course, if $D - R_1(v)$ has a transmitter, this process can be repeated. By application of this procedure to the digraph D of Figure 6.14, we find that $\{v_1, v_2\}$ is a 1-basis. Since any acyclic digraph has a point of indegree 0 and so do all its subgraphs, we have the following corollary.

Corollary 6.12a. Every acyclic digraph has a unique 1-basis.[2]

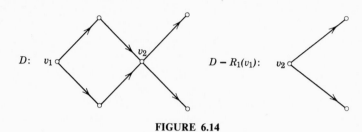

$D:$ v_1 v_2 $D - R_1(v_1):$ v_2

FIGURE 6.14

From this result it follows immediately that if a digraph $D^{(n)}$ is acyclic it has a unique 1-basis. And from Theorem 6.9 it follows that this 1-basis is a unique n-basis of the digraph D. It was this reasoning which led to the statement of Theorem 6.10 that every acyclic digraph has a unique n-basis for every n.

Theorem 6.12 gives one sufficient condition for a digraph to have a 1-basis. We shall present another and quite different one in Theorem 6.15. In order to do so, however, we need to make a brief excursion into the study of cycles of odd length. For brevity, we call a cycle of odd length an odd cycle.

Theorem 6.13. If D has a closed sequence of odd length, it has an odd cycle.

Let L be a closed sequence of D of odd length. By Theorem 2.7, D has a cycle. If this cycle is odd, the theorem is verified. But if it is even, we can form another closed sequence L_1 from L by deleting this cycle. Obviously, L_1 is also of odd length. We can continue deleting even cycles from the closed sequence L until we find an odd cycle, proving the theorem.

Theorem 6.14. A strong digraph has no odd cycles if and only if its points can be partitioned into two sets V_1 and V_2 such that every line has one point in each of these two sets.

To prove this theorem, we first take as given that D has no odd cycles. Let v be any point of D, let V_1 be the set of points of D at odd distances

[2] This result was first given by von Neumann and Morgenstern (1944).

from v, and let V_2 be the set of remaining points (at even distances from v). We shall show that there is no line joining two points of V_2. The corresponding argument for V_1 is similar. Let u and w be any two points of V_2. By the definition of V_2, there are paths L_1 from v to u and L_2 from v to w, both of even length. Since D is strong there is a path L_3 from w to v. The closed sequence L_2, followed by L_3 is also of even length, since any closed sequence of odd length contains an odd cycle (by Theorem 6.13) and, by hypothesis, D has no odd cycles. But if D were to contain line uw, then the closed sequence formed by L_1, then L_3, and uw would be odd. By Theorem 6.13, this closed sequence would contain an odd cycle, contrary to the hypothesis that D has no odd cycles.

We next take as given that the points of D can be partitioned into V_1 and V_2 so that every line has one point in each of these two sets. It follows at once that every cycle of D contains an even number of lines, since the points of any cycle must be alternately in V_1 and V_2.

Four corollaries of Theorem 6.14 may now be stated which give information concerning 1-bases of strong digraphs.

Corollary 6.14a. Every nontrivial strong digraph with no odd cycles has at least two 1-bases.

Let V_1 and V_2 be the two sets of Theorem 6.14. Thus, no two points in the same set are adjacent. Also, every point of V_2 is adjacent from some point of V_1, since if a point were not, D would not be strong. Therefore V_1, and similarly V_2, is a 1-basis.

Corollary 6.14b. A digraph consisting of an even cycle alone has exactly two 1-bases. A digraph consisting of an odd cycle alone has no 1-bases.

Let D be a digraph consisting of a single cycle. To construct a 1-basis, we may choose any point as the first to include. After that we must alternately exclude and include points as we proceed around the cycle. The last included point and the first are not adjacent if and only if the cycle is even. In this case there are exactly two 1-bases, both of which can be constructed in this manner. Shown in Figure 6.15 is a cycle of length 6 in which the two 1-bases are $\{v_1, v_3, v_5\}$ and $\{v_2, v_4, v_6\}$.

Corollary 6.14c. No more than one pair of 1-bases can partition the set V of points of a strong digraph so that every line has exactly one point in each set of this partition.

Suppose that there are two pairs of 1-bases, U_1 and U_2, V_1 and V_2, which thus partition V. Let v be a point in both U_1 and V_1. Then all

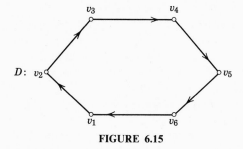

FIGURE 6.15

points adjacent from v must be in both U_2 and V_2. Since these are both 1-bases, all points at distance 2 from v must lie in both U_1 and V_1. By continuing, we see that $U_1 = V_1$ and $U_2 = V_2$, proving the corollary.

In the digraph of Figure 6.16, the sets $\{u_1, u_2, u_3\}$ and $\{v_1, v_2, v_3\}$ form the partition of Theorem 6.14 and hence are 1-bases. The points u_1 and v_1 also constitute a 1-basis, but in accordance with this corollary, $V - u_1 - v_1$ is not a 1-basis, for u_2 and v_3 are adjacent. The next corollary tells us, however, that this is a 1-cover.

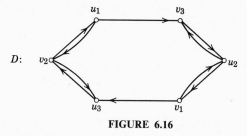

FIGURE 6.16

Corollary 6.14d. If B is a 1-basis of a strong digraph, then $V - B$ is a 1-cover.

Since D is strong, every point v of B is adjacent from some point u. Since B is a 1-basis, u must be in $V - B$. Hence $V - B$ is a 1-cover.

The corollaries of Theorem 6.14 gives sufficient conditions for a strong digraph to have a 1-basis. The next theorem[3] provides a sufficient condition, in addition to that of Theorem 6.12, for any digraph to have one.

Theorem 6.15. Any digraph with no odd cycles has a 1-basis.

We begin by condensing D to form D^*. Let S_1 be a transmitter or isolate of D^*. Since S_1 has no odd cycles, it has at least one 1-basis,

[3] The theorem is due to Richardson (1946).

by Corollary 6.14a. We then select all points in some 1-basis of S_1 and reject all points of D adjacent from these selected points. This set of rejected points contains all unselected points of S_1 and, possibly, other points of D. Let D_1 be the subgraph generated by the points of D not yet selected or rejected. We now repeat the process of selecting and rejecting points using the subgraph D_1. The process can be continued until all points of D are either selected or rejected.

We now show that at the end of this process the selected points form a 1-basis. They clearly form a 1-cover, since all points are either selected or rejected, and points are rejected if and only if they are adjacent from a selected point. Since all points adjacent from a selected point are rejected, no two selected points are adjacent. Therefore, the selected points form a 1-basis, proving the theorem.

The proof of Theorem 6.15 provides a constructive procedure for finding every 1-basis of a digraph with no odd cycles. In Figure 6.17 we illustrate both Theorem 6.15 and the construction process used in its proof.

The condensation D^* of the digraph D of Figure 6.17(a) is shown in Figure 6.17(b). Within S_1, whose points in D are v_1, v_2, v_3, v_4, we may choose (by the procedure of Corollary 6.14b) either v_1 and v_3 or v_2 and v_4 as the 1-basis for S_1. Choosing the former, the resulting selected and

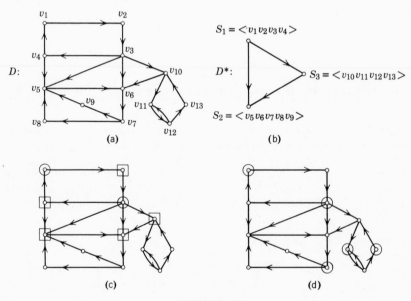

FIGURE 6.17

rejected points are shown respectively with circles and squares in Figure 6.17(c). The transmitters of the condensation of the subgraph generated by the remaining points are $\langle v_7 \rangle$ and $\langle v_{11}v_{12} \rangle$. We can complete our 1-basis by including v_7 and also including either v_{12} or both v_{11} and v_{13}, the latter choice being shown in Figure 6.17(d). Thus, our 1-basis consists of the points encircled in this figure.

Two Examples from Game Theory

The concept of 1-basis may be illustrated by two uses in the theory of n-person games. Both concern games involving the formation of coalitions among the players. The first use arises in the analysis of voting behavior of a political unit such as a presidential nominating convention. Let us assume that each player (e.g., the chairman of a state delegation) has a certain number of votes and that a candidate is elected if he garners a designated fractional majority of the total number of votes. A winning coalition is a collection of players with enough votes to elect a candidate. Since a winning coalition may expect to gain certain benefits (spoils) from their victory, there is an advantage to the players in forming a minimal winning coalition, i.e., one which contains no smaller one.

To provide a concrete example, let us consider a hypothetical "convention" consisting of only four players, t_1, t_2, t_3, t_5, having 1, 2, 3, and 5 votes respectively, with a total of six votes needed to elect a candidate. The winning coalitions are t_1t_5, $t_1t_2t_3$, $t_1t_2t_5$, $t_1t_3t_5$, t_2t_5, $t_2t_3t_5$, t_3t_5, and $t_1t_2t_3t_5$. This simple game can be conveniently represented as a digraph. We let the points of the digraph stand for the winning coalitions, and we draw a line from one point to a second if and only if the first coalition is a subset of the second. Figure 6.18 shows the digraph thus obtained.

From the construction of this digraph it is clear that every winning coalition is reachable from a minimal winning coalition in one step and that no minimal winning coalition is reachable from any other. Thus, the set of minimal winning coalitions is always a 1-basis of the digraph. It is also evident from the construction of the digraph that it must be acyclic. From Corollary 6.12b, we know that every acyclic digraph has a unique 1-basis. The unique 1-basis in Figure 6.18 consists of the coalitions t_1t_5, t_2t_5, t_3t_5, and $t_1t_2t_3$, which correspond to the transmitters of the digraph.

In our second example, the points and lines of a digraph are given quite different meaning. We are again interested in the formation of coalitions, but now we focus on the distribution of the payoff among the players. Let us assume that three players each contribute an equal

D:

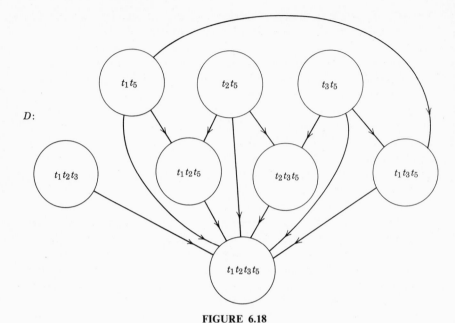

FIGURE 6.18

sum to a pool, and the game consists in deciding how to apportion the total. Suppose that the rules of the game allow any two players to enforce a mutual decision on the third. Of course, splitting the total equally among the three players amounts to not playing the game. The first two players might form a coalition, agreeing to split the pool equally between them at the expense of the unfortunate third player. Note that with the formation of a coalition we are hypothesizing an agreement on the splitting of the spoils.

If this coalition should form, the third player might try to entice the second to form a coalition with him instead. He would probably not succeed by offering an even split, since the second player is already promised half, but he might offer $\frac{3}{4}$ of the pool, keeping only $\frac{1}{4}$ for himself. Such an offer would be attractive to both the second and third players, since each stands to gain $\frac{1}{4}$ over his earnings under the first coalition. But this second coalition could be broken up if the first player offered to split the pot equally with the third.

The coalitions just discussed could be described by giving a payoff vector whose entries are the earnings of the three players. Thus, the first coalition is represented by $(\frac{1}{2}, \frac{1}{2}, 0)$, the second by $(0, \frac{3}{4}, \frac{1}{4})$, and the last by $(\frac{1}{2}, 0, \frac{1}{2})$. We have observed that of these vectors, the second is preferred (by two of the three players) to the first, and the third to the second. Thus the preference of one vector over another is asserted relative to a coalition. We need to examine this preference in more detail.

At the conclusion of the play of such a game there is a payoff made to (or collected from) each player, which is conveniently expressed in the form of a payoff vector with one component for each player. We call a coalition S effective for a payoff vector y if S has a strategy such that the minimum expected payoff to S as a result of this strategy is at least as great as the sum of the entries corresponding to S in y. For example, the coalition $\{2, 3\}$, consisting of the second and third player, is effective for the payoff vector $(0, \frac{3}{4}, \frac{1}{4})$, since this coalition can collect $\frac{3}{4} + \frac{1}{4}$ by the rules of the game. A payoff vector[4] y is said to dominate another, x, if there is an effective coalition S for y such that each player in S receives more under y than under x. Thus, in our example we have seen that $(0, \frac{3}{4}, \frac{1}{4})$ dominates $(\frac{1}{2}, \frac{1}{2}, 0)$ by means of its effective coalition consisting of the second and third players, since the second and third entries in the first payoff vector are greater than the corresponding entries in the second. Similarly, $(\frac{1}{2}, 0, \frac{1}{2})$ dominates $(0, \frac{3}{4}, \frac{1}{4})$ by means of the first and third players.

It is easy to see that the second player should not be enticed away from his coalition with the first by the offer of more than half the spoils, since he would put himself in danger of losing altogether. In fact, the more a player accepts for joining a coalition, the more the other players have to gain by joining forces against him. Thus the set of three vectors, each of which has one of its entries 0 and the others each $\frac{1}{2}$, has some "stability"—in the sense that if any payoff vector outside the set threatens to take hold, there will be a tendency to establish another inside the set. We see further that no vector in the set dominates any other. And while it is true that each is dominated by some payoff vector outside this trio, it is also true that every outside payoff vector is dominated by one of the trio!

This kind of stability has led to the definition of a solution of an n-person game as a set of payoff vectors[5] that have the two properties: (1) none of the payoff vectors dominates any other in the set, and

---

[4] The game under consideration is an example of a "cooperative n-person game." The discussion which follows is a greatly simplified treatment, suitable for our example, of some ideas from the von Neumann–Morgenstern theory of such games. For further details, see Luce and Raiffa (1957). The terms "dominate" and "solution" are properly defined for "imputations" (a technical term we shall not introduce) rather than for payoff vectors, but in this simple example there is no distinction.

[5] In the general treatment of n-person games the definition of solution is given in terms of imputations, not payoff vectors.

(2) every payoff vector not in the set is dominated by one in the set. The trio of payoff vectors just discussed has these two properties, and hence is a solution.

Let us construct a digraph whose points represent the payoff vectors of a game. We draw a line from one point to another if and only if the first payoff vector dominates the second. Such a representation is possible, since no vector can dominate itself. It should be noted that the digraph need not be transitive or acyclic. With this method of representation, the problem of finding a solution of an n-person game is exactly that of finding a 1-basis of the digraph. The equivalence of the two problems can be established by comparing the two properties required of a solution with the two required of a 1-basis.

Usually, as in our example, there are infinitely many payoff vectors, so the digraph of the dominance relation is infinite. In our example we can illustrate the application of the concept of 1-basis by restricting consideration to those payoff vectors where the members of the winning coalition split the pot and offer none to the other player. All these payoff vectors are shown in the digraph of Figure 6.19 by representing all vectors having entries other than 0 or $\frac{1}{2}$ by means of typical entries a and b, where $0 < a < \frac{1}{2}$, and $b = 1 - a$, so that $\frac{1}{2} < b < 1$. In this digraph it is easy to see that the trio of points whose vectors have one

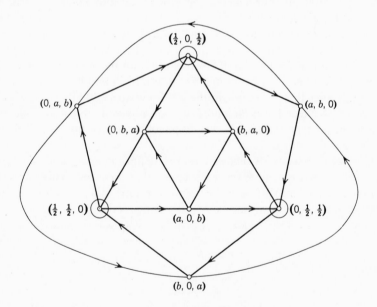

FIGURE 6.19

entry 0 and the others $\frac{1}{2}$ form a 1-basis, since there are no lines joining them, and every other point is adjacent from one of them. These points are encircled in Figure 6.19. To show that this trio constitutes a solution, we must verify that any vector whose entries are all positive is dominated by one of the trio. But since such a vector must have two entries each less than $\frac{1}{2}$, we see at once that this is the case. Thus if we restrict our consideration to payoff vectors having one entry 0, there is a unique solution to the game.

It is interesting to note that the application of digraphs to game theory has motivated most of the research concerning 1-bases. This research has consequently centered about conditions on a digraph under which a 1-basis can be found and further conditions which ensure that a digraph has a unique 1-basis. Although these problems have not been solved in general, the results presented in this chapter are applicable to many specialized circumstances.

DISTANCE INDEXES

In this final section we return to a consideration of some properties of digraphs that depend upon the distances among points. The *distance sum a_i from a point v_i* of D is the sum of the finite distances $d(v_i, u)$ for all u in D. Thus, a_i is the sum of the finite entries in the ith row of the distance matrix $N(D)$. The *distance sum b_j to a point v_j* is the sum of the finite distances $d(u, v_j)$ for all u in D. Thus, b_j is the sum of the finite entries in the jth column of $N(D)$. The *total distance Σd_{ij} within a digraph D* is the sum of all the finite distances $d(v_i, v_j)$ in D. Thus, Σd_{ij} is the sum of all the finite entries in $N(D)$.

Figure 6.20 shows four digraphs and their distance matrices. Let us assume that these digraphs represent communication networks and that a unit of cost is entailed in transmitting a message along each line. Then $d(u, v)$ indicates the minimum cost in getting a message from person u to person v. Suppose, further, that each person wishes to send a distinct message to every person reachable from him. Then, a_i is the minimum total cost entailed by person v_i, and Σd_{ij} is the minimum total cost entailed by all persons in the network.

Since digraphs D_1, D_2, and D_3 are all strong, it is possible for everyone to get a message to everyone else. We see, however, that the minimum total cost in these networks differ, ranging from 20 in D_2 to 50 in D_3. In D_1, v_3 is the best person from whom to distribute messages, since $a_3 = 6$ is the smallest distance sum from any person. In D_2 and D_3, all persons are equally good. In the strictly weak digraph D_4, point v_3 is the unique source, and hence person v_3 is the only one who can reach everyone. The minimum total cost in getting messages to everyone from v_3 is 6. Finally, we note that the total distance within D_4 is 8.

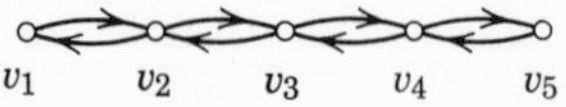

$$N(D_1) = \begin{bmatrix} 0 & 1 & 2 & 3 & 4 \\ 1 & 0 & 1 & 2 & 3 \\ 2 & 1 & 0 & 1 & 2 \\ 3 & 2 & 1 & 0 & 1 \\ 4 & 3 & 2 & 1 & 0 \end{bmatrix} \begin{matrix} a_i \\ 10 \\ 7 \\ 6 \\ 7 \\ 10 \end{matrix}$$

b_j $\quad$ 10 $\quad$ 7 $\quad$ 6 $\quad$ 7 $\quad$ 10 $\quad$ $\Sigma d_{ij} = 40$

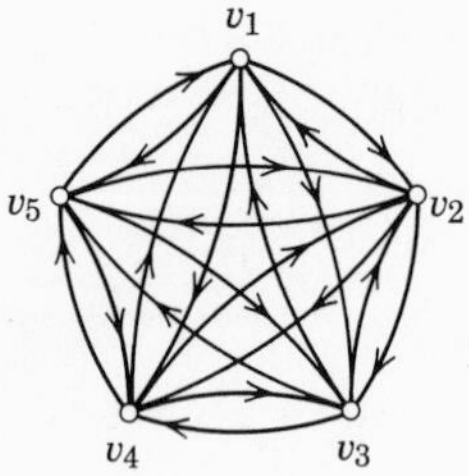

$$N(D_2) = \begin{bmatrix} 0 & 1 & 1 & 1 & 1 \\ 1 & 0 & 1 & 1 & 1 \\ 1 & 1 & 0 & 1 & 1 \\ 1 & 1 & 1 & 0 & 1 \\ 1 & 1 & 1 & 1 & 0 \end{bmatrix} \begin{matrix} a_i \\ 4 \\ 4 \\ 4 \\ 4 \\ 4 \end{matrix}$$

b_j $\quad$ 4 $\quad$ 4 $\quad$ 4 $\quad$ 4 $\quad$ 4 $\quad$ $\Sigma d_{ij} = 20$

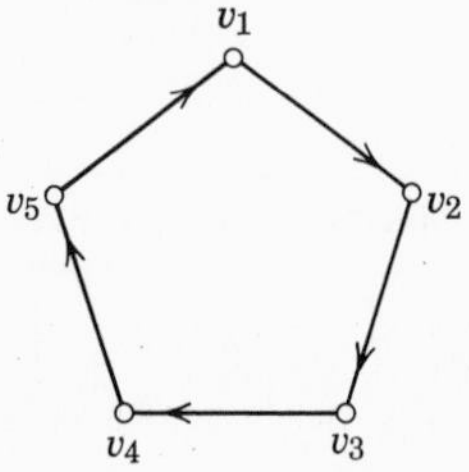

$$N(D_3) = \begin{bmatrix} 0 & 1 & 2 & 3 & 4 \\ 4 & 0 & 1 & 2 & 3 \\ 3 & 4 & 0 & 1 & 2 \\ 2 & 3 & 4 & 0 & 1 \\ 1 & 2 & 3 & 4 & 0 \end{bmatrix} \begin{matrix} a_i \\ 10 \\ 10 \\ 10 \\ 10 \\ 10 \end{matrix}$$

b_j $\quad$ 10 $\quad$ 10 $\quad$ 10 $\quad$ 10 $\quad$ 10 $\quad$ $\Sigma d_{ij} = 50$

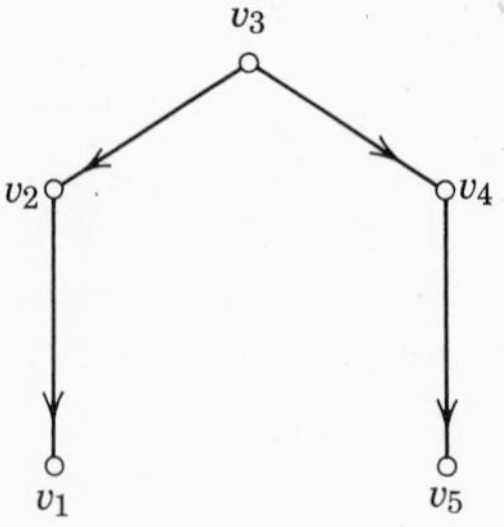

$$N(D_4) = \begin{bmatrix} 0 & \infty & \infty & \infty & \infty \\ 1 & 0 & \infty & \infty & \infty \\ 2 & 1 & 0 & 1 & 2 \\ \infty & \infty & \infty & 0 & 1 \\ \infty & \infty & \infty & \infty & 0 \end{bmatrix} \begin{matrix} a_i \\ 0 \\ 1 \\ 6 \\ 1 \\ 0 \end{matrix}$$

b_j $\quad$ 3 $\quad$ 1 $\quad$ 0 $\quad$ 1 $\quad$ 3 $\quad$ $\Sigma d_{ij} = 8$

FIGURE 6.20

This is much smaller than for the strong digraphs since there are so many infinite entries in $N(D_4)$.

We now consider bounds on a_i, b_j, and Σd_{ij}. It will be convenient to state them first for strong digraphs and then for any digraph.

Theorem 6.16. Let D be a strong digraph with p points, a distance sum from v_i of a_i, and a distance sum to v_j of b_j. Then,

$$p - 1 \leq a_i \leq \frac{p(p - 1)}{2}$$

and

$$p - 1 \leq b_j \leq \frac{p(p - 1)}{2}$$

We need prove only the first statement, since the second follows by directional duality. It is obvious that in a strong digraph the smallest distance sum from v_i occurs when every point is adjacent from v_i. Clearly, in this case $a_i = p - 1$. To verify the upper bound, we note that since D is strong there are $p - 1$ finite, nonzero entries in each row of $N(D)$. Thus from Theorem 5.21, it is clear that the sum of the row is at most

$$1 + 2 + \ldots + (p - 2) + (p - 1) = \frac{p(p - 1)}{2}$$

completing the proof.

Corollary 6.16a. Let D be any digraph with p points, a distance sum from v_i of a_i, and a distance sum to v_j of b_j. Then,

$$0 \leq a_i \leq \frac{p(p - 1)}{2}$$

and

$$0 \leq b_j \leq \frac{p(p - 1)}{2}$$

Clearly, if no point is adjacent from v_i, the distance sum from v_i is 0. The upper bound is the same as that in Theorem 6.16, since its value cannot be greater than in the case of a strong digraph.

Corollary 6.16b. Let D be a strong digraph with p points and a total distance of Σd_{ij}. Then,

$$p(p - 1) \leq \sum d_{ij} \leq \frac{p^2(p - 1)}{2}$$

This corollary follows immediately from Theorem 6.16, since the greatest total distance within D will occur when every a_i is maximum, and the least when every a_i is minimum. Therefore, all the values in the equation of Theorem 6.16 must be multiplied by p, the number of rows in $N(D)$.

In stating the next corollary, we let Z_p denote the digraph which consists of a single cycle of length p. Recall also that K_p is the complete symmetric digraph of p points. In Figure 6.20, $D_3 = Z_5$ and $D_2 = K_5$.

Corollary 6.16c. Let D be a strong digraph. Then, $\Sigma d_{ij} = p(p - 1)$ if and only if $D = K_p$. Also,

$$\sum d_{ij} = \frac{p^2(p - 1)}{2}$$

if and only if $D = Z_p$.

Since $D = K_p$ if and only if each $d_{ij} = 1(i \neq j)$, and $D = Z_p$ if and only if every point is at a distance $(p - 1)$ from some point, it is obvious that these digraphs take the minimum and maximum values of the preceding corollary.

Corollary 6.16d. Let D be any digraph with p points and with total distance Σd_{ij}. Then,

$$0 \leq \sum d_{ij} \leq \frac{p^2(p - 1)}{2}$$

The proof of this corollary follows from Corollary 6.16a by the argument presented in the proof of Corollary 6.16b.

Communication Example

The concepts of total distance within a digraph and distance sum from a point have been used by Bavelas (1950) in research on communication networks to construct an index of the "relative centrality" of a person. Stated in terms employed here, the relative centrality of v_i is

$$\frac{\Sigma d_{ij}}{a_i}$$

Figure 6.21 shows digraphs of four symmetric communication networks employed in this research, with the index of relative centrality indicated for each point. Experiments were conducted in which five-man groups

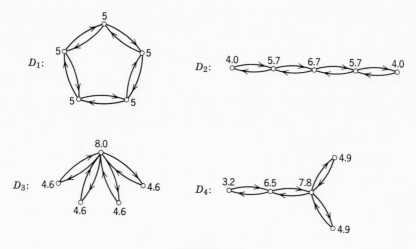

FIGURE 6.21

worked in each of these networks on a problem requiring the pooling of information. It was found that if a single person has highest relative centrality, then he is most likely to be chosen by the group as its leader. Thus, in the networks D_2, D_3, and D_4 it is possible to predict with considerable confidence who will emerge as leader by knowing the relative centrality of each person. But in D_1 no predictions can be made, since all have the same relative centrality. It was also found that an individual's morale is directly related to his relative centrality. Thus, the four networks have quite different distributions of morale among group members.

Status in an Organization

Consider the digraph of delegated authority in an organization. Call v an immediate subordinate of u if line uv is in this digraph. And in general, call v a subordinate of u if v is reachable from u. Call the *subordinate vector* of u the sequence $(e_1, e_2, \ldots, e_{p-1})$ where e_n is the number of points at distance n from u. In analyzing status phenomena in organizations, Harary (1959c) proposed the following as reasonable requirements for the status of a person. For any point u in this digraph, a status measure $s(u)$ is wanted such that (1) $s(u)$ is an integer, (2) $s(u)$ is 0 if and only if u has no subordinates, (3) if the subordinate vector of v is obtained from that of u by adding one subordinate (at any distance from v), the status of v is greater than that of u, and (4) if the subordinate vector of v is obtained from that of u by increasing the distance of any one subordinate, the status of v is again greater than that of u. In view of these considerations, the status of person v in an organization may be defined as the number of his immediate subordinates, plus twice the number of their immediate subordinates (who are not immediate subordinates of v), plus three times the number of their immediate subordinates (not already included), and so on. It can be shown that this particular definition gives the smallest possible measure satisfying these four requirements and, in this sense, is a natural one.

We can readily verify that under this definition the status of v_i equals a_i, the distance sum from v_i in the digraph of the organization. Figure 6.22 shows the digraphs of two small organizations, with the status indicated for each person.

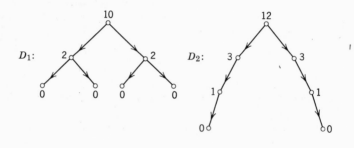

FIGURE 6.22

It will be noted that the status measures in these two organizations are rather different even though both organizations have the same number of people. Harary defines the gross status of an organization as the sum of the status measures of its members. Clearly, this is the same as Σd_{ij}, the total distance within the digraph of the organization. Furthermore, he defines the relative status of person v_i as the ratio of his status measure to the gross status of the organization, in other words, as

$$\frac{a_i}{\Sigma d_{ij}}$$

It is interesting to note that this definition of relative status is the reciprocal of that of relative centrality, given in the previous example, even though the two definitions were developed quite independently.

From Theorem 6.16 it follows that, in an organization of p people, person v will have maximum status if all members lie on a single path from v. And from Corollaries 6.16c. and 6.16d, it follows that the maximum gross status of an organization with p people occurs in one whose digraph consists of a single cycle. Obviously, few organizations (if any) have such a structure.

Since the status of person v_i is given by a_i, the distance sum from v_i, it is natural to ask what empirical property is measured by its directional dual b_j. Harary calls this the contrastatus of v_i, or "the amount of status weighing down on an individual from his superordinates," and he suggests that the net status of v_i, as given by $a_i - b_i$, may often be a better measure of his "prestige" than status itself.

SUMMARY

In this chapter we have focused attention upon certain properties of digraphs that depend upon the distances among points. We began by defining two numbers that may be associated with any point v of a digraph. The outnumber $o(v)$ is the distance to a farthest point from v, and the innumber $i(v)$ of a point v is the distance from a farthest point to v. If $o(v)$ is a finite number n, then v can reach every point of the digraph in n steps and we call v an n-source. Similarly, v is an n-sink if $i(v) = n$.

The minimum finite outnumber and the minimum finite innumber of the points of a digraph provide useful information about the digraph. A point with minimum finite outnumber is known as an outcentral point, and its outnumber is called the outradius of the digraph. Similarly, a point with minimum finite innumber is an incentral point, and its innumber is the inradius of the digraph. Thus, an outcentral point can reach every point within the distance given by the digraph's outradius, and every point can reach an incentral point within the distance given by the inradius. In other words, outcentral and incentral points are most favorably located with respect to reaching and being reached respectively. Every unilateral digraph has at least one outcentral point and at least one incentral point.

In any digraph, the maximum outnumber equals the maximum innumber, and these are finite if and only if the digraph is strong. A point with maximum finite outnumber is called an outperipheral point; one with maximum finite innumber is an inperipheral point. The outnumber of an outperipheral point (or the innumber of an inperipheral point) is known as the diameter of the digraph, which is the greatest distance between any two points of the digraph. The diameter, therefore, provides a useful index of the compactness of a digraph. Some theorems were presented which give bounds on the outradius, inradius, and diameter of a strong digraph and establish possible relationships among their values.

The concept of point basis, discussed in Chapter 4, has certain counterparts when distance considerations are imposed. An n-cover S is a set of points from which all points are reachable within distance n, that is, $R_n(S) = V$. A minimal n-cover is one which contains no n-cover as a proper subset. If a minimal n-cover has the additional property that none of its points is reachable within n steps from any other, then it is called an n-basis. We saw that if r is the length of a longest path in D, then any point basis of D is an n-basis for $n \geq r$. It remains an unsolved problem to find a general characterization for digraphs having an n-basis for any given value of n. It is possible, however, to reduce this problem to one of finding a characterization of digraphs having a 1-basis. Certain results concerning 1-bases were presented, and some uses of 1-bases in the theory of games were described.

In the final section of the chapter, some indexes were presented which make use of the distance sum a_i from a point v_i and the distance sum b_j to a point v_j. The chapter concluded with a description of some applications of these indexes to research on communication networks and on status in organizations.

We turn in the next chapter to consideration of the effects upon the connectedness of a digraph of removing some of its lines. This investigation is concerned with the vulnerability of digraphs with respect to the destruction or malfunctioning of its lines.

EXERCISES

1. (a) Find the outnumber and innumber for each of the points in the digraph of Figure 6.23. (b) What are its outcentral and incentral points? (c) What are its outperipheral and inperipheral points? (d) What is its outradius, inradius, and diameter?

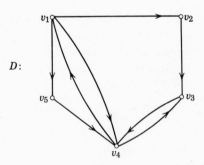

FIGURE 6.23

2. (a) In the above digraph, what is the total distance Σd_{ij}? (b) Do all outcentral points have the same distance sum a_i? (c) What is the relative centrality of each outperipheral and inperipheral point?

3. Let D be a digraph with 6 points and with $\Sigma d_{ij} = 90$. What is its outradius? Its inradius?

4. Plot the minimum values of p against all integer values of r_i from 1 to 10, for $r_0 = 5$.

5. If $r_0 = k$, for what value of r_i is p smallest?

6. Suppose that a researcher wishes to study processes of communication in a problem-solving group. To solve the problem, one person must get an item of information from every member of the group, perform an operation on these items, and then send this processed information to all members. Each person has a list of members to whom he can send messages, and messages can be sent only at designated time intervals. A procedure is wanted which will require at least five time intervals for any one person to obtain information from everyone and at least three time units for the processed information to reach everyone. (a) What is the smallest group that can be employed? (b) Draw a digraph of a communication network that will satisfy the above requirements.

7. (a) Show that the relative centrality of any person in a communication network whose digraph is K_p or Z_p is p. (b) Show that if $s(v_i)$ is the same for all points of any digraph, then $\Sigma d_{ij}/a_i = p$, for all points of D.

8. Let E be a strong subgraph of a strong digraph D with the same points as D. What are the relative magnitudes of the outradius of D and of E? The inradius? The diameter?

9. Prove or disprove: If every cycle of a strong digraph D has even length, every semicycle is also even.

10. Prove: If D consists of a cycle of length p, then D has an n-basis if and only if $p \leq n + 1$ or $p/(n + 1)$ is an integer.

11. Prove: Let D have an n-basis B and let r be the integer such that $n + r$ is the least distance between points of B. Then B is an s-basis of D for each s such that $n \leq s \leq n + r - 1$.

12. Prove: If D has an n-basis B and no point of B is reachable from another, B is an s-basis for every $s > n$.

13. Let D have an n-basis $B = \{v_1, v_2, \ldots, v_k\}$ such that no point of D is reachable from more than one point of B. Show that $R_n(v_1)$, $R_n(v_2)$, $\ldots$, $R_n(v_k)$ partitions the set V of points of D.

14. Use the procedure of Corollary 6.14b and find the 1-basis of digraph D in Figure 6.17 obtained by choosing v_2 and v_4 from S_1.

7 • Removal of Lines: Vulnerability

What therefore God hath joined together, let no man put asunder.
MATTHEW 19:6

Consider a communication network whose digraph is in a particular category of connectedness, let us say C_3. In this case, every pair of people can engage in two-way communication, and messages will pass along links of the network which correspond to lines of its digraph. Now, suppose that for some reason one of these links is removed from the network. Can all pairs of people still engage in two-way communication? To answer this question, we need more information about the effects upon the category of a digraph brought about by removing one of its lines. If, for example, the digraph of the original network is complete symmetric, the removal of any single line does not affect its category. But if the original digraph consists of a cycle, the removal of any one line reduces its category from C_3 to C_2, and two-way communication is no longer possible for any pair of people. Intuitively, we would say that the cycle is more vulnerable than the complete symmetric digraph.

In this chapter, we investigate how a digraph depends upon its various lines for its connectedness. We begin by examining several ways in which a line may be said to be "between" two points. This analysis leads to the identification of two fundamental types of lines, known as bridges and basic lines. It also leads to certain criteria for a line to have the property that its removal from a digraph of a given category results in one of another category.

With these results at hand, it is then possible to consider some of the effects of removing sets of lines from a digraph. This investigation yields three useful indexes that may be associated with any digraph: (1) the maximum number of lines of D whose removal does not affect the category of D, (2) the minimum number of lines whose presence is required to preserve the category of D, and (3) the minimum number of lines whose removal reduces the category of D.

In the final section, we consider some interesting properties of a collection of lines of a digraph such that, using these lines only, it is still possible to reach any point v from any point u whenever this can be done in the entire digraph.

BETWEENNESS OF LINES

Since the category of a digraph D is defined in terms of the joining of its pairs of points, if we wish to study the importance of a particular line x for the connectedness of D, we should examine the ways in which x enters into the joining of pairs of points. For this purpose, we often need to refer to the first point fx and the second point sx of a line x. Theorem 7.1 and its corollary provide results that are useful in the remainder of the discussion.

Theorem 7.1. If D has two points u and v joined by a semipath and all semipaths joining them contain a line x, then x itself is the only semipath joining fx and sx, and conversely.

Let L be a semipath joining u and v. By hypothesis, L contains x. Now assume there is a semipath L_1 in D joining fx and sx but not containing x. On replacing in L the occurrence of x and its two points by L_1, we obtain a semisequence joining u and v but not containing x. But this violates the hypothesis that all semipaths joining u and v contain x. Therefore, x must be the only semipath joining fx and sx.

The converse of this theorem is obvious, for if we let $u = fx$ and $v = sx$, then u and v are joined by a semipath, namely x, and all such semipaths contain x.

Corollary 7.1a. If D has two points u and v, such that there is a path from u to v and all paths from u to v contain a line x, then x itself is the only path from fx to sx, and conversely.

The proof of this corollary is similar to that of the theorem.

These results are illustrated by the digraph of Figure 7.1. It is readily seen that x_2 lies on all semipaths joining v_2 and v_5 as well as on all paths from v_1 to v_7. And in accordance with the theorem and corollary, x_2 is the only semipath joining its two points v_3 and v_4.

When a line lies on all semipaths (or paths) joining two points, it

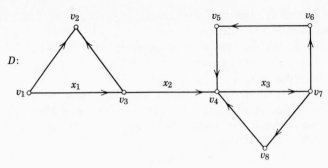

FIGURE 7.1

seems appropriate to say that it is, in some sense, "between" these two points. We shall now give precise meaning to this intuitive notion. To do so, we designate four kinds of betweenness. The definition of each specifies the way in which two points u and v are joined and the location of a line x with respect to semipaths (or paths) joining them.

A *line x is 1-between two points* u and v, written $(u\,x\,v)_1$, if u and v are 1-joined and every semipath joining them contains x.

A *line x is 2-between two points* u and v, written $(u\,x\,v)_2$, if u and v are 2-connected and every path joining them contains x.

A *line x is 3-between two points* u and v, written $(u\,x\,v)_3$, if u and v are 3-connected and every path joining them contains x.

A *line x is 3'-between two points* u and v, written $(u\,x\,v)_{3'}$, if u and v are 3-connected, and either every path from u to v contains x or every path from v to u contains x (but not both).

We say simply that a *line x is between two points* if it is i-between them, for $i = 1, 2, 3,$ or $3'$. If it is not true that x is i-between u and v, we write $\sim(u\,x\,v)_i$. It follows at once from the definitions that if $(u\,x\,v)_i$, then $(v\,x\,u)_i$ for $i = 1, 2, 3,$ or $3'$.

These definitions are illustrated by the digraph shown in Figure 7.1. Since the digraph is weak, every pair of points is 1-joined, satisfying the first condition of the definition of 1-betweenness. We see further that $(v_2 x_2 v_5)_1$, since all semipaths joining v_2 and v_5 contain x_2. However, x_1 is not 1-between v_2 and v_5, for there is a semipath joining these two points which does not contain x_1.

Consider now points v_1 and v_7 and line x_3. Clearly, v_1 and v_7 are 2-connected, and all paths joining them contain x_3. We know, therefore, that $(v_1 x_3 v_7)_2$.

The concept of 3-betweenness is illustrated by points v_5 and v_8 and line x_3. It can be verified that these two points are 3-connected and that all paths joining them (in both directions) contain x_3. Thus, we conclude that $(v_5 x_3 v_8)_3$.

Finally, we see that $(v_4 x_3 v_6)_{3'}$. This statement follows from the fact that v_4 and v_6 are 3-connected, and all paths from v_4 to v_6 contain x_3 but not all paths from v_6 to v_4 do.

Suppose that a digraph is taken to represent a communication network. Then knowledge of the betweenness of a line x with respect to two points u and v permits us to draw certain immediate conclusions about the flow of messages in the network. Thus, for example, in the digraph shown in Figure 7.1, we have seen that $(v_5 x_3 v_8)_3$. We may conclude, then, that in the corresponding communication network v_5 and v_8 can engage in two-way communication, but all of their messages must pass through x_3, that is, be transmitted directly from v_4 to v_7. This link is essential for all communication between v_5 and v_8, and v_4 and v_7 will know of any messages sent from one to the other.

In order to analyze further the ways in which the connectedness of a digraph depends upon one of its lines, we need to examine how the two points fx and sx of a line x may be joined in a digraph. For this purpose, we require the concept of a cyclic line. A line x of D is *cyclic* if there is a path from sx to fx. Clearly, a line is cyclic if and only if it lies on a cycle. A line that is not cyclic is *acyclic*. In Figure 7.1, line x_3 is cyclic, whereas x_1 is acyclic.

Theorem 7.2. The points fx and sx of any line x are 2-connected if and only if x is acyclic; they are 3-connected if and only if x is cyclic.

It is obvious that fx and sx must be 2-joined. If there is also a path from sx to fx, then x is cyclic and fx and sx are 3-connected. Otherwise x is acyclic, and the two points are 2-connected.

If we apply the definitions of betweenness to a line x and its two points fx and sx, we obtain the following corollaries.

Corollary 7.2a. No digraph has a line x such that $(fx \, x \, sx)_3$.

By the definition of 3-betweenness, if x is 3-between its two points, then fx and sx are 3-connected and all paths joining them contain x. Thus there is a path from sx to fx. But by definition of a path, no path from sx to fx can contain x. Therefore, it is impossible that $(fx \, x \, sx)_3$.

Corollary 7.2b. If $(fx \, x \, sx)_1$, then $(fx \, x \, sx)_2$.

From Theorem 7.2 it follows that fx and sx are either 2-connected or 3-connected, since they are 2-joined. By the definition of 1-betweenness we know that if $(fx \, x \, sx)_1$, all semipaths—and thus all paths—joining fx and sx contain x. But this means that fx and sx are not 3-connected, for no path from sx to fx can contain x. Therefore, fx and sx are 2-connected, and all paths joining them contain x, satisfying the definition of $(fx \; x \; sx)_2$.

The digraph of Figure 7.2 illustrates the various possibilities for the betweenness of a line x with respect to its points fx and sx. The betweenness of each of the four labeled lines of Figure 7.2 is shown in Table 7.1.

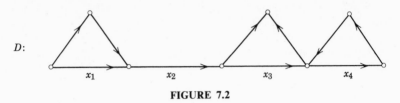

FIGURE 7.2

Table 7.1. Examples of betweenness of a line x with respect to fx and sx
Data from Figure 7.2.

x	$(fx \; x \; sx)_1$	$(fx \; x \; sx)_2$	$(fx \; x \; sx)_{3'}$
x_1	no	no	no
x_2	yes	yes	no
x_3	no	yes	no
x_4	no	no	yes

Bridges and Basic Lines

We are now ready to consider two important kinds of lines, known as bridges and basic lines. A line x is a *bridge* of a digraph D if x is the only semipath joining fx and sx. Thus, by definition of 1-betweenness, x is a bridge if and only if $(fx \; x \; sx)_1$. The next theorem gives a criterion for a line x to be a bridge.

Theorem 7.3. For any digraph D, the following statements are equivalent.

(1) $(fx \; x \; sx)_1$, that is, x is a bridge.
(2) There are two points u and v such that $(u \; x \; v)_1$.

Theorem 7.3 is really a previous one in disguise, for upon substituting the definition of 1-betweenness in statements (1) and (2), we obtain Theorem 7.1. This theorem tells us that if a digraph contains any two points u and v such that x is on all semipaths joining them, then x is a bridge. It is readily seen that in Figure 7.1 the line x_2 is a bridge; it lies on all semipaths joining each point of $\{v_1, v_2, v_3\}$ and each point of $\{v_4, v_5, v_6, v_7, v_8\}$.

The next theorem shows that it is impossible for a line to be 1-between any two points that are 3-connected.

Theorem 7.4. If u and v are 3-connected in D, then there is no line x of D such that $(u\, x\, v)_1$.

It is given that u and v are 3-connected. Thus, by definition there is a path from u to v and one from v to u. If x is 1-between these points, then x lies on all semipaths (and hence all paths) joining them. But this is impossible, for then there would be paths from u to fx and from v to fx, and the union of these is a semipath joining u and v but not containing x.

Corollary 7.4a. No strong digraph has a bridge.

In other words, no line of a strong digraph is 1-between any two points. This corollary follows immediately from Theorem 7.4, since every pair of points of a strong digraph is 3-connected.

Corollary 7.4b. If a unilateral digraph has a bridge, then it is strictly unilateral.

Since every unilateral digraph is either strictly unilateral or strong, Corollary 7.4b follows directly from the preceding one.

The digraph shown in Figure 7.2 is strictly unilateral and, as we have seen, contains exactly one bridge, x_2. Although lines x_3 and x_4 are not bridges, we note that each of these is the only path from its first point to its second point. A line x of a digraph is said to be *basic* if x is the only path from fx to sx. Thus, in Figure 7.2 lines x_3 and x_4 are basic, but x_1 is not. It is apparent, of course, that x_2 is basic. The next theorem gives five equivalent conditions for a line to be basic.

Theorem 7.5. The following statements are equivalent for any line x.
(1) x is the only path from fx to sx, that is, x is a basic line.
(2) Either $(fx\, x\, sx)_2$ or $(fx\, x\, sx)_{3'}$.
(3) x is between fx and sx.
(4) There are two points such that x is between them.
(5) There are two points u and v such that there is a path from u to v and all such paths contain x.

Note, first, that Corollary 7.1a gives the equivalence of (1) and (5). Obviously (2) implies (3), which implies (4). Hence to prove the equivalence of all these statements, we need only show that (1) implies (2) and that (4) implies (1).

(1) Implies (2). Clearly, fx and sx are either 2-connected or 3-connected. Since x is the only path from fx to sx, either $(fx \times sx)_2$, $(fx \times sx)_3$, or $(fx \times sx)_{3'}$, by definition. But by Corollary 7.2a, $(fx \times sx)_3$ is impossible. Therefore, statement (2) follows from statement (1).

(4) Implies (1). It is given that x is between two points. By Theorem 7.1 and its Corollary 7.1a, x is the only path from fx to sx. Thus, (4) implies (1), proving the theorem.

Before illustrating this theorem, we present three corollaries.

Corollary 7.5a. The following statements characterize any line that is between its first and second points.
1. $(fx \times sx)_2$ if and only if x is acyclic and basic.
2. $(fx \times sx)_{3'}$ if and only if x is cyclic and basic.

The equivalence of statements (2) and (3) of Theorem 7.5 provides that x is between its first and second points if and only if either $(fx \times sx)_2$ or $(fx \times sx)_{3'}$. The equivalence of (1) and (2) means that in either case x is basic. By Theorem 7.2, x is acyclic if and only if fx and sx are 2-connected, and x is cyclic if and only if fx and sx are 3-connected.

Since every line of a strong digraph is cyclic and every line of an acyclic digraph is acyclic, we obtain the next corollary.

Corollary 7.5b. Every basic line of a strong digraph satisfies $(fx \times sx)_{3'}$. Every basic line of an acyclic digraph satisfies $(fx \times sx)_2$.

The next corollary makes explicit some conclusions which result when a line is in a certain betweenness relation with a pair of points.

Corollary 7.5c. Let there be two points u and v such that $(u \times v)_i$.
1. If $i = 1$, then $(fx \times sx)_2$. In other words, every bridge is basic and acyclic.
2. If $i = 2$, then either $(fx \times sx)_2$ or $(fx \times sx)_{3'}$.
3. If $i = 3$ or $i = 3'$, then $(fx \times sx)_{3'}$.

To prove the first statement, we assume that there are two points such that $(u \times v)_1$. It follows from Theorem 7.3 that $(fx \times sx)_1$ and from Corollary 7.2b that $(fx \times sx)_2$. From Corollary 7.5a, we conclude that x is basic and acyclic.

The second result is a specific instance of the fact that statement (4) implies (2) in Theorem 7.5.

By the hypothesis of the third statement, x is 3-between or 3'-between u and v. Hence statement (4) of Theorem 7.5 is satisfied, and x is basic. From the definitions of betweenness, we know that u and v are 3-connected and that x lies on a path joining them. Therefore by Theorem 7.2,

x is cyclic. Since x is basic and cyclic, it follows from Corollary 7.5a that $(fx \times sx)_{3'}$.

Theorem 7.5 and its corollaries are illustrated by the digraphs of Figure 7.3. In digraph D, it is readily verified that there is only one path from v_9 to v_1 and that lines x_1, x_2, and x_3 lie on this path. Each of these lines, therefore, satisfies condition (5) of Theorem 7.5. Since v_9 and v_1 are 2-connected, each of these lines is also 2-between v_9 and v_1, satisfying condition (4). We know then that these are basic lines. We see, moreover, that x_1 is 2-between its two points and is acyclic, whereas x_2 is 3'-between its two points and is cyclic. Clearly, x_3 is a bridge, and in keeping with the first statement of Corollary 7.5c, is also acyclic. It should be noted, however, that the converse of this corollary is not true in general. For example, x_1 is basic and acyclic but not a bridge.

Certain implications of Corollary 7.5b should be noted. The first statement of this corollary applies, of course, to any strong component of a digraph. Thus, any basic line within a strong component is 3'-between its two points. Moreover, any basic line joining two points in different strong components is 2-between its two points. These conclusions are substantiated by lines x_1, x_2, and x_3 in Figure 7.3. Another consequence of this corollary is the statement that every basic line of a condensed digraph is 2-between its two points. In the digraph D^* of Figure 7.3, it can be seen that three of the lines are basic, and for each of these it is true that $(fx \times sx)_2$.

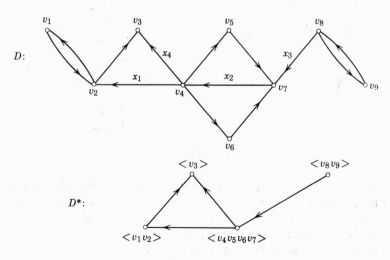

FIGURE 7.3

The next theorem states an important property of any basic line of a strong digraph.

Theorem 7.6. Let D be a strong digraph. Then x is in every complete closed sequence of D if and only if x is basic.

Since a complete closed sequence contains a path from fx to sx, x is in every complete closed sequence if and only if x is the only path from fx to sx, that is, x is basic.

This theorem may be illustrated by a hypothetical example. Suppose that a subway company wants to provide service for five stations. It has three requirements: (a) A customer must be able to start at any station, go to every other station, and return to his starting station. (b) Only one-way traffic is possible between any two adjacent stations. (c) If service breaks down between any one pair of adjacent stations, it must still be possible to meet requirement (a). Stated in terms of digraphs, the first requirement says that the digraph of the subway system is strong and, therefore, must have a complete closed sequence. The second asserts that the digraph must be asymmetric. Theorem 7.6 tells us that if any line of the digraph is basic, then the third requirement is not met. The problem consists, therefore, of constructing a strong digraph which is asymmetric and has no basic lines.

Digraph D_1 of Figure 7.4 satisfies the first two conditions, for it consists of a cycle. But it does not satisfy the third, since every line is basic.

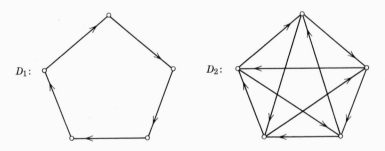

FIGURE 7.4

It can be suitably modified, however, by adding lines in such a way that for each line x there is a path from fx to sx not containing x. Digraph D_2 of Figure 7.4 shows one way of satisfying all three requirements.

The final theorem of this section specifies the conditions under which a line x lies in every complete open sequence of a strictly unilateral digraph.

Theorem 7.7. If x is a line of a strictly unilateral digraph D such that $(fx \times sx)_2$, then x is in every complete open sequence of D.

Let L be any complete open sequence from v_0 to v_n. Since L is complete, it contains the points fx and sx. Since it is given that $(fx \times sx)_2$, we know that x is acyclic. Hence there is no path, and thus no sequence, from sx to fx. Therefore, L consists of three subsequences: v_0 to fx, fx to sx, and sx to v_n. Moreover, since $(fx \times sx)_2$, then x is the only path from fx to sx. Hence, L must contain x.

This theorem may be illustrated by the strictly unilateral digraph of Figure 7.5. It can be seen that any one of the points v_1, v_2, or v_3 is the initial point of a complete open sequence. Moreover, v_4 is the terminal point of all such sequences. Clearly, x_1 and x_2 are both 2-between their two points. And, in keeping with Theorem 7.7, they both lie on every complete open sequence of the digraph. That the converse of this theorem is not true in general can be seen in this figure, since x_3 lies on every complete open sequence, but it is not 2-between its two points.

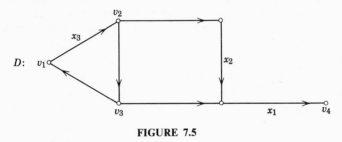

FIGURE 7.5

In the next section, we consider the effects upon the connectedness category of a digraph brought about by removing exactly one of its lines. It should come as no surprise that betweenness is fundamental to this analysis.

REMOVAL OF A LINE

Suppose that a digraph D is in connectedness category C_i. And suppose, furthermore, that we remove a line x from D. Is the connectedness of the new digraph stronger, weaker, or the same as D? In order to deal precisely with a question of this sort, we need some additional definitions.

A *spanning subgraph E of D* is a subgraph with the same set of points as D. The *removal of a line x from D* results in that spanning subgraph, $E = D - x$, containing all lines of D except x. Thus, when a line is removed from a digraph, its two points remain. If D is in connectedness category C_i and x is a line of D such that $D - x$ is in C_j, then x is called an i, j *line.*

The next theorem and its corollaries state some of the effects of removing a bridge from a digraph. These results provide equivalent conditions for x to be a bridge, in addition to the one given in Theorem 7.3. We denote the number of weak components of a digraph D by $k_w(D)$.

Theorem 7.8. Line x is a bridge of D if and only if

$$k_w(D - x) = 1 + k_w(D).$$

First, we take as given that x is a bridge. We know that x lies in exactly one weak component W (Theorem 3.2) and that there is a semipath joining any two points in W (Theorem 3.11). By definition of a bridge, all semipaths joining fx and sx contain x. Thus, in $D - x$ there is no semipath joining fx and sx. Consequently, fx and sx are in different weak components of $D - x$, and $D - x$ has at least one more weak component than D. Since every point in W is joined by a semipath with fx or sx, $D - x$ has exactly one more weak component than D.

Conversely, let $k_w(D - x) = 1 + k_w(D)$. This means that there is a set V_1 of points which generates one weak component in D but two weak components in $D - x$. Thus, every pair of points in V_1 is joined by a semipath in D, but at least one pair is not joined by a semipath in $D - x$. It follows that there are two points such that they are 1-joined in D and all semipaths joining them contain x. By Theorem 7.3, x is a bridge.

The digraph of Figure 7.6 illustrates this theorem. Clearly, $k_w(D) = 2$ and $k_w(D - x) = 3$, satisfying the formula of Theorem 7.8. Moreover, x is the only bridge of D, and the formula is not satisfied by any other line of D.

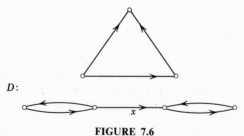

D:

FIGURE 7.6

Corollary 7.8a. If D is a weak digraph, then x is a bridge if and only if $D - x$ has exactly two weak components.

This corollary is a special case of Theorem 7.8. It can be rephrased to state that if D is a weak digraph, then x is a bridge if and only if $D - x$ is disconnected. This observation, together with the definition of an i, j line, leads to the next corollary.

Corollary 7.8b. In a weak digraph, x is a bridge if and only if x is an $i, 0$ line.

This corollary gives a criterion for a line of a weak digraph to be an $i, 0$ line. The next theorem shows, however, that this criterion cannot be satisfied in a strong digraph.

Theorem 7.9. No strong digraph contains a 3, 0 line.

By Corollary 7.8b, a 3, 0 line x would have to be a bridge. But by Corollary 7.4a, no strong digraph has a bridge.

Since the removal of a bridge from a weak digraph D reduces the category of D, the presence of the bridge may be said to strengthen D. In general, an i, j line is called a *strengthening line* of D if $i > j$, and a *neutral line* if $i = j$. Thus, the presence of a strengthening line is critical for preserving the connectedness of the digraph, and the presence of a neutral line makes no difference to the category of the digraph. The next theorem shows that we need not be concerned with i, j lines where $i < j$.

Theorem 7.10. There are no lines in any digraph whose removal increases its category.

This assertion can be easily verified. For if x is any line of D, any path or strict semipath in $D - x$ is already in D. Hence, the category of $D - x$ is at most that of D.

Corollary 7.10a. Every line of a disconnected digraph D is a $0, 0$ line.

Aside from the ones specified in Theorems 7.9 and 7.10, all other kinds of i, j lines may exist. An example of each of these is given in Figure 7.7, which shows four digraphs D_0, D_1, D_2, and D_3 such that D_i is in C_i. An ordered pair of integers i, j written near a line indicates that the line is an i, j line. The next theorem and corollary specify the relationship between basic lines and strengthening and neutral lines.

Theorem 7.11. If x is not a basic line, then x is neutral.

Since, by hypothesis, x is not basic, there is a path L from fx to sx not containing x. For any sequence (or semisequence) joining two points which contains x, we may obtain another joining the same two points on replacing x by L. Hence, in $D - x$, there is a sequence (or semi-sequence) joining any two points which are thus joined in D. Therefore, deleting x does not change the category of D. And, by definition, x is neutral.

Corollary 7.11a. Every strengthening line is basic.

This corollary is simply a restatement of Theorem 7.11 in view of the fact that every line is either basic or not basic and either neutral or strengthening.

Characterization of i, j Lines

With the background thus far in this chapter, we are able to characterize each possible kind of i, j line in terms of betweenness. The next three theorems give these results according to the category of the digraph.

Theorem 7.12. Let D be strictly weak.

1. x is a 1, 0 line if and only if it is a bridge, that is, there are two points u and v such that $(u \ x \ v)_1$.
2. x is a 1, 1 line if and only if it is not a bridge.

The theorem is an immediate consequence of Theorem 7.10, Corollary 7.8b, and Theorem 7.3. These observations are illustrated by digraph D_1 of Figure 7.7. It can be seen that x_1 is a bridge and a 1, 0 line, whereas x_2 is not a bridge and is a 1, 1 line.

Theorem 7.13. Let D be strictly unilateral.

1. x is a 2, 0 line if and only if it is a bridge, that is, there are two points u and v such that $(u \ x \ v)_1$.
2. x is a 2, 1 line if and only if it is not a bridge, and there are two points u and v such that $(u \ x \ v)_2$ or $(u \ x \ v)_3$.
3. x is a 2, 2 line if and only if there are no two points u and v such that $(u \ x \ v)_1$, $(u \ x \ v)_2$, or $(u \ x \ v)_3$; or equivalently, whenever x is between two points it is 3'-between them.

The first result follows immediately from Corollary 7.8b.

Next, given that x is a 2, 1 line, we know that it is not a bridge. Since $D - x$ is strictly weak, it has two points u and v with no path joining them. Since D is unilateral, u and v are 2-joined in D; and so every path joining them contains x. Hence if u and v are 2-connected, then $(u \ x \ v)_2$; if 3-connected, $(u \ x \ v)_3$.

Conversely, we are given that x is not a bridge; therefore $D - x$ is weak. We also are given that there are two points u and v such that $(u \ x \ v)_2$ or $(u \ x \ v)_3$. In either case, all paths joining u and v contain x, so that there are no paths joining them in $D - x$. Therefore, $D - x$ is strictly weak, and x is a 2, 1 line.

The third result follows from the preceding by elimination of possibilities.

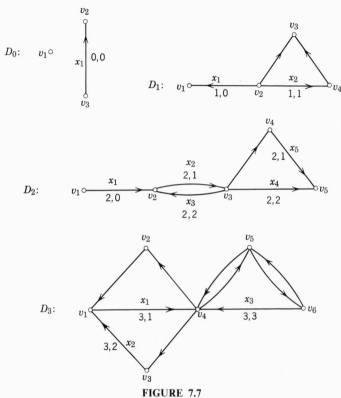

FIGURE 7.7

This theorem is illustrated by D_2 of Figure 7.7. First of all, x_1 is a bridge and a 2, 0 line. Secondly, x_2, which satisfies $(v_1 \, x_2 \, v_3)_2$ but is not a bridge, is a 2, 1 line. Thirdly, we see that x_3 is not 1-, 2-, or 3-between any two points and is a 2, 2 line.

Theorem 7.14. Let D be strong.

1. x is a 3, 1 line if and only if there are two points u and v such that $(u \, x \, v)_3$.

2. x is a 3, 2 line if and only if there are two points u and v such that $(u \, x \, v)_{3'}$ and no two points u and v such that $(u \, x \, v)_3$.

3. x is a 3, 3 line if and only if there are no two points u and v such that $(u \, x \, v)_3$ or $(u \, x \, v)_{3'}$.

If x is a 3, 1 line, then every pair of points in D is 3-connected and there are two points u and v with no paths joining them in $D - x$. Therefore, every path of D joining u and v contains x, and so $(u \times v)_3$, by definition.

Conversely, if there are two points u and v such that $(u \times v)_3$, it follows by definition that every path joining them contains x. Therefore, $D - x$ contains no path joining u and v, and so x is either a 3, 1 or a 3, 0 line. Since there are no 3, 0 lines, x is a 3, 1 line.

We next prove the third statement, leaving the second until later. Assume that x is a 3, 3 line. From the preceding result we know that there are no two points u and v such that $(u \times v)_3$. Moreover, there are no two points u and v such that $(u \times v)_{3'}$, since if there were, all paths in one direction joining u and v would contain x, and u and v would not be 3-connected in $D - x$.

Conversely, if there are no points u and v such that $(u \times v)_3$ or $(u \times v)_{3'}$, then all points in $D - x$ are 3-connected and x is a 3, 3 line.

The second result of the theorem now follows by elimination of possibilities.

This theorem is illustrated by digraph D_3 of Figure 7.7. We can see that $D_3 - x_1$ is in C_1, since in it only strict semipaths join v_2 and v_3. Therefore, since D_3 is strong, x_1 is a 3, 1 line. Moreover, v_2 and v_3 are 3-connected in D_3 and all paths joining them contain x_1; hence $(v_2 \, x_1 \, v_3)_3$. Clearly, $D_3 - x_2$ is in C_2, since in this subgraph v_3 is a receiver and any two other points are 3-connected. Hence, x_2 is a 3, 2 line. We also have $(v_3 \, x_2 \, v_1)_{3'}$, and since there is a path from v_1 to v_3 not containing x, there are no two points u and v such that $(u \times v)_3$. Line x_3 is a 3, 3 line, since $D_3 - x_3$ is clearly strong. Moreover, every two points of D_3 are mutually reachable by paths not containing x_3. Therefore, there are no points such that x_3 is 3- or 3'-between them.

A summary of the criteria for x to be an i, j line, as established in the preceding theorems, is given in Table 7.2. Results are presented only for weak digraphs since by Corollary 7.10a every line of a disconnected digraph is a 0, 0 line. The criteria are stated in terms of betweenness of x with respect to two points of the digraph. For example, the 3, 2 entry of the table presents information included in Theorem 7.14, namely, that in a strong digraph x is a 3, 2 line if and only if there are two points u and v such that $(u \times v)_{3'}$, and there are no two points u and v such that $(u \times v)_3$.

Under certain conditions, an i, j line can be characterized just in terms of its betweenness relation to its two points. In these cases, we need to be concerned only with x and its two points fx and sx. The next three theorems provide such criteria.

Table 7.2. Criteria for x to be an i, j Line of a Weak Digraph

In this table an empty cell means that there is no such line; $n = 1, 2, 3,$ or $3'$ means that there are two points u and v in D such that $(u\, x\, v)_n$; $\sim n$ means that there are no two points u and v such that $(u\, x\, v)_n$.

i	0	1	2	3
1	1	~ 1		
2	1	~ 1 / 2 or 3	~ 1 / ~ 2 / ~ 3	
3		3	$3'$ / ~ 3	$\sim 3'$ / ~ 3

(column heading: j)

Theorem 7.15. Let D be strictly weak.
1. x is a $1, 0$ line if and only if $(fx\, x\, sx)_1$.
2. x is a $1, 1$ line if and only if $\sim(fx\, x\, sx)_1$.

These results are obtained by applying the definition of a bridge to Theorem 7.12.

Theorem 7.16. Let x be an acyclic line of a strictly unilateral digraph.
1. x is a $2, 0$ line if and only if $(fx\, x\, sx)_1$.
2. x is a $2, 1$ line if and only if $(fx\, x\, sx)_2$ and $\sim(fx\, x\, sx)_1$.
3. x is a $2, 2$ line if and only if $\sim(fx\, x\, sx)_2$.

The first result follows immediately from the definition of a bridge and Theorem 7.13. The third requires the observation from Theorem 7.2 that since x is acyclic, $(fx\, x\, sx)_{3'}$ is impossible; Theorems 7.5 and 7.13 then complete the proof. The second result follows by elimination.

Theorem 7.17. If D is strong, the following statements are equivalent.
1. x is a $3, 3$ line.
2. $\sim(fx\, x\, sx)_{3'}$.
3. x is not basic.

The first two statements are equivalent by Corollary 7.5c and Theorem 7.14. In addition, since D has no line such that $(fx\, x\, sx)_2$, x is not basic if and only if $\sim(fx\, x\, sx)_{3'}$, by Theorem 7.5, completing the proof.

Determining the i, j Value of a Line

In principle, it is possible to determine the i, j value of any line of a weak digraph by means of the procedures summarized in Table 7.2.

Since these may be cumbersome, especially in large digraphs, simpler procedures would be preferable. It is often relatively easy to ascertain whether a line is a bridge. If x is a bridge, then Corollary 7.8b tells us that x is either a 1, 0 or a 2, 0 line, depending upon the category of D. And since every line of a strictly weak digraph is either 1, 0 or 1, 1, we can readily determine the i, j values of all lines when D is in C_1.

It is usually not difficult to discover whether a line is basic. And since Theorem 7.11 asserts that every line which is not basic is neutral, we can readily find 1, 1, 2, 2, and 3, 3 lines, and, of course, all other lines are strengthening. It is not so easy, though, to identify lines that are 2, 1, 3, 2, or 3, 1. If a line of a strictly unilateral digraph is acyclic, then we know from Theorem 7.16 that it is a 2, 1 line if and only if it is basic but not a bridge. However, in all other cases we must use the more tedious criteria of Table 7.2.

If the given digraph is quite complicated, we may wish to employ matrix methods to find i and j. The procedure will not be reviewed in detail, but it will be recalled from Chapter 5 that the connectedness matrix $C(D)$ can be derived from the adjacency matrix $A(D)$ using certain operations. Likewise of course, $C(D - x)$ is obtainable from $A(D - x)$. The two matrices $A(D)$ and $A(D - x)$ are identical except that the entry of 1 in $A(D)$, which reflects the presence of x, is an entry of 0 in $A(D - x)$. To find the i, j value of x, then, we take $A(D)$, obtain $A(D - x)$ and derive the matrices $C(D)$ and $C(D - x)$. The minimum entry of $C(D)$ is the i-value of x, that of $C(D - x)$ is its j-value.

Realization of i, j Lines

We have seen that if any single line x is removed from a digraph, its category of connectedness is either reduced or left unchanged. In other words, x is a strengthening line or a neutral one. A digraph is vulnerable, in this sense, at its strengthening lines. It follows that any empirical property uniquely associated with the category of a digraph will be destroyed by a change that corresponds to the removal of strengthening line. Thus, for example, in a strong communication network, every pair of people can engage in two-way communication. However, the failure of a single link to function will destroy this capacity if and only if the link corresponds to a strengthening line of the associated digraph. Similarly, if a strengthening link of a strictly unilateral network fails to function, it will no longer be possible for a message to reach everyone from a single originator.

Betweenness plays a crucial role in determining the dependence of a digraph upon a line for its category of connectedness. In Theorem 7.5, we saw that a line is basic if and only if it is between its two points. And in Theorem 7.11, we saw that every line which is not basic is neutral. Thus, if a line x is not between its two points, the digraph is not vulnerable at x. If, therefore, we wish to construct an invulnerable structure, we must be sure that no line of the associated digraph is between its two points.

If a line x is 1-between its two points, it is a bridge. A digraph is especially vulnerable at a bridge, since x is an $i, 0$ line of a weak digraph if and only if x is a bridge. In the sociometric example discussed earlier, we saw that the residents of a housing project will tend to associate in a single grouping if and only if the digraph of their choices is weak. The group is, therefore, vulnerable at each bridge x, for if fx does not choose sx the group will break in two. We have seen, however, that no strong digraph can have a bridge and hence a $3, 0$ line. Thus, in a strong sociometric structure the continued existence of the group is not dependent upon any single choice.

REMOVAL OF A SET OF LINES

Thus far we have considered some of the effects of removing a single line from a digraph. A more general problem is to investigate the effects of removing a set of lines from a digraph. Unfortunately, a thorough investigation of these effects becomes extremely complicated. Certain useful results, however, can be obtained rather easily. In this section, we present only an introduction to this area of investigation.

The *removal of a set Y of lines from D* results in that spanning subgraph, $D_1 = D - Y$, containing all lines of D except those in Y. Thus, if D is a digraph whose sets of points and lines are V and X, then $D - Y$ is that digraph whose set of points is also V and whose set of lines is $X - Y$. If a digraph D is in category C_i and Y is a set of lines of D such that $D - Y$ is in C_j, then Y is called an i, j *set of lines* of D. Just as a line may be strengthening or neutral, so may a set of lines. An i, j set is *strengthening* if $i > j$ and *neutral* if $i = j$.

These concepts are illustrated by the digraphs of Figure 7.8. It can be verified readily that D is in C_2. The set Y_1 is neutral, for $D - Y_1$ is also in C_2. It can be seen that sets Y_2, Y_3, and Y_4 are strengthening sets, for $D - Y_2$ is in C_1 while $D - Y_3$ and $D - Y_4$ are each in C_0.

In the remainder of this section, we consider three useful indexes that may be associated with any digraph.

The *line requirement* of a digraph D, denoted $\mathrm{lr}(D)$, is the smallest number of lines whose presence is required in order for the category of D not to be decreased. The *line surplus* of a digraph D, denoted $\mathrm{ls}(D)$,

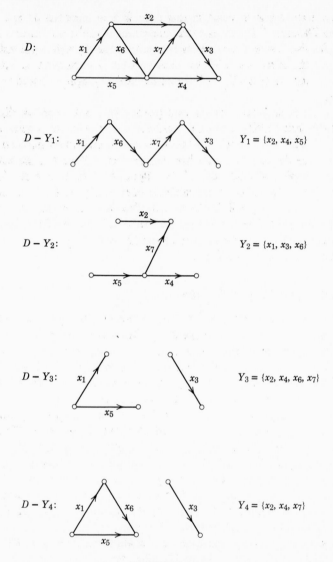

FIGURE 7.8

is the maximum number of lines in any neutral set Y of D. Obviously, in any digraph the sum of the line requirement and the line surplus is the total number of lines. In other words, if Y_1 is a largest neutral set of lines of D, then the line requirement of D is the number of lines in $D - Y_1$. Clearly, the line requirement of the digraph D of Figure 7.8 is 4.

Theorem 7.18. The following formulas, in which D_i is a digraph in C_i, give the line requirement of any digraph in each category:

$lr(D_0) = 0,$

$lr(D_1) = p - 1,$

$lr(D_2) = $ the minimum number of distinct lines in any complete open sequence,

$lr(D_3) = $ the minimum number of distinct lines in any complete closed sequence.

To prove this theorem, we first observe that since a digraph with p points and no lines is (totally) disconnected, $lr(D_0) = 0$.

Any spanning subgraph of D_1 that has no semicycles is also strictly weak and has $p - 1$ lines. By Theorem 3.15, any digraph with p points and fewer than $p - 1$ lines is disconnected. Hence, the line requirement of D_1 is $p - 1$.

By Theorem 3.10, a strictly unilateral digraph D_2 has a complete open sequence. Thus any spanning subgraph of D_2 which does not have a complete open sequence is not unilateral. Therefore, any spanning subgraph of D_2 that is unilateral and has the fewest possible number of lines contains the lines in a complete open sequence. Hence, the minimum number of lines in any complete open sequence of D_2 is its line requirement.

Finally, we observe that a similar argument establishes the formula for $lr(D_3)$, since by Theorem 3.9 every strong digraph contains a complete closed sequence.

The *line vulnerability* of a digraph D, denoted $lw(D)$, is the minimum number of lines in any strengthening set Y of D. In other words, this index gives the smallest number of lines whose removal reduces the category of a digraph. Thus, any property of D that depends upon the category of D may be destroyed if the number of lines removed equals or exceeds the line vulnerability of D. Clearly, however, the lines that are removed must all be contained in the same strengthening set of D.

The next theorem provides useful information concerning the line vulnerability of strong digraphs. For convenience of notation, we let id_{min} denote the minimum indegree of any point of D and od_{min} denote the minimum outdegree of any point of D.

Theorem 7.19. If D is strong, its line vulnerability satisfies the inequalities:

$$lw(D) \leq od_{min} \quad \text{and} \quad lw(D) \leq id_{min}$$

Thus, $lw(D) \leq$ the smallest row or column total of the adjacency matrix $A(D)$.

We first prove that $lw(D) \leq id_{min}$. Let u be a point of D with minimum indegree. If we remove all lines to u, then u is a transmitter and the resulting digraph is not strong. The number of lines removed is $id(u)$. Hence, the line vulnerability of D is at most $id(u) = id_{min}$. The directional dual of this argument establishes that $lw(D) \leq od_{min}$, completing the proof.

The next corollary is a paraphrasing of a theorem due to Luce (1952).

Corollary 7.19a. If D is strong, then $lw(D) \leq q/p$.

To prove this corollary, we note that $id_{min} \leq \overline{id}$, where $\overline{id}$ is the average indegree of the points of D. By Corollary 1.1a, $\overline{id} = q/p$. It follows from Theorem 7.19, then, that $lw(D) \leq \overline{id} = q/p$.

The inequality in the preceding sentence immediately implies the next corollary.

Corollary 7.19b. If D is strong and $lw(D) = q/p$, then for each point v, $id(v) = od(v) = q/p$.

Corollary 7.19c. If D is strong, then $lw(D) = p - 1$ if and only if D is the complete symmetric digraph K_p.   .

First, we take as given that $lw(D) = p - 1$. By Corollary 7.19a, $lw(D) \leq q/p$. It follows that $p - 1 \leq q/p$. This inequality may be rewritten $q \geq p(p - 1)$. Since no digraph has more than $p(p - 1)$ lines and K_p is the only digraph with $p(p - 1)$ lines, we conclude that D is K_p.

We now prove that if D is K_p then $lw(D) = p - 1$. For any two points u and v, there are $p - 1$ paths from u to v which pairwise have no lines in common: the path uv and the paths uv_iv, for the remaining $p - 2$ points. Hence, for there to be no path from u to v, at least $p - 1$ lines must be removed, so $lw(D) \geq p - 1$. But $lw(D) \leq od_{min} = p - 1$. Hence $lw(D) = p - 1$.

Corollary 7.19d. For any strong digraph D, the line vulnerability satisfies the inequality $1 \leq lw(D) \leq p - 1$.

Obviously, $1 \leq lw(D)$. Since the largest number of lines in any strong digraph occurs in K_p, we have, from Corollary 7.19c, $1 \leq lw(D) \leq p - 1$.

These results concerning the line vulnerability of strong digraphs are illustrated by the digraphs of Figure 7.9. It can be verified that each of these satisfies the inequalities given in Theorem 7.19 and Corollaries 7.19a and 7.19d. Digraphs D, F, and G all illustrate Corollary 7.19b.

And, the complete symmetric digraph G satisfies Corollary 7.19c, since $lw(G) = p - 1$.

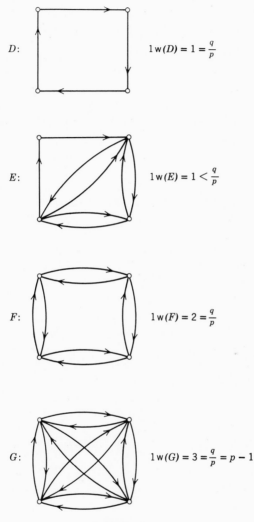

$$1w(D) = 1 = \frac{q}{p}$$

$$1w(E) = 1 < \frac{q}{p}$$

$$1w(F) = 2 = \frac{q}{p}$$

$$1w(G) = 3 = \frac{q}{p} = p - 1$$

FIGURE 7.9

In summary, we have examined three indexes that may be associated with any digraph. Two of these, line surplus and line requirement, are complements of each other. They give, respectively, the maximum number of lines that may be removed from D without changing its category, and the minimum number of lines whose presence in D is required in order to preserve the category. The third index, line vulnerability, gives the smallest number of lines whose removal from the digraph reduces its category. These three indexes, together with the category of a digraph, provide useful information about its connectivity with respect to its lines.

LINE BASES

Thus far we have been concerned with the effects upon the category of a digraph of removing one or more of its lines. In this section, we are still interested in the removal of a set of lines but with a different emphasis. Consider two points u and v of a digraph D such that v is reachable from u. Clearly, D may contain a line x such that v is still reachable from u in $D - x$. In general, D may contain a set of lines Y whose removal results in a spanning subgraph in which whenever u can reach v in D it can also do so in $D - Y$. In matrix terms, $D - Y$ has the same reachability matrix as D; that is, $R(D - Y) = R(D)$. Now if the set Y has the property that the removal of even one additional line from $D - Y$ no longer results in a digraph with the same reachability matrix as D, then the lines of $D - Y$ constitute a minimal collection of lines which preserves the reachability matrix of D. Such a set of lines is the focus of this section.

A *line basis* of a digraph is a minimal collection of lines which preserves reachability. In other words, a line basis of D is the set of lines in a minimal spanning subgraph E such that $R(E) = R(D)$, that is, for any points u and v, whenever u is reachable from v in D, then u is also reachable from v in E. A *subgraph* $\langle Y \rangle$ *generated by the set* Y *of lines of* D is the subgraph whose line set is Y and whose point set consists of all points of D that are the first or second point of a line of Y. Since a line basis is a set of lines, we may speak of the subgraph generated by a line basis.

It follows from Theorem 5.4 that any two digraphs with the same reachability matrix have the same transitive closure; therefore, we have the next result.

Theorem 7.20. The subgraph generated by a line basis of a digraph D has the same transitive closure as D.

Figure 7.10 presents the complete symmetric digraph K_4 and three digraphs generated by different line bases of K_4. Since K_4 is strong, any line basis must also generate a strong spanning subgraph. Moreover, the removal of even one line from any of these subgraphs will weaken it. We see that one line basis of K_4 contains six lines, one contains five lines, and one contains four so that not all line bases of a digraph need have the same number of lines. Let us assume that the digraph K_4 represents a communication network. Since K_4 is strong, a message can originate with any person, reach everyone, and return to its originator. Since each subgraph generated by a line basis of K_4 is also strong, we see that this property of the network will be preserved even if only those lines in a line basis are actually used. Of course, the line vulnerability of the subgraph generated by any line basis is 1.

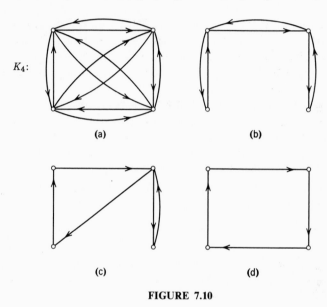

K_4:

(a)   (b)

(c)   (d)

FIGURE 7.10

Theorem 7.21. Every digraph has a line basis.[1]

Clearly, every digraph has a set of lines which preserves reachability, namely all the lines of D. Therefore, it has a minimal set, and so every digraph has a line basis.

The following procedure always results in a line basis of a digraph D. If D has no line whose removal results in a spanning subgraph with the same reachability relation, then by definition all lines of D form a line basis. Otherwise, there is a line x_1 such that $D - x_1$ has the same reachability relation as D. We now apply the same process to $D - x_1$.

[1] This theorem and other related results on line bases are developed in König (1936, Ch. VII, §2).

Thus if $D - x_1$ is not already a line basis for D, then there is a subgraph $D - x_1 - x_2$ with the same reachability relation. This process must terminate, since the number of lines in D is finite. By definition, the lines in the last digraph obtained by such a process form a line basis.

We now relate the concept of basic line to that of line basis. In Theorem 7.5, we have five equivalent conditions for a line to be basic; the next theorem provides still another.

Theorem 7.22. In a digraph D, x is basic if and only if it is in every line basis of D.

We first take as given that x is basic. By Theorem 7.5, there are two points u and v such that there is a path from u to v and all such paths contain x. Thus, in $D - x$, u cannot reach v. It follows that x is in every spanning subgraph of D which preserves reachability. By definition, then, x is in every line basis.

Now assume that x is in every line basis of D. By definition, x is in every minimal spanning subgraph which preserves reachability. This means that there are two points u and v such that u can reach v in D but not in $D - x$. Thus all paths from u to v must contain x. By definition, then, x is in every line basis.

Corollary 7.22a. If there is a unique path L from u to v, then every line of L is in every line basis of D.

This corollary follows immediately, since every line of L is basic by Theorem 7.5.

If the set of lines of a digraph D constitutes a line basis of D, we speak of D as being its own line basis, by an abuse of language. The next corollary characterizes such digraphs.

Corollary 7.22b. A digraph is its own line basis if and only if every line is basic.

First, if every line x is basic, by Theorem 7.22, x is in every line basis, and hence D is its own line basis. Conversely, if D is its own line basis, it obviously has only one, and this one contains every line x. Thus, by the theorem, x is basic, proving the result.

Recall that a digraph is unipathic if whenever v is reachable from u, there is a unique path from u to v. The next corollary, then, is an immediate consequence of the two preceding ones.

Corollary 7.22c. If a digraph is unipathic, it is its own line basis.

Any property of a digraph D that depends only on the reachability relation of D is also a property of any spanning subgraph of D generated by one of its line bases. Let us illustrate this general statement by means of a unilateral digraph D of a communication network N. Since D is unilateral, we know that it contains a complete open sequence, and a message can reach everyone in N from a single originator. This statement is true also for any spanning subgraph generated by a line basis of D. Thus, the communication network will be undisturbed, with respect to this property, by the destruction or malfunctioning of communication links so long as a line basis remains intact. And since a basic line is in every line basis, the removal of even one basic line will destroy this property of the network. We see in the unilateral digraph of Figure 7.11 that there is a unique path from v_1 to v_2, consisting of lines x_1, x_2, and x_3. By Corollary 7.22a, we know that each of these lines is in every line basis of the digraph. Thus, if any one of these lines is removed, the digraph no longer contains a complete open sequence.

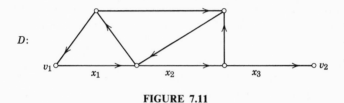

FIGURE 7.11

The next theorem gives conditions for a set of lines of a digraph to be a line basis.

Theorem 7.23. A set Y of lines of a digraph D is a line basis of D if and only if the following two conditions hold:
1. Y preserves reachability in D.
2. Every line of Y is basic in $\langle Y \rangle$.

To prove this theorem we need only show that, given preservation of reachability, condition (2) is equivalent to minimality. First, if Y is a line basis of D, clearly Y is a line basis of $\langle Y \rangle$, and hence every line of Y is basic in $\langle Y \rangle$. Conversely, if each line of Y is basic in $\langle Y \rangle$, Y is its own line basis. Therefore, the removal of any line from Y destroys reachability in $\langle Y \rangle$, establishing the minimality property. Thus, Y is a line basis of D.

The next corollaries describe some properties of line bases for strong digraphs.

Corollary 7.23a. A set Y of lines of a strong digraph D is a line basis if and only if $\langle Y \rangle$ is a minimal strong spanning subgraph of D.

This result follows from the above theorem and Theorem 7.17, which implies the equivalence of strengthening and basic lines in strong digraphs.

Among all line bases of D, there is at least one with the smallest possible number of lines. We call such a set a *minimum line basis*. The next corollary connects this concept with that of line requirement, and is an immediate result.

Corollary 7.23b. The line requirement of a strong digraph is the number of lines in a minimum line basis.

Corollary 7.23c. A line basis of K_p is minimum if and only if it generates a complete cycle.

By Theorem 7.18, the line requirement of K_p is p; hence a minimum line basis of K_p has p lines. Moreover, a strong digraph of p points has exactly p lines only if it is a complete cycle. Conversely, a cycle of p points is a line basis for K_p; and since it has p lines, it is minimum. Figure 7.10(d) shows a line basis with four lines for K_4, and it generates a complete cycle.

In the next theorem we establish an important result concerning line bases of an acyclic digraph, and hence of the condensation D^* of any digraph D.

Theorem 7.24. Every acyclic digraph has a unique line basis consisting of all its basic lines.

Let B be the set of basic lines of an acyclic digraph D. To show that B is a line basis we first demonstrate that B preserves reachability. If point v is reachable from u in D, then we must show that it is also reachable from u in $\langle B \rangle$. Let L be a maximal path from u to v, that is, one whose set of points is contained in no other path from u to v. We show that all lines of L are basic. If x is a line of L, then for any path from fx to sx whose other points are not in L, replacing x in L by this path would contradict the maximality of L. But no path from fx to sx can contain another point of L; for if L_1 were a path from fx to sx containing a point w occurring after sx in L, then that part of L_1 from w to sx together with that portion of L from sx to w would form a closed sequence, contradicting the acyclicity of D. A similar argument applies if w precedes fx. Thus all lines of L are basic. Clearly, then, B contains all lines of all maximal paths between points of D, and hence B preserves reachability. Thus some subset of B (possibly B itself) is a line basis. By Theorem 7.22, every line of B is in every line basis. Hence no proper subset of B is a line basis, and B itself must be a line basis.

To prove uniqueness, let Y be any line basis of D. By Theorem 7.22, Y contains B. But since every line basis is minimal and B is a line basis, $Y = B$.

This theorem is illustrated by the acyclic digraph shown in Figure 7.12. It can be verified that each labeled line of this digraph is basic. By Theorem 7.22, it follows that all of these lines are contained in every line basis of the digraph. And, if we construct the spanning subgraph generated by this set of basic lines, we obtain a line basis. Thus, this line basis is unique and consists of all basic lines of the digraph.

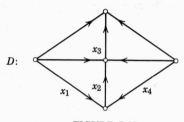

D:

FIGURE 7.12

Implication Digraphs

The concept of line basis is especially interesting when applied to implication digraphs.[2] In Chapter 1 we saw that an implication digraph is one in which each point corresponds to a proposition and a line uv means that proposition u implies proposition v. It will be recalled that the relation of implication is transitive. Thus, if D is an implication digraph, its transitive closure D^t is also an implication digraph; all the new lines of D^t correspond to valid implications implicit in D.

Recall that a total implication digraph displays all possible implications among the propositions corresponding to its points. Since the relation of implication is transitive, it follows that a total implication digraph is the transitive closure of any of its spanning subgraphs which preserve reachability. In particular, by Theorem 7.20, it is the transitive closure of the subgraph generated by any of its line bases. Thus, if we wish to establish the validity of a particular total implication digraph, it is sufficient to prove the implications represented by one of its line bases. The remaining implications are obtained simply by forming the transitive closure of the subgraph generated by the line basis.

The digraph D^t shown in Figure 7.13 displays the information provided by Theorems 7.3, 7.8, and the first part of Corollary 7.5c. This

[2] For a discussion of implication digraphs, see König (1936, pp. 105–107).

digraph is interpreted as an implication digraph in which the points have the following meanings:

v_1: x is a bridge of D.

v_2: There are two points u and v in D such that $(u \, x \, v)_1$.

v_3: The number of weak components of $D - x$ is one more than the number of weak components of D.

v_4: x is a basic line of D.

It can readily be determined that the digraph D of Figure 7.13 is the subgraph of D^t generated by a line basis of D^t. Thus, the validity of D^t can be established simply by proving the implications displayed in D.

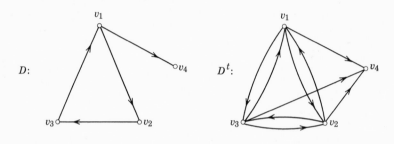

FIGURE 7.13

From propositional logic it is known that a set of propositions are all equivalent if and only if their total implication digraph is complete symmetric. In view of this fact, Corollary 7.23c can be quite useful, for it characterizes a minimum line basis of a complete symmetric digraph, namely, one which generates a complete cycle. Thus, a set of propositions are proved to be logically equivalent if it can be shown that the implication digraph of these propositions contains a complete cycle. And since the number of lines in a complete cycle is the number of points of the digraph, a set of p propositions can be shown to be equivalent by proving as few as p implications.

Finally, we note that any total implication digraph has a particular structure, as given by Corollary 5.4b. If a digraph D is a total implication digraph, then it has the following structure: Every strong component is complete symmetric and whenever there is a path from a point of strong component S_1 to a point of S_2, there is a line from each point of S_1 to each point of S_2. It is apparent that digraph D^t of Figure 7.13 has this structure.

SUMMARY

This chapter has focused attention upon the lines of a digraph. We have found four ways in which a line x may be said to be between two points. Upon applying these concepts to a line x and its two points fx and sx, it is possible to identify two important kinds of lines—bridges and basic lines—which play a critical role in determining the connectedness of a digraph.

One indication of the importance of a line for the connectedness of a digraph is the effect of its removal upon the category of the digraph. If a digraph D is in C_i and $D - x$ is in C_j, then x is said to be an i, j line. A line x is strengthening if $i > j$; x is neutral if $i = j$. The principal result of this analysis is a set of criteria, stated in terms of betweenness, for each permissible type of i, j line. The importance of bridges and basic lines is exemplified by two findings: the removal of a bridge disconnects a weak digraph, and every strengthening line is basic.

Study of the effects of removing a set of lines from a digraph raises more difficult problems. Certain results, however, are obtained readily. Of particular value are three indexes which specify the line requirement, line surplus, and line vulnerability of any digraph D. Formulas were provided for the line requirement and line surplus of any digraph, and bounds established for the line vulnerability of strong digraphs.

The final section introduced the concept of line basis, that is, a minimal set of lines of D which preserves the reachability relation of D. Thus, if a point v is reachable from u in D, then v is still reachable from u in the subgraph generated by a line basis of D. The major result of this section is that line x is in every line basis of D if and only if x is a basic line. Additional findings were presented concerning line bases of strong and of acyclic digraphs.

Throughout the chapter, suggestions were made concerning realizations that have to do with the vulnerability of a structure with respect to the destruction or malfunctioning of its links (empirical relationships). In the next chapter, we consider analogous problems concerning the removal of points.

EXERCISES

1. Disprove: A line x of D is 2-between some pair of points if and only if x is 2-between its own points.
2. Prove: In a symmetric digraph, x is between u and v if and only if $(u \times v)_{3'}$.
3. Prove or disprove: If D is unilateral and x is a line of D such that x is between its two points, then x lies on every complete sequence of D.

4. If od(fx) = 1, then x is basic. State and prove the directional dual of this statement.

5. Prove or disprove: If x is basic and v is reachable from fx, then x lies on every shortest path from fx to v.

6. (a) Prove: If D has a cyclic nonbasic line x, then D has a cycle not containing x. (b) Disprove: If D has a cyclic nonbasic line x, then D has a cycle containing fx and sx but not x.

7. Construct a digraph containing a 2, 2 basic line.

8. Disprove the following statements: (a) If x is an acyclic nonbasic line, then x is not contained in any line basis. (b) If every line of D is basic, then D is unipathic.

9. (a) Show that K_3 has exactly 5 line bases. (b) Show that the number of lines in a minimum line basis of D is sometimes greater than the number of basic lines in D.

10. Show that v is in a point basis of D if and only if v is in a point basis of the subgraph generated by a line basis of D.

11. Prove: If D is a strictly unilateral acyclic digraph, then lr(D) = $p - 1$.

12. Demonstrate that the following equations are true: (a) lr(K_p) = p, (b) ls(K_p) = $p(p - 2)$.

13. Let the digraph D of Figure 7.8 represent a communication network. What is the largest number of lines that can be destroyed without making it impossible for M to reach everyone in the network from a single person?

14. Disprove: If D is strong and id(v) = od(v) = q/p for each point v of D, then lw(D) = q/p. Compare Corollary 7.19b.

15. The total implication digraph of Theorem 7.5 is K_5, since its five propositions are equivalent. Draw the subgraph of the proof of the theorem, as given.

16. Draw the implication digraph of the proof given for Theorem 3.7. In this proof it was already known that conditions (2), (3), and (4) are equivalent. In what other ways could the proof have been completed?

17. Show that every strong digraph with no carrier points has a neutral line.

18. Prove the following statements: (a) Two points u and v of D are mutually reachable if and only if there is a path from u to v in which every line is cyclic. (b) Thus, D is strong if and only if it is weak and every line is cyclic.

19. Show that if line uv is 2-between u and v, then D and $D - uv$ have the same cyclic lines.

20. Prove or disprove: If a strong digraph D contains a symmetric pair of lines x_1 and x_2 whose removal results in a disconnected digraph, then $D - x_1$ is in C_2.

21. In Figure 7.10, line bases of K_4 are shown with 6, 5, and 4 lines. Is there a line basis of K_4 having 7 lines?

22. What is the maximum number of lines in a line basis of K_p?

8 · Removal of a Point

Out, damned spot! out, I say!
WILLIAM SHAKESPEARE, *Macbeth*

The purpose of this chapter is to study for points some of the properties considered in the preceding chapter for lines. We begin by defining betweenness of points, and we shall see that definitions may be made which are entirely analogous to those for betweenness of lines. We then consider the effects of removing a point from a digraph. Although this analysis can proceed in a way similar to that of the preceding chapter, questions involving the removal of a point from a digraph are more complicated than the corresponding questions for the removal of a line. The reason is that although a digraph cannot have a line whose removal results in a more strongly connected digraph, it may have such a point. Thus, in characterizing i, j points we must also consider cases where $i < j$.

Since every line is either strengthening or neutral, realizations of the removal of a line were cast in terms of vulnerability; a digraph is vulnerable at its strengthening lines. But since points may be weakening as well as strengthening or neutral, realizations of the removal of a point encompass a broader range of possibilities. We shall want to consider a digraph as vulnerable at its strengthening points; but it has an opposite sort of property at its weakening points since the removal of one of these will put the digraph in a stronger category of connectedness. Thus, for example, if a sociometric structure has two weak components, one being a single isolate, it is disconnected; but it can be made weakly connected by removing just this one person from the group. And, if a communication network is strictly unilateral, it may be possible to make it strong by removing one person from the network.

THE REMOVAL OF A POINT AND BETWEENNESS

The *removal of a point* v from a nontrivial digraph D results in that digraph $D - v$ which is the maximal subgraph of D not containing v. In other words, $D - v$ has as its set of points all the points of D except v, and has as its set of lines all lines of D except those lines incident with v. Thus, for any point v and line x of a digraph D with p points and q lines, $D - x$ has p points but $q - 1$ lines, while $D - v$ has $p - 1$ points and $q - \text{td}(v)$ lines.

These observations are illustrated in Figure 8.1. The digraph D has four points and five lines. The other digraphs are $D - v_i$ for each of the points of D. Obviously, each of these digraphs has $p - 1 = 3$ points. Since the total degree of v_1 is 1, $D - v_1$ has $q - \text{td}(v_1) = 5 - 1 = 4$ lines. Clearly, the removal of v_2 is much more disruptive, for $D - v_2$ has only 1 line.

In discussing the effects of removing a line from a digraph, we made use of the concept of betweenness of lines. We now develop the analogous concept of betweenness of points. The statement that *point v is i-between*

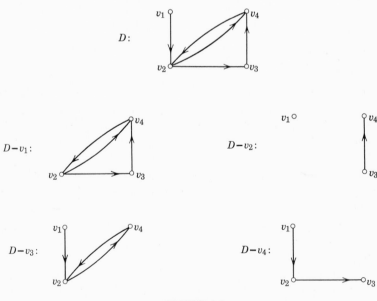

FIGURE 8.1

two other points u and w is abbreviated: $(u\,v\,w)_i$, for $i = 1$, 2, 3, or $3'$. The detailed definitions of these four kinds of betweenness for points are as follows:

$(u\,v\,w)_1$ means u and w are 1-joined and every semipath joining them contains v;

$(u\,v\,w)_2$ means u and w are 2-connected and every path joining them contains v;

$(u\,v\,w)_3$ means u and w are 3-connected and every path joining them contains v;

$(u\,v\,w)_{3'}$ means u and w are 3-connected and either every path from u to w contains v or every path from w to u contains v (but not both).

We say simply that a point is *between* two points if it is i-between them for any i.

An immediate consequence of these definitions is that betweenness displays a kind of symmetry. Thus, for any three distinct points u, v, and w, $(u\,v\,w)_i$ if and only if $(w\,v\,u)_i$, where $i = 1$, 2, 3, or $3'$.

The four kinds of betweenness are illustrated by the digraph of Figure 8.2. Thus, for example, we see that $(v_1 v_2 v_3)_1$, $(v_1 v_2 v_3)_2$, $(v_2 v_3 v_4)_3$ and $(v_2 v_3 v_5)_{3'}$.

The first theorem relates betweenness of points with betweenness of lines.

Theorem 8.1. Let u and w be two points which are not incident with line x. If $(u\,x\,w)_i$, then $(u\,fx\,w)_i$ for $i = 1, 2, 3$. If $(u\,x\,w)_{3'}$, then $(u\,fx\,w)_{3'}$ or $(u\,fx\,w)_3$. The same conclusions also hold for sx.

Once we have demonstrated these statements for fx, their validity for sx follows at once by applying the principle of directional duality.

By hypothesis, line x is i-between points u and w, which are not incident with x. If $i = 1$, 2, or 3, then it follows immediately from the definitions of betweenness of points and of lines that fx is i-between u and w. If $i = 3'$, then fx is on every path joining u and w in one direction, but it may or may not be on all paths in the other direction. Therefore, either $(u\,fx\,w)_3$ or $(u\,fx\,w)_{3'}$.

A specific instance of this theorem is found in the digraph of Figure 8.2. We see that $(v_1\,x\,v_5)_2$, and in keeping with Theorem 8.1, that $(v_1 v_2 v_5)_2$ and $(v_1 v_3 v_5)_2$.

It is clear from the definitions of betweenness of points that for any three points u, v, w at most one of the following statements is true: $(u\,v\,w)_2$, $(u\,v\,w)_3$, and $(u\,v\,w)_{3'}$. However, for points, just as for lines,

1-betweenness does not preclude 2-betweenness or 3-betweenness. The next theorem formalizes these relationships.

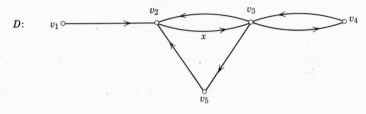

$$D: \quad v_1 \quad\quad v_2 \quad\quad v_3 \quad\quad v_4$$
$$x$$
$$v_5$$

FIGURE 8.2

Theorem 8.2. Let u, v, and w be points of a digraph such that $(u\,v\,w)_1$. If u and w are 2-connected, then $(u\,v\,w)_2$. If u and w are 3-connected, then $(u\,v\,w)_3$.

It is given that $(u\,v\,w)_1$. Thus, v is on every semipath and hence every path joining u and w. Therefore, by definition, if u and w are 2-connected, then $(u\,v\,w)_2$; and if u and w are 3-connected, then $(u\,v\,w)_3$.

In Figure 8.2, we see that $(v_1v_2v_4)_1$, v_1 and v_4 are 2-connected, and $(v_1v_2v_4)_2$, in keeping with Theorem 8.2. Similarly, we find that $(v_2v_3v_4)_1$, v_2 and v_4 are 3-connected, and $(v_2v_3v_4)_3$.

The next theorem provides a connection between the removal of a point and betweenness.

Theorem 8.3. Let u, v, and w be distinct points of a digraph D. The point v is between u and w if and only if u and w are more strongly connected in D than in $D - v$.

This result follows from the consideration of all possible cases: $(u\,v\,w)_1$ if and only if u and w are 1-joined in D and 0-connected in $D - v$; $(u\,v\,w)_2$ if and only if u and w are 2-connected in D and either 1- or 0-connected in $D - v$; $(u\,v\,w)_3$ if and only if u and w are 3-connected in D and either 1- or 0-connected in $D - v$; and $(u\,v\,w)_3$, if and only if u and w are 3-connected in D and 2-connected in $D - v$.

In the proof of the preceding theorem, it was noted that if v is 1-between u and w in D, then u and w are not joined in $D - v$. For this reason, a point which is 1-between two others is called a *cut point*. Examples of cut points are the points v_2 and v_3 in Figure 8.2, and the removal of either leaves a disconnected digraph. A cut point of a weak digraph is sometimes defined as one whose removal results in a disconnected digraph. The next theorem lists several equivalent statements, each of which could be used to define a cut point.

Theorem 8.4. The following statements are equivalent for a point v of a weak digraph D.

(1) There exist points u and w such that $(u\,v\,w)_1$, that is, v is a cut point.

(2) $D - v$ is disconnected.

(3) There exists a partition of $V - \{v\}$ into subsets V_1 and V_2 such that for any two points v_1 in V_1 and v_2 in V_2, $(v_1\,v\,v_2)_1$.

(4) There exist points u and w adjacent with v such that $(u\,v\,w)_1$.

This theorem is proved in a cyclic order.

(1) Implies (2). If v is 1-between points u and w, then u and w are not 1-joined in $D - v$, so $D - v$ is disconnected.

(2) Implies (3). Let V_1 be the set of points in one weak component of $D - v$, and let $V_2 = V - V_1 - \{v\}$. Then for any v_1 in V_1 and any v_2 in V_2, $(v_1\,v\,v_2)_1$ since D is weak and there is no semipath joining v_1 and v_2 in $D - v$.

(3) Implies (4). It follows from the hypothesis of (3) that there is a point u in V_1 and a point w in V_2 such that both u and w are adjacent with v. By using the points u and w for v_1 and v_2 in (3), we find that $(u\,v\,w)_1$, proving (4).

(4) Implies (1). This is immediate, for if there are two points adjacent with v such that all semipaths joining them contain v, then *a fortiori* there are two points such that all semipaths joining them contain v.

The following corollary provides a criterion for a point of any digraph to be a cut point.

Corollary 8.4a. A point v of a digraph D is a cut point if and only if $D - v$ has more weak components than D has.

To illustrate one application of this theorem, let us consider a group of people whose communication network corresponds to a strong digraph such as that shown in Figure 8.3. It is evident that v_4 is a cut point, since there are two points, for example v_2 and v_5, such that v_4 is 1-between them. If v_4 is removed, the resulting digraph is disconnected and has exactly two weak components, both of which are strong. It follows from Theorem 8.4 that all the people in the network, other than v_4, can be placed in two disjoint subgroups so that all semipaths joining a person in one subgroup with a person in the other contain v_4. In this example, these two subgroups are $\{v_1, v_2, v_3\}$ and $\{v_5, v_6\}$. Since every path is a semipath, it follows that all messages going from one subgroup to the other must pass through v_4. Clearly, v_4 has an important location with respect to these two subgroups, and he may be referred to as a liaison person or a bottleneck, depending upon whether his behavior facilitates or inhibits the flow of communication between the two subgroups. In any case, the flow will be especially heavy at this point.

It is obvious that since the removal of a point cannot introduce new paths or semipaths, it cannot increase the strength of connectedness of any two other points. The next theorem, which will be useful later, gives some circumstances in which the removal of a point cannot decrease the strength of connectedness of other points.

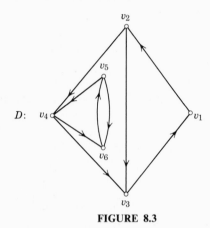

FIGURE 8.3

Theorem 8.5.   Let u, v, and w be points of a digraph D. For $i = 1$, 2, or 3, if u and w are i-joined in D but u and v are not, then u and w are also i-joined in $D - v$.

In proving this theorem, we consider each value of i separately. If $i = 1$, there is a semipath joining u and w, but none joining u and v. Hence, u and w are 1-joined in $D - v$. If $i = 2$, there is a path joining u and w, but none joining u and v. Thus u and w are 2-joined in $D - v$. Finally, if $i = 3$ then u and w are mutually reachable but u and v are not. Hence, v is not on any of the paths joining u and w, since all three points would be mutually reachable. Therefore, u and v are 3-joined in $D - v$.

PROPERTIES OF i, j POINTS

In discussing the line vulnerability of digraphs, we saw how each line can be classified according to the effect of its removal upon the connectedness category. Analogously, a point v of a digraph D is called an i, j *point* if D is in category C_i and $D - v$ is in C_j. The i, j point v

is called a *strengthening point* if $i > j$; it is a *neutral point* if $i = j$; and it is a *weakening point* if $i < j$. Intuitively, a strengthening point is one whose presence makes its digraph "stronger" than it would be without the point, and a weakening point is one whose presence "weakens" the digraph. If a digraph has a neutral point, its category of connectedness is the same whether the neutral point is present or removed.

The next theorem establishes the fact that with one exception all kinds of i, j points may occur.[1]

Theorem 8.6. There are no 1, 3 points in any digraph. However, all other i, j types of points do occur.

To see that it is not possible for a digraph in C_1 to have a 1, 3 point, we assume the contrary and consider such a digraph D as given. Thus D is in C_1 and has a point v such that $D - v$ is strong. But then there must be a line x in D joining v with some point u of $D - v$. Since $D - v$ is strong, for every point w there is a path in D joining v with w. This path consists of the line x joining v and u, and a path joining u with w in the strong digraph $D - v$. Hence any two points of D are joined by a path. This means that D is unilateral, which contradicts the assumption that D is in C_1.

To complete the proof of the theorem, we next demonstrate by a series of examples that all kinds of i, j points other than 1, 3 points can occur. The four digraphs shown in Figure 8.4 illustrate all possible kinds of $0, j$ points. For $j > 0$, the $0, j$ points are isolates.

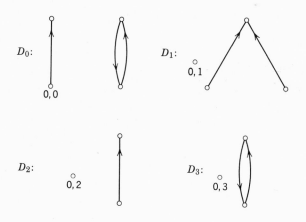

FIGURE 8.4

[1] For a discussion of i, j points, see Ross and Harary (1959).

Figure 8.5 shows a strictly weak digraph consisting of a strict semi-path. The classification of each point is designated, and we see an example of each possible type of 1, *j* point.

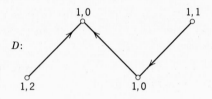

FIGURE 8.5

The digraph of Figure 8.6 is strictly unilateral and has four points, one of each 2, *j* type.

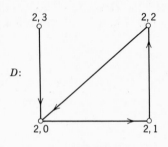

FIGURE 8.6

Finally, Figure 8.7 shows a strong digraph with five points which contains a point of each of the four 3, *j* types.

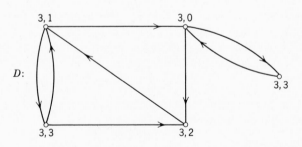

FIGURE 8.7

Weakening Points

Although no digraph has lines whose removal increases the strength of connectedness, we have already seen examples of weakening points. From the definition of weakening points and Theorem 8.6 we see that the following are all possible types of weakening points: 0, 1,   0, 2,   0, 3, 1, 2,   2, 3. The next three theorems characterize these types of points.

Theorem 8.7. A point v of a digraph D is a 0, j point, for $j = 1$, 2, or 3, if and only if D has exactly two weak components — one of which is the point v and the other is itself a digraph in C_j.

If v is a 0, j point, then clearly it is an isolate and D consists of v and a weak component in C_j. Conversely, if v is an isolate of a digraph which consists of v and a weak component in C_j, then v is a 0, j point.

Theorem 8.8. A point v of a strictly weak digraph D is a 1, 2 point if and only if no two points distinct from v are 1-connected.

If v is a 1, 2 point clearly no two other points can be 1-connected in D, since they are 2-joined in $D - v$. Conversely, if all pairs of other points are 2-joined, then there is a point u such that v and u are 1-connected. Let w_1 and w_2 be two points in $D - v$. By hypothesis, there is a path joining them in D, say from w_1 to w_2. If the path does not contain v, they are 2-joined in $D - v$. If every such path contains v, by Theorem 8.5 there are paths joining u with w_1 and u with w_2. There can be no path from u to w_1 or from w_2 to u, since then v and u would be joined by a path. Therefore, there must be paths from w_1 to u and from u to w_2 not containing v. Hence, any two points w_1 and w_2 are 2-joined in $D - v$, and v is a 1, 2 point since by Theorem 8.6 there are no 1, 3 points.

Theorem 8.9. A point v of a strictly unilateral digraph D is a 2, 3 point if and only if no two points distinct from v are 2-connected.

If v is a 2, 3 point of D, then no two other points can be 2-connected, since they are 3-joined in $D - v$. Conversely, if no points different from v are 2-connected, then there is a point u which is 2-connected with v and 3-connected with all other points. Hence, by Theorem 8.5, all points are mutually reachable with u in $D - v$, so $D - v$ is strong, and v is a 2, 3 point.

The preceding three theorems can be combined into the following result, which characterizes weakening points.

Theorem 8.10. Let D be a digraph in C_i. Then v is a weakening point of D if and only if no two points distinct from v are i-connected.

There are three corollaries of this theorem which give some further results concerning weakening points.

Corollary 8.10a. No weakening point of a digraph lies on a cycle.

Let v be any point on a cycle of D, and let w be any other point on this cycle. For any other point u of D, u and v are i-connected if and only if u and w are. By Theorem 8.10, if v is a weakening point then there is a point u that is i-connected with v and not i-connected with any other point. But we have just seen that this is not true for v. Hence v is not a weakening point.

Corollary 8.10b. Every weakening point of a unilateral digraph is a transmitter or a receiver.

By the hypothesis of the corollary, v is a 2, 3 point. Assume that v is neither a transmitter nor a receiver. Then there are lines uv and vw in D. Since $D - v$ is strong, it contains a path from w to u. Hence v is on a cycle, and by Corollary 8.10a, v is not a weakening point.

Corollary 8.10c. Any digraph D contains at most two weakening points.

Let u and v be weakening points of D. By Theorem 8.10, v is i-connected with some point, and if it is i-connected with a point other than u, then u is not a weakening point. Thus any two weakening points are i-connected, and no other point is i-connected with either of them. It follows that no other point is a weakening point.

A Sad Story. A group of men chartered a plane to go on a hunting trip in the north woods. As they were about to depart they discovered that weight restrictions required them to leave one man behind. Assume that the group will be more cohesive the higher the connectedness category of the digraph of its sociometric choices. Thus, in order to maximize cohesiveness, they choose to leave behind a weakening member (if there is any). Corollary 8.10a shows that no man contained in a cycle of choices will be left behind. In particular, no mutual friendships will be broken. Corollary 8.10b says that if the associated digraph is unilateral, any man to be thus excluded from the trip must either have given or received no choices. And Corollary 8.10c guarantees that there are at most two candidates for exclusion. If the digraph of Figure 8.8 represents the sociometric structure of the group and you were person v_5, how would you feel?

After a weakening point has been removed from a digraph, the resulting digraph may still have weakening points. For example, the digraph of Figure 8.9 is strengthened by the removal of v_3, but it then has two weakening points. If either of these is removed, the other still weakens the resulting digraph.

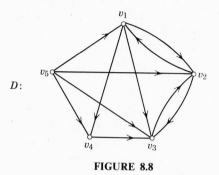

D:

FIGURE 8.8

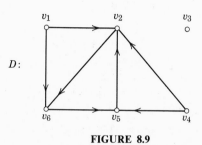

D:

FIGURE 8.9

It is also possible for a digraph with two weakening points to be left with two weakening points after one is removed. This is illustrated by D_1 of Figure 8.10 where, after the removal of v_1 or v_3, both the remaining points are weakening. (This example shows that if a group

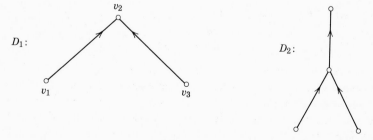

$D_1:$ $\qquad$ $D_2:$

FIGURE 8.10

increases its cohesiveness by repeatedly expelling a weakening member, it may end up with a strongly cohesive group consisting of a single member!) If a digraph has two weakening points and one is removed, it is not necessarily true that the other is weakening in the resulting digraph, as in D_2 of Figure 8.10.

Neutral Points

We now consider neutral points. It will be recalled that if v is a neutral point, its removal does not change the connectedness category of the digraph. In other words, the presence of v neither weakens nor strengthens D. Since a digraph in any connectedness category may have a neutral point, we must consider each category. The next four theorems give criteria for neutral points.

Theorem 8.11.   A point v of a disconnected digraph D is a 0, 0 point if and only if D has at least three weak components or v is not an isolated point.

This result follows immediately from Theorem 8.7.

An alternative phrasing of Theorem 8.11 asserts that a point is a 0, 0 point of a digraph if and only if there are two other points not joined by a semipath. This resembles the following criterion for a neutral point in a strictly weak digraph.

Theorem 8.12.   A point v of a strictly weak digraph is a 1, 1 point if and only if it is not a cut point and there are two other points which are 1-connected.

If v is a 1, 1 point, then it is clearly not a cut point. By Theorem 8.8, if no two other points are 1-connected, v is a 1, 2 point, contradicting the hypothesis.

Conversely, if v is not a cut point and there are two other points that are 1-connected in D, then $D - v$ is strictly weak and so v is a 1, 1 point.

Theorem 8.13.   A point v of a strictly unilateral digraph is a 2, 2 point if and only if there are no two points u and w such that $(u\ v\ w)_2$ or $(u\ v\ w)_3$, and there are two points distinct from v that are 2-connected.

Let v be a 2, 2 point. Then in both D and $D - v$ every pair of points is 2-joined. Therefore, in D there are no two points u and w such that $(u\ v\ w)_2$ or $(u\ v\ w)_3$. Moreover, there are two points distinct from v that are 2-connected, for otherwise it follows from Theorem 8.9 that v is a 2, 3 point.

Conversely, if D is in C_2 and v is not 2- or 3-between any two points, it follows that every pair of points in $D - v$ is 2-joined, so $D - v$ is unilateral. Since there are two points other than v that are 2-connected in D, they are not 3-joined in $D - v$. Hence, v is a 2, 2 point.

Theorem 8.14.   A point v of a nontrivial strong digraph is a 3, 3 point if and only if it is not between any two points.

If v is a 3, 3 point it cannot be between any two points since $D - v$ would not be strong. Conversely, if v is not between any points of a strong digraph, then $D - v$ is strong so v is a 3, 3 point.

Strengthening Points

Since a strengthening point is one whose removal reduces the strength of connectedness, only a weak digraph can have one. The following three theorems characterize strengthening points according to the strength of the resulting digraph.

Theorem 8.15.   Let D be a digraph in C_i, where $i = 1, 2,$ or 3. A point v is an $i, 0$ point if and only if it is a cut point, that is, v is 1-between two points.

This statement is a rephrasing of the part of Theorem 8.4 which characterizes cut points.

Theorem 8.16.   Let D be a digraph in C_i, where $i = 2$ or 3. A point v is an $i, 1$ point if and only if it is not a cut point and it is 2- or 3-between some pair of points.

If v is an $i, 1$ point, then by Theorem 8.15 it is not a cut point. Moreover, it must be 2- or 3-between some two points, since otherwise every pair of points in $D - v$ would be 2-joined, and $D - v$ would not be strictly weak.

Conversely, if v is not a cut point, then $D - v$ is weak. And if v is 2- or 3-between two points, they are not 2-joined in $D - v$, so v is an $i, 1$ point, for $i = 2$ or 3.

Theorem 8.17.   A point v of a strong digraph is a 3, 2 point if and only if it is 3'-between some two points but not 3-between any two points.

This result follows by elimination of possibilities specified in Theorems 8.14, 8.15, and 8.16.

The following theorem summarizes some of the results about strengthening points.

Theorem 8.18.   Every strengthening point of a digraph D is between some pair of points.

1. If D is in C_1, then a point is strengthening if and only if it is 1-between two points.
2. If D is in C_2, then a point is strengthening if and only if it is 2- or 3-between two points.
3. If D is in C_3, then a point is strengthening if and only if it is 3- or 3'-between two points.

Who Are the Important People? In discussing the sad story of the hunting trip, we made the assumption that a group is more cohesive the higher the connectedness category of the digraph of its sociometric choices. From this assumption it follows that the cohesiveness of a group will be reduced if it loses a member who corresponds to a strengthening point. It is, in this sense, vulnerable at these points, and people in these locations are important to the group. Theorem 8.18 tells us that all of these important people are between some pair of individuals in the digraph of the group's sociometric choices. Since the removal of a cut point from a weak digraph disconnects it, people corresponding to these points are especially important. Clearly, the vulnerability of a group and the relative importance of its members depend upon the pattern of choices and not merely upon the particular choices of the individual members.

Summary of Criteria

For convenience of reference, the criteria for i, j points of a weak digraph are summarized in Table 8.1. The criteria given in the i, jth cell of this table are necessary and sufficient conditions for a point v of a digraph D in C_i to be an i, j point.

Table 8.1 gives a convenient guide for ascertaining the i, j type of points in relatively simple weak digraphs. We begin by finding the category C_i of D. Any cut points of D are easily recognized by inspection as $i, 0$ points. To ascertain the i, j type of the remaining points, we employ the criteria in the appropriate row of the table going successively from left to right. Suppose that D is in C_1. We then discover for each point v_k whether there are two points distinct from v_k that are 1-connected. If so, v_k is a 1, 1 point; otherwise it is a 1, 2 point. Suppose that D is in C_2. We then ask for each point v_k whether it is 2-between or 3-between any two points. If so, v_k is a 2, 1 point. If not, we ask whether any two points distinct from v_k are 2-connected. If so, v_k is a 2, 2 point; otherwise it is a 2, 3 point. Finally, suppose that D is in C_3. We ascertain for each point v_k whether it is 3-between any two points. If so, v_k is a 3, 1 point. If not, we ask whether v_k is 3'-between any two points. If so, v_k is a 3, 2 point; otherwise it is a 3, 3 point.

Table 8.1.   Criteria for v to be an i, j Point of a Weak Digraph

In this table, $n = 1, 2, 3$, or 3' means that there are two points u and w such that $(u \, v \, w)_n$; $\sim n$ means that there are no such points; P_m means that there are two points u and w distinct from v such that u and w are m-connected, $m = 1, 2$; $\sim P_m$ means that there are no such points.

i	0	1	2	3
		~ 1		none
1	1	P_1	$\sim P_1$	exists
		~ 1	~ 2	
2	1		~ 3	$\sim P_2$
		2 or 3	P_2	
	1	~ 1	~ 3	~ 3
3		3	3'	$\sim 3'$

The i, j type of any point v_k can also be obtained by use of the connectedness matrix $C(D)$, described in Theorem 5.18. It will be recalled that the category C_i of D is given by the minimum entry in this matrix. For any point v_k, the category C_j of $D - v_k$ can be obtained in the same manner, giving the i, j value of v_k. For digraphs that are large but not too large, these procedures are easily programmed for the computer. It should be noted that any weakening points of D can be found from inspection of $C(D)$. If all minimum entries of $C(D)$ lie in the kth row and column, then v_k is a weakening point.

REMOVAL OF A SET OF POINTS

Thus far we have considered the effects upon the connectedness of a digraph of removing just one of its points at a time. Analysis of the effects of removing more than one point at a time is very complicated, and we shall not attempt a comprehensive treatment of this problem here. However, a useful result is readily available concerning the removal of a set of points from a weak digraph which results in a disconnected digraph. It is obvious that if D is complete and S is any proper subset of points of D, then $D - S$ is also complete; hence D cannot be disconnected by the removal of any set of points. The purpose of the next theorem[2] is to provide an upper bound for the smallest number of points of a weak digraph which is not complete, whose removal will result in a disconnected digraph.

Theorem 8.19. If D is weak and not complete, then the smallest number of points in a set S such that $D - S$ is disconnected is at most the minimum total degree occurring in D.

By hypothesis D is weak and not complete. Let n be the smallest number of points in a set S such that $D - S$ is disconnected. Let v be a point of D whose total degree td(v) is minimum among all the points of D. Then $n \leq$ td(v) for the following reason. If all the points of D adjacent with v are removed from D, the resulting digraph must be disconnected, since it contains v as an isolated point and must contain another weak component besides v because D is not complete.

Suppose that the sociometric choices of the residents of a housing project form a weak digraph which is not complete. Since the digraph is weak, we know from conclusion C3.1 (p. 76) that all residents will tend to associate in the same social activities. If the removal of a subgroup of residents results in a disconnected digraph, then the remaining residents will not show this tendency. Theorem 8.19 tells us how to determine an upper bound on the size of the smallest subgroup whose removal will disconnect the group. Specifically, we calculate for each person the sum of his choices given and choices received, that is, the total degree of the corresponding point in the digraph of choices. The size of the smallest subgroup whose removal will disconnect the group cannot exceed the smallest sum of choices for any individual.

The digraph of Figure 8.11 provides a simple example. We see that the minimum total degree is 3. Thus, the digraph can be disconnected by the removal of as few as 3 people. For example, the removal of either $\{v_2, v_4, v_6\}$ or $\{v_2, v_4, v_7\}$ will disconnect this digraph.

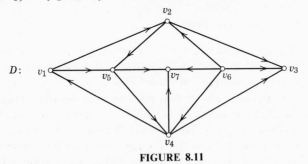

FIGURE 8.11

[2] This theorem is due to Whitney (1932).

SUMMARY

In this chapter, we have examined some of the effects of removing a point from a digraph. The treatment is like that for lines presented in Chapter 7. The concept of betweenness is applicable in both cases, being defined similarly for points and for lines. Moreover, i, j points and i, j lines are defined analogously. If in either case $i > j$, the point or line is said to be strengthening and the digraph is vulnerable in this respect. If $i = j$, the point or line is neutral. There is, however, one major difference between the removal of points and lines. Although there are no i, j lines such that $i < j$, there are points of this kind, which are known as weakening points. Thus, although a digraph cannot be strengthened by removing one of its lines, this can be accomplished in certain digraphs by removing a point. Therefore, a wider variety of effects may result from the removal of a point than the removal of a line. In fact, the only kind of i, j point that cannot exist is a 1, 3 point.

Although weakening points do exist, it turns out that no digraph can have more than two of them. Furthermore, no weakening point of any digraph lies on a cycle. And if a digraph is unilateral, then each of its weakening points is a transmitter or a receiver.

Just as for lines, the characterization of i, j points makes considerable use of the concept of betweenness. The criteria for v to be an i, j point of a weak digraph are summarized in Table 8.1. It can be seen there that every strengthening point of a weak digraph is between two other points.

In analyzing the point vulnerability of digraphs, the concept of a cut point plays an especially important role. A point is a cut point if it is 1-between two points and thus is analogous to a bridge. In a weak digraph, v is an $i, 0$ point if and only if it is a cut point. In other words, the removal of a point v from a weak digraph results in a disconnected one if and only if v is a cut point. In the next chapter, we shall examine in greater detail the properties of digraphs that have no cut points.

EXERCISES

1. Show that every point of a nontrivial digraph D is a weakening point if and only if D has exactly two points and is not strong.

2. Prove or disprove: Every weakening point of a strictly weak digraph is a transmitter or a receiver.

3. (a) Can a digraph have a cut point but no bridge? (b) Can a digraph have a bridge but no cut points?

4. (a) If D is a weak acyclic digraph, what kinds of i, j points can occur? (b) If D is a weak digraph with no semicycles, what kinds of i, j points can occur?

5. Construct digraphs having: (a) A 2, 1 point but no 2, 1 line. (b) A 2, 1 line but no 2, 1 point. (c) A 3, 1 point but no 3, 1 line. (d) A 3, 1 line but no 3, 1 point. (e) A 3, 2 point but no 3, 2 line. (f) A 3, 2 line but no 3, 2 point.

6. Prove or disprove: If a point of a strictly unilateral digraph is 3-between two points, then it is also 2-between some pair of points.

7. Consider a relation on a set of points of an arbitrary digraph which is defined so that two points are in this relation if and only if there is no point which is 1-between them. Show that this is an equivalence relation on the set of all points which are not cut points.

8. Show that every point of a strong symmetric digraph is either neutral or a cut point.

9. Show that if D has two weakening points u and v and $D - u$ also has two weakening points, then D is either digraph D_1 of Figure 8.10 or its converse.

10. Show that there is no strong digraph with four points in which each point is of a different $3, j$ type.

11. Prove: The following statements are equivalent for a point v of a strong digraph D. (a) v is between two points u and w. (b) $D - v$ is not strong. (c) There exists a partition of $V - \{v\}$ into nonempty subsets V_1 and V_2 such that for any two points v_1 in V_1 and v_2 in V_2, v is between v_1 and v_2. (d) v is between two points adjacent with it.

12. Prove: A point v is 3- or 3'-between two points of a digraph D if and only if $D - v$ has more strong components than D.

9 · Blocks

This was the most unkindest cut of all.

WILLIAM SHAKESPEARE
Julius Caesar

The preceding two chapters have discussed the vulnerability of a digraph with respect to the removal of one of its lines or one of its points. In the present chapter, we pursue this topic further. Consider the three digraphs shown in Figure 9.1. If they are interpreted as communication networks, it is possible in each for any two people to engage in two-way communication, since each is strong. It can be seen also that D_1 has a cut point v_0 but that D_2 and D_3 have no cut points. Thus network D_1, in contrast to D_2 and D_3, is vulnerable in the sense that the removal of a person will disconnect the network.

These networks may also be compared in terms of restrictions they impose on paths of communication. In digraph D_3, for every three points u, v, and w there is a path from u to w that contains v as well as one that excludes v. In such a network any two people can include any third person in their two-way communication or they can exclude him. Thus D_3 imposes relatively little restriction on communication. Network D_2 is more restrictive, for although any two people can engage in two-way communication to the exclusion of a third, there is no path from v_1 to v_3 going through v_2. Finally, D_1 is most restrictive in that all messages in either direction between a person u_i and a person w_j must go through v_0.

The analysis of phenomena of this sort makes use of the concept "block." We shall see that the relatively vulnerable and restrictive digraph D_1 contains two blocks, $\langle u_1u_2u_3v_0 \rangle$ and $\langle w_1w_2w_3v_0 \rangle$, but that D_2 and D_3 each consists of just one block. In the first section of the

243

chapter, we investigate some properties of blocks, and in following sections we examine some less vulnerable and less restrictive classes of strong blocks. In the final section, we consider several special kinds of strong digraphs which are uniformly vulnerable in the sense that the removal of any line produces the same effect on the connectedness category.

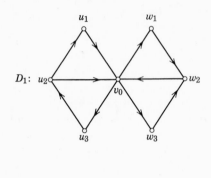

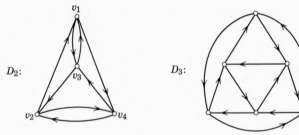

FIGURE 9.1

SOME PROPERTIES OF BLOCKS

A *block* B of a digraph D is a maximal weak subgraph of D, which has no point v such that $B - v$ is disconnected. Although a block B has no point whose removal disconnects B, it may contain a cut point of the entire digraph. In the digraph D_1 of Figure 9.1, it is evident that $\langle u_1 u_2 u_3 v_0 \rangle$ and $\langle w_1 w_2 w_3 v_0 \rangle$ are blocks since each of these is a maximal weak subgraph having no point whose removal will disconnect it. We see, however, that both blocks contain the point v_0, which is a cut point of D_1. An entire digraph is called a block if it has only one block. Thus, D_2 and D_3 are blocks, but D_1 is not.

Before discussing the properties of blocks, it will be useful to have some preliminary results concerning disjoint paths. Two distinct paths from u to v are called *point-disjoint* if the only points they have in common are u and v. Two paths from u to v are *line-disjoint* if they have no lines in common. Point-disjoint and line-disjoint semipaths are defined similarly.

Theorem 9.1. There are two point-disjoint paths from u to v in a digraph D if and only if there is a path from u to v of length greater than 1, and no point other than u and v is on every path from u to v.

Obviously, if there are two point-disjoint paths from u to v, one is of length greater than 1, and no other point is on every path from u to v.

The proof of the converse is much more difficult. (Fortunately, its complete comprehension is not required for understanding the remainder of the chapter.) We take as given that there is no point other than u and v on every path from u to v and that there is a path L_1 of length greater than 1 from u to v. Let U be the set of points w such that there are two point-disjoint paths from u to w. Our proof is completed once we show that v is in U.

Let w_1 be the second point of L_1, and let L_2 be a path from u to v not containing w_1. Since v is on both L_1 and L_2, we can find a point w_0 on L_1 which is the first point after u that is also on L_2. Then w_0 is clearly in U, so U is not empty.

We now suppose that v is not in U and then proceed to a contradiction. Let w be a point of U such that $d(w, v)$ is minimal among points of U. Let L_3 be a shortest path from w to v, and let L_4 and L_5 be two point-disjoint paths from u to w, as illustrated in Figure 9.2(a). By hypothesis, there is a path L_6 from u to v not containing w. Let v_0 be the first point of L_6 which is in L_3, and let u_0 be the last point in L_4 or L_5 that is also in the part of L_6 from u to v_0. Such points exist since, in particular, v is in both L_6 and L_3, and u is in both L_6 and L_4. Without loss of generality, we take u_0 in L_4, as in Figure 9.2(b). Now, let L_7 be the path from u to v_0 consisting of the union of L_5 and the subpath of L_3 from w to v_0, and let L_8 be another path from u to v_0 which is the union of the subpath of L_4 from u to u_0 and the subpath of L_6 from u_0 to v_0. Then L_7 and L_8 are two point-disjoint paths from u to v_0, so v_0 is in U. But since v_0 is on a shortest path from w to v, $d(v_0, v) < d(w, v)$. This contradicts the choice of w as a point in U nearest to v. Hence our assumption that v is not in U is false. Therefore, there are two point-disjoint paths from u to v, and the theorem is proved.

A Case of Sabotage. An underground movement has a group of agents operating in enemy territory. Agent H is the head of the movement and Agent D is a dynamiter. Communication occurs among

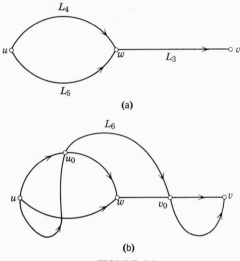

(a)

(b)

FIGURE 9.2

agents only when two agents arrange a clandestine meeting. Agent H can send instructions to Agent D only through intermediary agents, and the communication network has been constructed so that no agent is on all paths from Agent H to Agent D. Agent H wishes to instruct Agent D when to blow up a bridge, but he wants no other agent to know when the bridge is to be destroyed. Being a graph theorist, Agent H knows from Theorem 9.1 that there are two point-disjoint paths from him to Agent D. Therefore, he prepares two messages: (1) "Blow up the bridge when Operation S is put into effect," and (2) "Operation S begins at dawn on May 1." He sends these messages along the two point-disjoint paths, and the mission is successfully accomplished.

Corollary 9.1a. There are two point-disjoint semipaths joining u and v if and only if there is a semipath joining them of length greater than 1 and no other point is in every semipath joining them.

The corollary can be proved by forming the symmetrized digraph and applying Theorem 9.1 to it. The proofs of the following theorem and corollary are similar and are omitted.

Theorem 9.2. There are two line-disjoint paths from u to v if and only if v is reachable from u and no line is in every path from u to v.

Corollary 9.2a. There are two line-disjoint semipaths joining u and v if and only if u and v are 1-joined and no line is in every semipath joining them.

Theorems 9.1 and 9.2 are special cases of a more general theorem[1] which we present here for completeness. It will not be used in this chapter and its proof is omitted.

Theorem 9.3. If u is not adjacent to v in D, then the maximum number of point-disjoint paths from u to v in D is the minimum number of other points whose removal from D results in a digraph in which v is not reachable from u. The maximum number of line-disjoint paths from u to v is the minimum number of lines whose removal from D results in a digraph in which v is not reachable from u.

The analogous results may be formulated for semipaths.

We now turn to a consideration of blocks. The digraph shown in Figure 9.3 has two blocks, namely $\langle v_1 v_2 v_3 v_4 \rangle$ and $\langle v_4 v_5 v_6 \rangle$. Although the cut point v_4 is in both blocks, each other point and each line is in exactly one. Moreover, the two blocks have but one point in common. These facts suggest the content of our next two theorems about blocks.

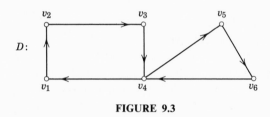

FIGURE 9.3

Theorem 9.4. Two distinct blocks of a digraph have at most one point and no lines in common.

Assume that two distinct blocks of D have a line or more than one point in common. Then their union is a weak subgraph of D that has no cut points and hence is a block. This contradicts the maximality property of a block of D.

Corollary 9.4a. Every line of a digraph lies in exactly one block.

Since a line x of a digraph is itself a weak digraph without cut points, it lies in a maximal such subgraph, or block, B. By Theorem 9.4, then, x is in exactly one block.

Theorem 9.5. Every point of a digraph other than a cut point lies in exactly one block. Every cut point lies in more than one block.

[1] This is a well-known theorem due to Menger (1932).

Corollary 9.4a shows that every line, and hence every point, lies in a block. We must show that a point is a cut point if and only if it lies in more than one block.

Let v be a cut point. Then, by Theorem 8.4, adjacent with v there must be points v_1 in block B_1 and v_2 in B_2 such that no semipath of $D - v$ joins v_1 and v_2. Then the lines joining v with v_1 and with v_2 are respectively in B_1 and B_2, showing that v is in both blocks.

Next, assume that a point v is in two distinct blocks B_1 and B_2. Suppose that v is not a cut point of D. By Theorem 9.4, B_1 and B_2 have no other point in common, so there must be a semipath L in $D - v$ joining a point of B_1 and a point of B_2. But then the union of L, B_1, and B_2 is a subgraph which has no point whose removal would disconnect it, and this arrangement is impossible since B_1 and B_2 are distinct blocks. Therefore, v is a cut point, which is what we wanted to show.

Corollary 9.5a. Whenever two points u and w of a weak digraph D do not lie in a common block, there is a cut point v that lies on every semipath joining them.

This corollary is a restatement of Corollary 9.1a, in terms of blocks. It follows that if D is strong and two points lie in different blocks, then there is a cut point on every path from each point to the other.

The next theorem provides equivalent conditions for a digraph to be a block.

Theorem 9.6. The following statements are equivalent for any weak digraph D with more than two points.

(1) D is a block, that is, D is weak and has no cut points.

(2) Every pair of lines lies on a semicycle.

(3) Every pair of points lies on a semicycle.

(4) For any three distinct points u, v, and w, there is a semipath joining u and w which contains v.

(5) For any three distinct points u, v, and w, there is a semipath joining u and w which does not contain v.

In proving this theorem, we show the equivalence of (1), (3), (4) and (5) in a cyclic order, and then show that (2) and (3) are equivalent.

(1) Implies (3). Let u and v be any two points of a block D. Since D has no cut points, no point is in every semipath joining u and v. By Corollary 9.1a, therefore, there are two point-disjoint semipaths joining u and v. The union of these two semipaths is a semicycle containing u and v.

(3) *Implies* (4). Let u, v, and w be three distinct points of D. By condition (3), there is a semicycle Z_1 containing u and v and a semicycle Z_2 containing v and w. If either w is on Z_1 or u is on Z_2, there is clearly a semipath joining u and w containing v. Thus, we need only consider the case where w is not on Z_1 and u is not on Z_2. Begin with u and go along Z_1 until reaching the first point u_0 of Z_2, then take the semipath on Z_2 joining u_0 and w which contains v. This constitutes a semipath joining u and w that contains v.

(4) *Implies* (5). Let u, v, and w be three distinct points of D. By condition (4), there is a semipath L joining u and v which contains w. There is then contained in L a semipath joining u and w that does not contain v.

(5) *Implies* (1). By condition (5), for every pair of points, u and w, there is no point on every semipath joining u and w. Hence D has no cut points, so it is a block.

(3) *Implies* (2). Let u_1v_1 and u_2v_2 be any two lines of D. Let Z_1 be a semicycle containing u_1 and u_2. We first form a semicycle Z_2 containing u_1v_1 and u_2 as follows. If the point v_1 is in Z_1, then Z_2 is formed as the union of u_1v_1 and that portion of Z_1 joining u_1 and v_1 which contains u_2. If v_1 is not in Z_1, since (3) implies (5) there is a semipath L joining v_1 and u_2 which does not contain u_1. Let w be the first point of L in Z_1. Then Z_2 is formed as the union of u_1v_1, that portion of L joining v_1 and w, and that portion of Z_1 joining w and u_1 which contains u_2. By the same process, we form a semicycle Z containing u_1v_1 and u_2v_2.

(2) *Implies* (3). Let u and v be any two points of D. Since D is weak, there are lines x_1 and x_2 incident with u and v, respectively. By condition (2), D has a semicycle Z containing x_1 and x_2. Hence, u and v lie on a semicycle. This completes the proof of the theorem.

A Sociometric Example. In Chapter 3 we suggested an empirical assumption E3.1 (p. 52) which led to the conclusion that the residents of a housing project will tend to associate in groupings that correspond to weak components of the digraph of their sociometric choices. We now consider the case where the sociometric choices correspond to a digraph D which is a block. We know, of course, that the residents will tend to associate in a single grouping, since every block is weak. Moreover, the project has no resident whose departure will make the group break up, since by definition D has no cut points. The conditions of Theorem 9.6 lead us to expect that this group will be highly resistant to disruption. Since by condition (2) every pair of lines lies on a semicycle, it follows that if any one person withdraws one of his choices, any two residents will still be bound together by a semipath of choices.

By condition (3), moreover, every pair of residents is bound together by two semipaths. And by condition (4), every two residents u and w are linked together by semipaths between each of them and a third resident v. But by condition (5) the linkage of u and w does not depend upon the continued presence of v. These observations suggest that, in general, if the sociometric structure of a group forms a block, then the group is very cohesive.

We turn next to a study of the kinds of connectedness of a digraph in terms of the connectedness of its blocks. There are exactly three categories of blocks: strong, strictly unilateral, and strictly weak. Note that in Figure 9.4 blocks $\langle v_1 v_2 v_3 \rangle$ and $\langle v_3 v_4 \rangle$ are strictly unilateral, block $\langle v_4 v_5 v_6 v_7 \rangle$ is strictly weak, and block $\langle v_4 v_8 \rangle$ is strong.

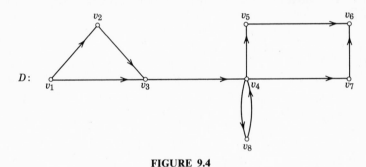

FIGURE 9.4

Theorem 9.7. A weak digraph is strong if and only if all its blocks are strong.

Let D be strong and let u and v be two points in some block B of D. Then there is a path in D from u to v. Such a path cannot contain a point w outside B, for if it did, the subgraph formed by B and this path would be strong and would have no cut point, contradicting the maximality of the block. Thus the paths from u to v (and also from v to u) in D are in B, and hence it is strong.

On the other hand, let all the blocks of the weak digraph D be strong. Then for two blocks having a point v in common, it is possible to go from any point of one block to any point of the other via the cut point v. And given any two points u and w of D, since D is weak we can find a sequence of strong blocks successively intersecting one another such that u is in the first and w in the last. Thus we can find a path in each direction between u and w, and so D is strong.

The first corollary of Theorem 9.7 gives a sufficient condition for a weak digraph to be strictly unilateral.

Corollary 9.7a. Let D be a weak digraph with one strictly unilateral block and all other blocks strong. Then D is strictly unilateral.

By hypothesis, D is weak and all its blocks are strong except for one block B which is strictly unilateral. By the theorem, D is not strong. After forming the condensation, we find that $D^* = B^*$. But by Corollary 3.4a, B^* is strictly unilateral and so is D.

For strictly weak digraphs we have the following corollary.

Corollary 9.7b. A strictly weak digraph has either a strictly weak block or two strictly unilateral blocks.

If D is strictly weak and has no strictly weak blocks, then by the preceding corollary it must have more than one strictly unilateral block.

By an argument analogous to that used in the first part of the proof of Theorem 9.7, we can establish the following result.

Theorem 9.8. If D is unilateral, then all of its blocks are unilateral.

Any digraph consisting of a strict semipath shows that the converse of Theorem 9.8 is not true. All blocks of such a digraph are unilateral, but the digraph is strictly weak.

We now examine some relationships between blocks and centrality. In Chapter 6 we saw that two outcentral (or two incentral) points need not be adjacent to one another. Figure 9.5 shows a digraph of this

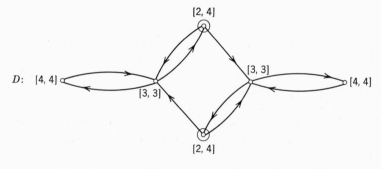

FIGURE 9.5

sort. In this figure, the associated number pair is indicated for each point, and the outcentral points are circled. We see that even though the outcentral points are not adjacent to each other, they do lie in the same block.

Theorem 9.9.   The outcentral points of a strong digraph lie in a common block. By duality, the incentral points also lie in a block.

This theorem is proved by contradiction. Assume that two outcentral points u and w do not lie in the same block. By Corollary 9.5a, there must be a cut point v on every path joining them. Let v' be a point for which the distance from v to v' is a maximum. Then this distance is the outnumber $o(v)$ of v. Since D is strong, there are paths from v' to u and from v' to w. But since v is a cut point, every path from one of these (for instance, w) to v' must go through v. Then the length of a shortest path L from w to v' must be greater than $o(v)$. But $o(w)$ is at least the length of L, and hence $o(w) > o(v)$, contrary to the fact that w is outcentral.

Although the outcentral points of a strong digraph lie in a block and the incentral points lie in a block, the two kinds of central points need not lie in the same block. Figure 9.6 illustrates this fact.

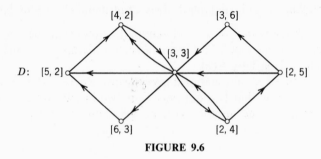

D:

[4, 2]   [3, 6]

[3, 3]

[5, 2]   [2, 5]

[6, 3]   [2, 4]

FIGURE 9.6

INVULNERABLE DIGRAPHS

A strong digraph is *point invulnerable* if all its points are 3, 3; it is *line invulnerable* if all its lines are 3, 3. The deletion of any point from a point invulnerable digraph leaves the digraph strong, as does the deletion of any line from a line invulnerable digraph. In this section, we look into the properties of these two kinds of strong digraphs and the relationship between them.

It is immediately evident that a point invulnerable digraph is a strong block, since if every point is 3, 3 then no point can be a cut point. But a point invulnerable digraph has certain additional characteristic properties which are described in the next theorem.

Theorem 9.10.   Let D be a digraph with at least three points. The following statements are equivalent.

(1) D is a point invulnerable digraph, that is, every point of D is 3, 3.

(2) For any three distinct points u, v, and w in D, there is a path from u to w not containing v.

(3) For any two distinct points u and v in D, there are two point disjoint paths from u to v.

We prove the equivalences in a cyclic order.

(1) Implies (2). If u, v, and w are points of a point invulnerable digraph, then $D - v$ is strong. Hence, there is a path of D from u to w not containing v.

(2) Implies (3). This follows immediately from Theorem 9.1.

(3) Implies (1). It is given that for any two distinct points u and v, there are two point disjoint paths from u to v. Hence, for any other point w, there is a path from u to v in $D - w$. By the same argument, there is a path from v to u in $D - w$. Hence, w is 3, 3.

In Figure 9.7, digraph D_1 has every point 3, 3. It can be readily verified that statements (2) and (3) of Theorem 9.10 are satisfied by this digraph. Let us suppose that this digraph represents a communication network and see what Theorem 9.10 tells us about such a network. Statement (1) asserts, of course, that there is no person in the network whose removal will prevent any other two persons from engaging in

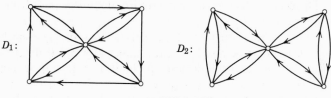

FIGURE 9.7

two-way communication. In a network satisfying statement (2), for any three people, it is possible for one of them to communicate to another with the third excluded. A network whose digraph satisfies statement (3) has two disjoint channels from any person to any other. This not only allows an alternate channel in case one fails, but it allows the transmission of two messages from any person u to any other v in such a way that no other person will receive them both. Theorem 9.10 says that a communication network satisfying any one of these three statements automatically satisfies the other two.

Corollary 9.10a. Every point invulnerable digraph with at least three points is line invulnerable.

Let x be a line of a point invulnerable digraph D. By Theorem 9.10 there is a path L, other than x, from fx to sx, so that x is not basic. By Theorem 7.17, x is therefore a 3, 3 line, and thus D is line invulnerable.

It can be readily verified that the point invulnerable digraph D_1 of Figure 9.7 is also line invulnerable. In other words, every point is 3, 3 and every line is 3, 3. The converse of Corollary 9.10a does not hold, since a line invulnerable digraph may not even be a block. Digraph D_2 shown in Figure 9.7 has the same number of points and lines as D_1 and is line invulnerable. However, D_2 obviously has a 3, 0 point and, therefore, is neither point invulnerable nor a block.

The next theorem gives a characterization of line invulnerable digraphs.

Theorem 9.11. The following statements are equivalent for any nontrivial weak digraph.
(1) D is line invulnerable, that is, every line is 3, 3.
(2) For any line x and any two distinct points u and v, there is a path from u to v not containing x.
(3) For any two distinct points u and v, there are two line-disjoint paths from u to v.

The proof of these equivalences is given cyclically.

(1) Implies (2). If x is a line of a line invulnerable digraph, then $D - x$ is strong. Hence, for any two points u and v, there is a path from u to v not containing x.

(2) Implies (3). This is an immediate consequence of Theorem 9.2.

(3) Implies (1). Let x be any line and u and v any two distinct points of D. Since there are two line-disjoint paths from u to v in D, there is a path from u to v in $D - x$. Similarly, there is a path from v to u in $D - x$; hence, $D - x$ is strong. Since x was chosen arbitrarily, D is line invulnerable.

In the digraphs of Figure 9.7 it can be seen that for any two points and any line there is a path joining the points which does not contain the line. Viewed as communication networks, this means that in both of these a person can send a message to every other person without making use of any given link. However, as noted above, in the network represented by D_2 it is not true that a person can send a message to every other person without engaging any particular third person.

FLEXIBLE DIGRAPHS

A digraph with at least three points is *flexible* if for any three points u, v, and w in it there is a path from u to w containing v. Referring back to Figure 9.1, we see that D_3 is flexible but that D_1 and D_2 are not. The definition of a flexible digraph is reminiscent of one of the equivalent conditions for a point invulnerable digraph, namely that for any three points u, v, and w there is a path from u to w *not* containing v. Although these two descriptions sound somewhat opposite in character, we shall show that a flexible digraph is point invulnerable. Then, by Corollary 9.10a, it is also line invulnerable. We shall also show that it has the property that every two points lie on a cycle.

In a communication network corresponding to a flexible digraph, any two individuals u and w can communicate on a path that includes, or on one that excludes, any third person v. There are two communication paths from u to w which have no other points in common. Any person can send a message to any other individual without making use of any given link. And there is a path from u to w and a return path from w to u that have no other points in common. It is because of the freedom in choosing paths that these digraphs are called flexible.

Theorem 9.12.   A flexible digraph is point invulnerable.

This theorem is proved by showing that for any three distinct points u, v, and w in a flexible digraph D, there is a path from u to w not containing v. By the definition of flexible, there is a path L from u to v containing w. The subpath of L from u to w is then a path not including v, as desired.

Theorem 9.13.   In any flexible digraph, every pair of points lies on a cycle.

Let u and v be points of a flexible digraph D. If u is adjacent to v, then the line uv together with any path from v to u forms a cycle containing both points. If u is not adjacent to v, let w be any point adjacent from u. Since D is flexible, there is a path from w to u containing v. The union of this path and the line uw is then a cycle containing u and v.

The two digraphs of Figure 9.8 illustrate Theorems 9.12 and 9.13. We see that D_1 is flexible, since for any three points in it there is a path

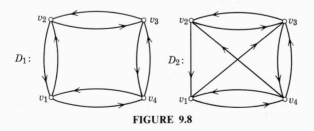

FIGURE 9.8

from the first to the third containing the second. It is also easy to verify that every point of D_1 is 3, 3 and that every two points lie on a cycle. Digraph D_2 shows, however, that the converses of these theorems are not true. This digraph is point invulnerable, and every two points in it lie on a cycle; but it is not flexible, since there is no path from v_1 to v_4 containing v_2.

In a communication network corresponding to a digraph in which every pair of points lies on a cycle, it is possible for any two people u and v to communicate with each other using just the cycle containing them for their communication channels. In such a network no other individual can hear messages sent in both directions, thereby ensuring a degree of secrecy of communication. As we have seen, not every point invulnerable digraph has this property, but by Theorem 9.13 all flexible digraphs do.

Both digraphs of Figure 9.8 are, of course, strong blocks, since both are point invulnerable. It is easy to see that any digraph in which every pair of points lies on a cycle has no 3, 0 and no 3, 1 points, since the deletion of any point from a cycle results in a path. Inasmuch as it has no cut points, such a digraph is a strong block. A digraph consisting of just a cycle is an example. Clearly, it is a strong block, but it is neither point invulnerable nor flexible. Figure 9.9 illustrates the fact that in a point invulnerable digraph, it is not necessary for every two points to lie on a cycle.

D:

FIGURE 9.9

Thus far in this chapter we have considered blocks, strong blocks, point and line invulnerable digraphs, digraphs in which every two points lie on a cycle, and flexible digraphs. We have studied relations among these concepts, which are summarized in the implication digraph of Figure 9.10.

Examples have been presented to show that each implication shown in Figure 9.10 is strict, or one-way. However, this is not the case for symmetric digraphs.

Theorem 9.14.   If a digraph D with at least three points is a symmetric block, then D is flexible.

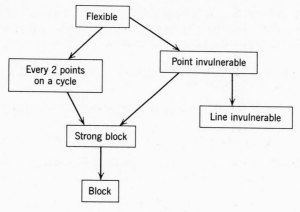

FIGURE 9.10

Let u, v, and w be distinct points of a symmetric block D. By Theorem 9.6, there is a semipath from u to w containing v. Since D is symmetric, there is also a path from u to w containing v; hence D is flexible.

From Theorem 9.14 we see at once by the implication digraph of Figure 9.10 that all its concepts except line invulnerability are equivalent for symmetric digraphs.

Corollary 9.14a. For a symmetric digraph D with at least three points, the following statements are equivalent.

(1) D is a block.
(2) D is a strong block.
(3) Every two points of D lie on a cycle.
(4) D is point invulnerable.
(5) D is flexible.

This corollary may be illustrated by reference to the communication example. In ordinary oral communication, if person u can talk directly to person v, then v can talk back to u. Therefore, a network constructed from such communication possibilities corresponds to a symmetric digraph. In order to assure that it is flexible, we need only guarantee that there is no cut point.

UNIFORMLY LINE VULNERABLE DIGRAPHS

In this final section, we study digraphs having the special property that all lines are strengthening and have the same i, j value. Such digraphs are called *uniformly line vulnerable digraphs*.

For strictly weak digraphs the only possible case is the digraph in which every line is 1, 0. The first theorem characterizes such digraphs. Its proof is straightforward and is omitted.

Theorem 9.15.   Every line of a strictly weak digraph D is 1, 0 if and only if D has no semicycles.

In the case of strictly unilateral digraphs, there are two possibilities: every line is 2, 0 or every line is 2, 1. The next theorem characterizes digraphs in which every line is 2, 0; its proof is also omitted.

Theorem 9.16.   Every line of a digraph D is 2, 0 if and only if D is a path.

Now we observe that there is no digraph in which every line is 2, 1.

Theorem 9.17.   In every strictly unilateral digraph there is at least one line that is not 2, 1.

To prove this theorem, we note first that D either has a bridge or it does not. If it has a bridge, this bridge is a 2, 0 line, and there is nothing further to prove.

We now show that if D has no bridge, then D has a 2, 2 line. Since D is unilateral, it follows from Theorem 3.10 that D has a complete open sequence L from a point v_1 to a point v_n. Let us order the strong components of D according to their occurrence in L. Clearly, then, for each S_i and S_{i+1}, L contains a line x_i such that fx_i is in S_i and sx_i is in S_{i+1}. Now consider the line x_1 whose first point is in S_1 and whose second point is in S_2. Since x_1 is not a bridge, there exists a semipath joining fx_1 and sx_1 but not containing x_1. This semipath must contain a line $x \neq x_1$ such that fx is in S_1 and sx is in S_i, where $i > 1$, since S_1 is a transmitter of D^*. Therefore, x is a 2, 2 line, for $D - x$ contains the complete open sequence L, completing the proof.

We turn now to uniformly line vulnerable strong digraphs. Since by Theorem 7.9, no digraph contains a 3, 0 line, we need to consider just two cases: digraphs having only 3, 1 lines and those having only 3, 2 lines. However, the next theorem shows that only the second of these cases exists.

Theorem 9.18.   Any digraph with a 3, 1 line has at least four lines that are not 3, 1.

We first note that in any complete closed sequence L of a digraph, every pair of points are mutually reachable so that each 3, 1 line must appear twice in L. Let D be a digraph with a 3, 1 line x that is 3-between u and v. Let L_1 be a shortest complete closed sequence of D. Since u

and v are in L_1, each of them is in a cycle which is a subsequence of L_1. Because x cannot occur twice in one cycle, u and v are in distinct cycles Z_1 and Z_2. Each of these cycles Z_i contains a point v_i which appears only once in L_1—since otherwise the sequence that results when Z_i is deleted from L_1 is complete, closed, and shorter than L_1, which is impossible. Then the two lines incident with each v_i must also appear only once in L_1 and hence are not 3, 1. Points v_1 and v_2 are not adjacent in L_1, for otherwise they would lie in a common cycle. Therefore, D contains at least four lines which are not 3, 1.

Theorem 9.18 is illustrated by the digraph of Figure 9.11, where it can be seen that line x is a 3, 1 line since it is 3-between points v_3 and v_4 (Theorem 7.14). The other four lines of this digraph are 3, 2 lines. Thus this is the smallest digraph containing a 3, 1 line.

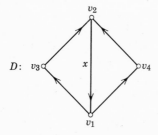

FIGURE 9.11

We now consider strong digraphs in which every line is 3, 2. The digraph Z_p, which consists of a cycle of length p, is clearly such a digraph, for the removal of any line results in a single path. We shall see that any strong digraph in which every block is a cycle also has every line 3, 2. But these are not the only such digraphs. For example, the digraph of Figure 9.12 is a strong block which is not a cycle, and yet each of its lines is 3, 2.

The next theorem gives a necessary and sufficient condition for a strong digraph to have every line 3, 2.

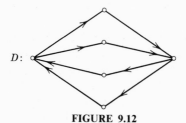

FIGURE 9.12

Theorem 9.19. Every line of a strong digraph is 3, 2 if and only if every line is basic and for every pair of points u and v, whenever there is a line x_1 which is in every path from u to v there is a line x_2 in every path from v to u.

First, let D be a digraph in which every line is 3, 2. Then by Theorem 7.17, every line of D is basic. Suppose u and v are two points such that a line x_1 is in every path from u to v. Since x_1 is 3, 2, u is not in the strong component $S(v)$ of $D - x_1$, but v can reach u in $D - x_1$. The condensation $(D - x_1)^*$ is a complete path, since it is unilateral, acyclic, and every line is basic. Therefore, there is precisely one other strong component S_0 which has any points adjacent from a point of $S(v)$. Also, there is only one line x_2 in D from any point of $S(v)$ to any point of S_0, since x_2 is a basic line. Thus, because u is not in $S(v)$, line x_2 is in every path from v to u in $D - x_1$. Since by the same argument x_2 is in every path from v to fx_1 in $D - x_1$, it is in every path from v to u in D.

To prove the converse, let D be a strong digraph in which every line is basic, and for any two points u and v, whenever there is a line x_1 in every path from u to v, there is a line x_2 in every path from v to u. By Theorem 7.17, since every line of D is basic, it has no 3, 3 lines. Now suppose it has a 3, 1 line x. Then there are points u and v such that x is in every path joining u and v, that is, $(u \, x \, v)_3$. Let L be a path from u to v. Let u_0 be the first point of L such that $(u \, u_0 \, v)_3$, and let v_0 be the last point of L such that $(u \, v_0 \, v)_3$. There are such points, in particular, fx and sx. Hence there are two line-disjoint paths from v_0 to u_0 (via u and via v). This results in a contradiction, since x is in every path from u_0 to v_0.

Corollary 9.19a. If D is strong and every block is a cycle, then every line is 3, 2.

This corollary follows at once from the theorem. For, every line of D is basic, and whenever there is a line that lies in every path from v to u, there is also a line lying in every path from u to v.

To summarize, we have seen that the only uniformly line vulnerable digraphs are those in which every line is 1, 0, every line is 2, 0, or every line is 3, 2.

We now consider an interesting special class of digraphs in which every line is 3, 2. A *symmetric tree* is a strong digraph with no cycle of length greater than 2. Figure 9.13 displays all symmetric trees with 2, 3, and 4 points.

The next theorem gives five equivalent criteria for a digraph to be a symmetric tree.

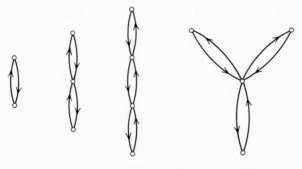

FIGURE 9.13

Theorem 9.20.   The following statements are equivalent for a strong digraph D.
1. D is a symmetric tree, that is, D has no cycle of length greater than 2.
2. Every block of D is a cycle of length 2.
3. D is unipathic, and the paths joining two points are converses.
4. D is symmetric, and $q = 2p - 2$.
5. D is symmetric, and the removal of any symmetric pair of lines results in a disconnected digraph.

We prove the equivalence of these five statements in the usual cyclic order.

(1) Implies (2).   Let D be a symmetric tree. Since D is strong, every line is cyclic. And inasmuch as D contains no cycles of length greater than 2, D is symmetric. Hence, each block of D contains a cycle of length 2. Let B be a block containing more than one such cycle. Let uv and vw be lines of B. By Corollary 9.14a, the subgraph B is point invulnerable, so there is a path L from w to u not containing v. The union of L, uv, and vw is a cycle of length greater than 2, contrary to the hypothesis. Therefore, each block consists of a cycle of length 2.

(2) Implies (3).   Let every block of a strong digraph D consist of a cycle of length 2. Let u and v be points of D and let L_1 be a path from u to v, with uv_1 the first line of L_1. Since every line is in a block and every block of D consists of a cycle of length 2, the cycle uv_1u must be a block. Therefore, the line v_1u is in D. By continuing in this way, we see that the converse L_1' of the path L_1 must be in D. Now we show the uniqueness of these paths joining u and v. Suppose that L_2 is another path from length greater than 2 and this cycle will be in some block. This is a contradiction, thereby proving the implication.

(3) Implies (4).   Let D be unipathic, and let the paths joining any two points be converses. Thus, the converse of each line is in D, so D is

symmetric. It follows from Theorem 3.15 that a weak symmetric digraph has at least $q = 2(p - 1)$ lines. Moreover, if D has more than $2p - 2$ lines, it has a cycle of length greater than 2, so that D would not be unipathic since it is symmetric. Therefore, $q = 2p - 2$.

(*4*) *Implies* (*5*). Let D be a symmetric digraph with $2p - 2$ lines, and let uv be a line of D. We need to show that $D - uv - vu$ is disconnected. Suppose it is weak. Then $D - uv - vu$ is a weak symmetric digraph with p points. As such it has at least $2p - 2$ lines, as noted above. Since this is impossible, the digraph resulting from the removal of any symmetric pair of lines of D is disconnected.

(*5*) *Implies* (*1*). Let (5) be given, and assume that the digraph has a cycle of length greater than 2. Then the removal of a symmetric pair of lines with one line in that cycle results in a weak digraph, which is a contradiction.

Corollary 9.20a. If D is a symmetric tree, then every line of D is 3, 2.

From Theorem 9.20, we know that if D is a symmetric tree, then every block of D is a cycle of length 2. Since, by definition, a symmetric tree is strong, it follows from Corollary 9.19a that every line of D is 3, 2.

SUMMARY

The major portion of this chapter is devoted to a study of structures known as blocks. A block B of a digraph is a maximal weak subgraph having no point v such that $B - v$ is disconnected. A digraph is a block if it consists of just one block. We began the chapter by considering some of the most important properties of blocks. We then turned to digraphs that are strong blocks, concentrating upon three special kinds of strong blocks.

The first of these is a digraph in which every two points lie on a cycle. The second is one in which every point is a 3, 3 point and is known as a point invulnerable strong digraph. The third, called a flexible digraph, has the property that for any three points u, v, and w, there is a path from u to w containing v. The relationships among these classes of strong blocks are summarized in the implication digraph shown in Figure 9.10. In the course of this analysis we found that every point invulnerable strong digraph is line invulnerable, that is, every line is a 3, 3 line. However, a line invulnerable strong digraph need not even be a block.

In the final section of the chapter we investigated digraphs all of whose lines are strengthening and in the same i, j category. Such digraphs are uniformly line vulnerable, since the removal of any line weakens the digraph and does so to the same extent. The chapter closes by investigating a special class of these, known as symmetric trees. These are defined as strong digraphs with no cycle of length greater than 2. In such a digraph, every line is a 3, 2 line.

EXERCISES

1. Show that every weak component of a digraph D is a block if and only if D has no cut points.
2. If D is a block, can it have a bridge?
3. Determine which of the digraphs in Figure 9.14 are blocks, strong blocks, point invulnerable, line invulnerable, uniformly line vulnerable, or flexible.

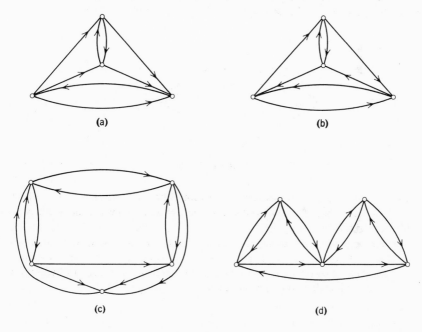

(a)   (b)

(c)   (d)

FIGURE 9.14

4. Give an example of a point invulnerable digraph which is not flexible but in which every two points lie on a cycle.
5. Show that for any positive integer n, a digraph can be found containing n that are 3, 1 lines and four that are 3, 2 lines.
6. Prove: A weak digraph D with more than one line has the property that for every pair of lines there is a cycle containing them if and only if D is itself a cycle.

7. Determine the implication digraph of the following statements for a weak digraph D with at least three points. (a) D is a block. (b) Any line uv and any other point w lie on a semicycle. (c) Every pair of lines of D lies on a cycle of D^s. (d) Every three points lie on a semicycle.

8. Prove: Every line of a strictly weak digraph D is 1, 0 if and only if D has no semicycles (Theorem 9.15).

9. Prove: Every line of a digraph D is 2, 0 if and only if D is a path (Theorem 9.16).

10. Let D be a digraph in which every two points lie on a cycle. Show that for any point v, $D - v$ is unilateral.

11. Prove: For a strong digraph D, a line is a 3, 2 line of D if and only if it is a 3, 2 line of its block.

12. (a) Verify that the digraph shown in Figure 9.15 is uniformly line vulnerable.
    (b) Find a point of each type: 3, 0,   3, 1,   3, 2, and 3, 3 in this digraph.

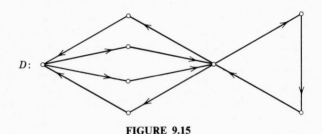

$D:$

FIGURE 9.15

13. (a) Prove that every symmetric tree with more than one point has a carrier.
    (b) Prove that in a nontrivial symmetric tree every point is either a cut point or neutral.

14. Let D be a nontrivial digraph. Prove that (a) D has at least two points that are not cut points; (b) D has at least two points that are not 2, 1 points; (c) D has at least two points that are not 3, 1 points. Thus, the only "uniformly point vulnerable" digraphs are those with every point 3, 2.

10 • *Acyclic Digraphs*

It is impossible to reduce human society to one level.

POPE LEO XIII

We turn now to a consideration of digraphs having no cycles. Such digraphs are not strong and, in fact, contain no two mutually reachable points. Therefore, any communication structure whose digraph is acyclic does not permit two-way communication or "feedback."

It will become apparent in this chapter and the following one that acyclic digraphs play a special role in the ordering of sets of points. Hence, the chapter begins with a discussion of partial orders and complete orders. We next consider the question of assigning "levels" to the points of a digraph and find that a certain kind of level assignment is possible if and only if the digraph is acyclic. An even more stringent requirement for assigning levels is investigated in the following section.

With this background, we are able to begin the study of a class of acyclic digraphs possessing especially interesting properties. Such digraphs are complete and, as we shall see, are complete orders. Investigation of their properties is continued in the next chapter.

The final section of the present chapter contains a brief discussion of a class of digraphs having no semicycles. Such a digraph is a "tree from a point" and is encountered in the theory of organizations, the structural analysis of language, probability theory, and game theory.

PARTIAL AND COMPLETE ORDERS

It will be recalled from Chapter 1 that a relation R on a set V of points which is irreflexive, asymmetric, and transitive is called a partial order.

If, in addition, R is complete, then R is a complete order. Obviously, every complete order is a partial order, but there exist partial orders that are not complete. Since both are irreflexive relations, we are concerned with digraphs which are partial orders or complete orders.

The relation "less than" on real numbers is a complete order and indeed any complete order R can be interpreted by assigning numbers to its points in such a way that for any two points u and v, uRv if and only if the number assigned u is less than that assigned v. It should be noted, however, that the differences between these numbers need not be the same for all pairs of adjacent points. In other words, a complete order yields an ordinal scale but not an interval scale. Complete orders are also known as transitive tournaments and are the topic of intensive study in the next chapter.

To illustrate partial and complete orders, let us consider a person who is deciding on the purchase of one of six cars. If no two of the cars have the same price, he can assign a distinct rank to each car with respect to price so that the first car costs less than each of the others, the second costs less than each of the remainder, and so on. The relation "costs less than" is, therefore, a complete order on these six cars. Similar considerations apply, of course, to the horsepower of the cars. Let us assume that the ranking of the cars with respect to price, from cheapest to most expensive, is A, B, C, D, E, F, and that the ranking with respect to horsepower, from most to least, is B, C, A, E, D, F. We assume further that our hypothetical buyer is interested only in price and horsepower. In forming a combined preference for one car from each pair, he prefers the first to the second if and only if the first is cheaper and has more horsepower than the second; otherwise he cannot decide. The digraph of his combined preferences is that shown in Figure 10.1. Inspection of this digraph shows that it is asymmetric and transitive and is, therefore, a partial order. We see that A is preferred to D, E, and F and that

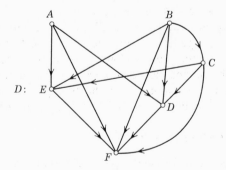

FIGURE 10.1

B is preferred to C, D, E, and F. But our buyer cannot choose between A and B since for him they are incomparable. Since the digraph of combined preferences is not complete, it is not a complete order. In this example, we find that the set of comparisons corresponds to a digraph that is transitive. This is not always the case. Sometimes a person will indicate a preference of u to v, v to w, but w to u, thus forming a cycle of preferences. Whenever this happens the digraph is neither a partial nor a complete order. Such a result creates difficulties in scaling, and the person giving such preferences is sometimes alleged to be inconsistent.

If a digraph is acyclic, then clearly it is asymmetric, since it has no cycles of length 2. Thus, the transitive closure D^t of an acyclic digraph D is a partial order, being irreflexive, asymmetric, and transitive. We know that the condensation D^* of any digraph D is acyclic. Hence, the transitive closure of D^* is a partial order. Therefore, if the condensation D^* of a digraph D is transitive, it is possible to make D into a partial order simply by treating its strong components as if they were single points. We see, then, that there is a close interrelationship between acyclic digraphs and partial orders. In fact, every partial order is an acyclic digraph.

LEVEL ASSIGNMENTS

In Chapter 3 we discussed acyclic digraphs and found five equivalent conditions for a digraph to be acyclic (Theorem 3.7). In this section we present three more. The new conditions stem from the possibility of assigning numerical values to the points of a digraph. For each point v_i let us denote by n_i the integer assigned to it. A digraph D has an *ascending level assignment*, and the integers are *levels*, if for each line v_iv_j of D the corresponding integers satisfy $n_i < n_j$. Thus the lines of D are directed from lower to higher levels. Of course, if a digraph has a cycle, it has no ascending level assignment. Figure 10.2(a) shows a digraph with an ascending level assignment.

Of course, a dual assignment of levels could be made so that the lines run from points of one level to those at a lower level. In this case, we speak of a digraph with a *descending level assignment*. Figure 10.2(b) shows the same digraph as Figure 10.2(a) but with a descending level assignment. We shall consider only ascending level assignments and refer to them briefly as *level assignments* henceforth.

The assignment of levels to a given digraph is, of course, not unique. For example, doubling all levels again results in a level assignment. Moreover, the relative level of two points of a weak digraph D that are

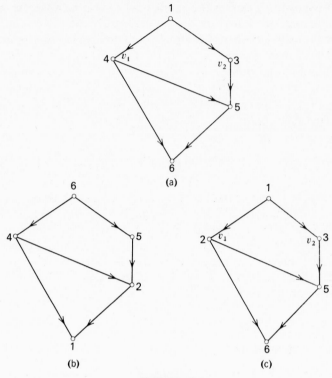

FIGURE 10.2

not joined by a path is not determined by D but is dependent upon the level assignment. Thus, Figures 10.2(a) and (c) show level assignments for the same digraph, but the relative levels of points v_1 and v_2 are reversed in the two figures.

One of the eight equivalent conditions for a digraph to be acyclic makes use of a new definition concerning matrices. A square matrix is *upper triangular* if all its nonzero entries are on or above the main diagonal.

Theorem 10.1. The following properties of a digraph D are equivalent.

(1) D has no cycles.
(2) Every strong component of D consists of one point.
(3) D^* is isomorphic to D.
(4) D and D^* have the same number of points.
(5) Every sequence of D is a path.

(6) It is possible to order the points of D so that its adjacency matrix is upper triangular.

(7) It is possible to assign levels n_i to the points v_i in such a way that if $v_i v_j$ is in D then $n_i < n_j$.

(8) D^t is a partial order.

The equivalence of the first five conditions was shown in Theorem 3.7. We shall prove the rest by showing that (7) implies (8), (8) implies (1), (1) implies (6), and (6) implies (7).

(7) *Implies* (8). We need only show that if D satisfies (7), then D^t is asymmetric, since D^t is transitive by definition. If $v_i v_j$ is in D^t, there is a path from v_i to v_j in D, each point of which has a higher level than the preceding, and so $n_i < n_j$; hence, $v_j v_i$ is not in D^t.

(8) *Implies* (1). If D satisfies (8) it is acyclic. For if D has a cycle containing v_i and v_j, D^t contains $v_i v_j$ and $v_j v_i$, contrary to (8).

(1) *Implies* (6). We make use of Theorem 3.8, which tells us that if D has no cycles, then it has at least one point of indegree 0. We label one such point v_1. Now since D has no cycles, $D - v_1$ also has no cycles. By Theorem 3.8, $D - v_1$ has a point v_2 whose indegree is 0. By continuing the process we find in $D - \{v_1, v_2\}$ a point v_3 and in general in $D - \{v_1, v_2, \dots, v_n\}$ a point v_{n+1} of indegree 0. With the points of D ordered in this way, let $A = [a_{ij}]$ be its adjacency matrix. Since by construction there is no line $v_i v_j$ in D if $i \geq j$, the corresponding entry a_{ij} is 0, proving (6).

(6) *Implies* (7). Suppose the points of D have been ordered so that $A(D)$ is upper triangular. If v_i corresponds to the ith row and column, assign it level i. Since $a_{ij} = 0$ if $i > j$, it follows that there is no line from a point of one level to one of a lower level, proving (7). This completes the proof of Theorem 10.1.

As an interesting consequence of showing that (6) implies (7), we have the following corollary.

Corollary 10.1a. Let D be an acyclic digraph with p points. Then (1) the integers from 1 through p can be assigned to the points of D in such a way that no two points have the same level, and (2) for every line $v_i v_j$ in D the level of v_i is less than that of v_j.

Figures 10.3 and 10.4 illustrate the theorem and its corollary. Figure 10.3 shows a digraph and the adjacency matrix formed using the given labeling of its points, $u_1, u_2 \dots, u_5$. The points are to be reordered in accordance with condition (6). Since D is acyclic, it has a point, u_5, of indegree 0 and one, u_2, of outdegree 0. In the adjacency matrix, therefore, the fifth column and second row consist of zeros. To follow through the

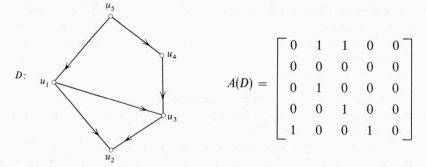

$$A(D) = \begin{bmatrix} 0 & 1 & 1 & 0 & 0 \\ 0 & 0 & 0 & 0 & 0 \\ 0 & 1 & 0 & 0 & 0 \\ 0 & 0 & 1 & 0 & 0 \\ 1 & 0 & 0 & 1 & 0 \end{bmatrix}$$

FIGURE 10.3

ordering of the points suggested in the proof that (1) implies (6), we note that u_5 is the only point of indegree 0, so we label it v_1. In $D - v_1$, u_1 and u_4 are both points of indegree 0, so we can label either v_2. Letting u_1 be labeled v_2, Figure 10.4 shows one labeling of the points that can be obtained, together with the resulting adjacency matrix, which is of course upper triangular.

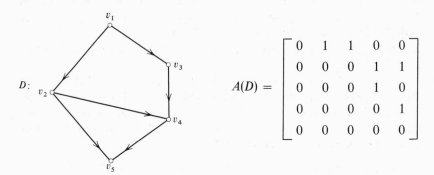

$$A(D) = \begin{bmatrix} 0 & 1 & 1 & 0 & 0 \\ 0 & 0 & 0 & 1 & 1 \\ 0 & 0 & 0 & 1 & 0 \\ 0 & 0 & 0 & 0 & 1 \\ 0 & 0 & 0 & 0 & 0 \end{bmatrix}$$

FIGURE 10.4

The next theorem states the smallest possible number of levels in any acyclic digraph.

Theorem 10.2.   Let D be an acyclic digraph and let n be the length of a longest path of D. Then $n + 1$ is the smallest number of levels in any level assignment of D.

Since the levels of the points in a path must all be distinct, we cannot have fewer than $n + 1$ levels. We now construct a level assignment using only the integers from 0 to n. Let U be the set of transmitters of D

and assign the integer 0 to each point of U. To every other point assign the length of a longest path to it from any point of U. We now show that this is a level assignment. Let $v_i v_j$ be any line of D and let L be a longest path to v_i from a point u in U. Then v_j is not in L, since otherwise that portion of L from v_j to v_i together with $v_i v_j$ forms a cycle. Hence, L followed by $v_i v_j$ is a path from u to v_j of length one greater than L, so v_j has a higher level assignment than v_i. This level assignment has precisely $n + 1$ levels since the longest path has length n.

Corollary 10.2a. Let D be an acyclic digraph with p points. Then p is the smallest number of levels in any level assignment if and only if D is unilateral.

Since the longest path in a unilateral acyclic digraph has all p points, Theorem 10.2 shows that the fewest levels it can have is p. And if the fewest levels in any assignment is p, then it has a path of p points, that is, a complete path. By Theorem 3.10, it is unilateral.

The idea of level assignment can be generalized from acyclic digraphs to all digraphs. A *quasi-level assignment* of a digraph D associates with each point v_i a positive integer n_i, called its *quasi-level*, such that: (1) if $v_i v_j$ is a line of D, then $n_i \leq n_j$, and (2) $n_i = n_j$ if and only if v_i and v_j are mutually reachable.

Theorem 10.3. Every digraph has a quasi-level assignment.

It is not surprising that the proof of this theorem uses the condensation of a digraph, which is acyclic. Let D be any digraph whatsoever. By Corollary 10.1a, D^* has a level assignment in which no two points have the same level. Assign to each point v_i of D the level n_i of its strong component in D^*. We now verify that this is a quasi-level assignment. Let $v_i v_j$ be any line of D. If v_i and v_j lie in the same strong component, then $n_i = n_j$. If not, the strong component containing v_j has a higher level than the one containing v_i, so $n_i < n_j$. Obviously, two points have the same assigned integer if and only if they are mutually reachable. Thus, this is a quasi-level assignment.

Of course, for strong digraphs, a quasi-level assignment is not interesting since all points are assigned the same integer. For unilateral digraphs, Theorem 10.3 can be reformulated as in Corollary 10.3a.

Corollary 10.3a. Quasi-levels can be assigned to points of a unilateral digraph so that if v_i and v_j are assigned quasi-levels n_i and n_j, respectively, then $n_i \leq n_j$ if and only if there is a path from v_i to v_j.

By Theorem 10.3, quasi-levels can be assigned to the points of a unilateral digraph D. We shall show that such a quasi-level assignment also satisfies the condition of the Corollary. From condition (1) above we see that $n_i \leq n_j$ if there is a path from v_i to v_j. To complete the proof we must show that if $n_i \leq n_j$ there is a path from v_i to v_j. Assume, on the contrary, there is none. Then because D is unilateral there is a path from v_j to v_i, since any two points are 2-joined. By (1) it then follows that $n_j \leq n_i$. Since we already know $n_i \leq n_j$, we conclude $n_i = n_j$. But then (2) asserts that v_i and v_j are mutually reachable. Thus our hypothesis that there is no path from v_i to v_j is false, and the corollary is proved.

Figure 10.5 shows a strictly unilateral digraph D with six points. Its condensation D^* is a unilateral acyclic digraph with three points. We see, in accordance with Corollary 10.2a, that D^* has three levels. The quasi-level assignment shown for D is derived from this level assignment for D^*. We see that it satisfies the conditions of Corollary 10.3a.

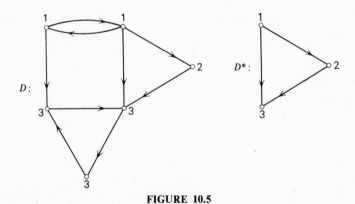

FIGURE 10.5

Levels and Status in an Organization

To illustrate the use of level assignments, let us consider a small research group consisting of seven people. We call the Principal Investigator v_1, the Assistant Investigators v_2 and v_3, the Research Assistant v_4, the Lab Technician v_5, the Secretary v_6, and the Clerk-Typist v_7. Let us assume that the digraph of direct supervision is that shown in Figure 10.6. We see that the Principal Investigator, wishing to maintain close control, directly supervises everyone.

The Personnel Department is asked to develop a compensation plan, based upon the levels of supervision in this staff. They assign level 0 to the Principal Investigator and higher numbered levels to the remaining

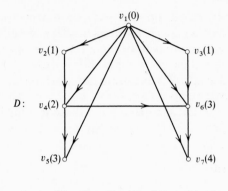

$$
N(D) = \begin{array}{c} \\ v_1 \\ v_2 \\ v_3 \\ v_4 \\ v_5 \\ v_6 \\ v_7 \end{array}
\begin{array}{ccccccc|c}
v_1 & v_2 & v_3 & v_4 & v_5 & v_6 & v_7 & a_i \\
\left[\begin{array}{ccccccc} 0 & 1 & 1 & 1 & 1 & 1 & 1 \end{array}\right. & & & & & & & 6 \\
\infty & 0 & \infty & 1 & 2 & 2 & 3 & 8 \\
\infty & \infty & 0 & \infty & \infty & 1 & 2 & 3 \\
\infty & \infty & \infty & 0 & 1 & 1 & 2 & 4 \\
\infty & \infty & \infty & \infty & 0 & \infty & \infty & 0 \\
\infty & \infty & \infty & \infty & \infty & 0 & 1 & 1 \\
\infty & \infty & \infty & \infty & \infty & \infty & 0 & 0
\end{array}
$$

FIGURE 10.6

staff in such a way that anyone supervised by another has a higher level than his immediate supervisor. They want to have as few levels as possible. Being rational and well informed, they know about Theorem 10.2. Thus, they know that the smallest possible number of levels will be the number of points on a longest path. Since v_1 is the unique source of the digraph, they assign each person a level equal to the length of a longest path to him from v_1. The resulting level assignments are those shown in parentheses in Figure 10.6.

We may ask how the level assigned to a person relates to his status in the organization. In Chapter 6 we discussed a status index according to which the status of an individual v_i is the distance sum a_i in the digraph of supervision. From the distance matrix $N(D)$ shown in Figure 10.6, we obtain the status of each individual. It can be seen that the status of v_2 is higher than that of v_1 even though v_2 is directly supervised by v_1. This rather surprising outcome results from the fact that v_1 gives direct supervision to everyone while v_2 does not. It is, of course, an open empirical question whether this index of status corresponds to some identifiable property of the real world.

Kemeny and Snell (1962, pp. 104–105), in commenting upon the possibility of such an outcome, have suggested another definition of status. Their proposal amounts to defining the status of v as the sum of the differences between the level of v and the level of each person reachable from v in the digraph of supervision (using a level assignment with the smallest possible number of levels). With this definition, status assignments along a chain of supervision will necessarily be consistent with level assignments.

Combining Rank Orders

Suppose that several judges are asked to rank order a collection of objects, with no ties permitted. Each judge's ranking can be portrayed by a digraph in which a line $v_i v_j$ indicates that the ith object immediately precedes the jth object in his ranking. This digraph is unilateral, since it consists of a complete path. We wish to pool these rankings in order to obtain a consensual ordering of the objects.

Let us assume that there are three judges, whose rankings give us digraphs D_1, D_2, and D_3, as shown in Figure 10.7. We may form a new digraph D from these by including a line $v_i v_j$ in D if and only if the corresponding line occurs in any one of the digraphs of the individual rankings. Since D contains the ranking of each judge, it contains a complete path and is, therefore, unilateral. If all judges agree completely, then of course the combined digraph is isomorphic with that of each judge. If, however, they do not agree (as in Figure 10.7), the combined digraph is not acyclic. Now, we cannot employ the level assignment given in Theorem 10.1, but we can assign quasi-levels to the points of D in accordance with Corollary 10.3a, as indicated in Figure 10.7.

What information does this assignment provide? If $n_i < n_j$, then v_i is ranked before v_j by all judges, and there is no v_k such that one judge ranks v_k before v_i and some other judge ranks v_j before v_k. If $n_i = n_j$, there is a closed sequence of objects $v_i \ldots v_j \ldots v_i$ such that each is ranked before the next by some judge, although it is possible that all judges rank v_i before v_j. For example, in Figure 10.7 each judge ranks b before c, but in the combined digraph D, there is also a path from c to b.

To form a consensual ranking, we require that if all judges rank v_i ahead of v_j, then v_i is to be ranked ahead of v_j in the consensus. In particular, objects at one quasi-level of the combined digraph must precede all objects at a higher quasi-level. The problem then reduces to one of ranking the objects within each quasi-level. If there is more than one point at a given quasi-level, these points generate a strong component of the combined digraph. Since it contains a cycle, the preferences

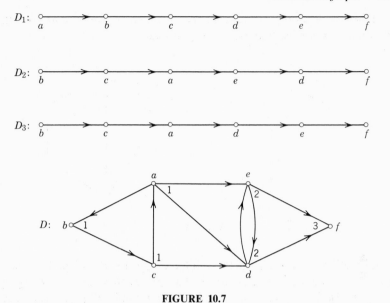

FIGURE 10.7

expressed in the combined digraph are not all consistent. Such inconsistencies pose serious problems for achieving a consensual ranking. We can form a rank order among these objects by deleting enough lines from the combined digraph to leave a complete path, but there is clearly more than one way of doing so. We can also obtain a ranking of a subset of the objects by removing from consideration enough of the objects to obtain a complete path. Then the consensual ranking will have at least as many ranks as there are quasi-levels in the combined digraph. Neither of these procedures is entirely satisfactory, and in general no *a priori* solution to the problem of inconsistency is available.[1]

GRADABLE DIGRAPHS

From Theorem 10.1, we know that every acyclic digraph has a level assignment such that if line v_iv_j is in D then $n_i < n_j$. We have seen, however, that under such an assignment the difference in levels of adjacent points need not all be the same. In this section, we examine digraphs in which the difference in levels of every two adjacent points is exactly 1. A *graded level assignment* of an acyclic digraph D is one such that for each line v_iv_j in D, $n_j = n_i + 1$. A *gradable digraph* is one which has a graded level assignment. Figure 10.8 shows two

[1] For a further discussion of these problems, see Cogan, *et al.* (1958, pp. 27–45).

digraphs with level assignments, one of which is graded and the other is not. We shall see that D_2 is not gradable.

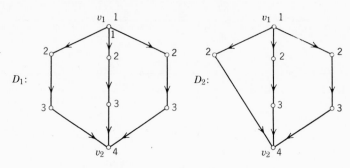

FIGURE 10.8

Inspection shows that in the gradable digraph D_1 all paths from v_1 to v_2 have the same length, but in digraph D_2 they do not. A digraph is *equipathic* if for every pair of points u and v in it, all paths from u to v have the same length. Obviously, every unipathic digraph is equipathic.

Theorem 10.4.   Every gradable digraph is equipathic.

Let L be any path from v_i to v_j. Since D is gradable, each point of L must have a level one greater than the preceding point, so that the difference between n_i and n_j is the number of lines of L. Thus all paths from v_i to v_j have the same length, and D is equipathic.

Corollary 10.4a.   Every line of a gradable digraph is basic.

Let x be a line of a gradable digraph D. By Theorem 10.4, every path from fx to sx has length 1. Thus, x is the only path from fx to sx, and x is basic.

These observations are illustrated by digraph D_1 of Figure 10.8, which has a graded level assignment. We see that for any point v which is reachable from a point u, the distance from u to v equals the absolute difference of their levels. Thus, all points reachable from a point u having the same level are at the same distance from u. Moreover, for every line x of D_1, x is the only path from fx to sx. If this digraph is interpreted as a communication network, then any message originating with v_1 will reach all persons at the same level in the same amount of time. Analogous interpretations are of course possible for other empirical phenomena where distance is coordinated to such variables as cost or distortion.

Theorem 10.4 shows that every gradable digraph is equipathic. And since every gradable digraph has a level assignment, it is also acyclic. Digraph D_1 of Figure 10.9 shows that the converses of these statements are not true in general, for D_1 is equipathic and acyclic but has no graded level assignment.

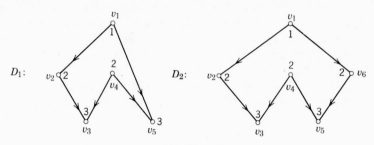

FIGURE 10.9

Our next theorem provides some criteria for a digraph to be gradable, but it requires additional definitions. A line x of a semipath L joining two points u and v is *oriented from* u if the semipath contained in L joining u and fx is shorter than that joining u and sx. The *orientation index of L from u to v*, denoted $m(L, u, v)$, is defined as the number of lines of L oriented from u minus the number oriented from v. To illustrate these concepts, consider the semipath L_1 of length 4 joining v_1 and v_5 in digraph D_1 of Figure 10.9. It has three lines oriented from v_1: v_1v_2, v_2v_3, and v_4v_5. Thus, $m(L_1, v_1, v_5) = 3 - 1 = 2$. Two observations may be made about orientation indexes. If L is a semipath joining u and v, then $m(L, u, v) = -m(L, v, u)$. Also, if w is any other point of L, and L_1 and L_2 are the semipaths contained in L joining w with u and v, respectively, then

$$m(L_1, u, w) + m(L_2, w, v) = m(L, u, v).$$

The *cyclic orientation index of a semicycle Z*, which we denote $m(Z)$, is the minimum number of lines of Z whose direction must be reversed to obtain a cycle. Thus, the cyclic orientation index of the semicycle of D_1 of Figure 10.9 is 2, since the reversing of v_4v_3 and v_1v_5 produces a cycle.

Theorem 10.5. The following statements are equivalent for a weak digraph D.
(1) D is gradable.
(2) The cyclic orientation index of every semicycle is one-half its length.

(3) For every pair of points, the orientation index from one to the other of all semipaths joining them is the same.

The proof of the equivalence is given cyclically.

(*1*) *Implies* (*2*). Suppose that Z is any semicycle of a digraph with a graded level assignment n_i. Take the length of Z as k, and let v_iv_j be a line of Z. Denote by L the semipath $Z - v_iv_j$ joining v_i and v_j. By definition $n_j = n_i + 1$, so there must be one or more line of L oriented from v_i than from v_j. Since the length of L is $k - 1$, and since the reversal of all lines of L oriented from v_j transforms Z into a cycle, it is readily verified that $m(Z) = k/2$, as was to be shown.

(*2*) *Implies* (*3*). Let D be a digraph in which every semicycle has cyclic orientation index equal to half its length. Let L_1 and L_2 be any semipaths joining points u and v. We must show that $m(L_1, u, v) = m(L_2, u, v)$.

We first consider the case where $L_1 \cup L_2$ is a semicycle Z. Let M be the set of lines of L_1 that are oriented from u to v together with those of L_2 oriented from v to u, and let $\bar{M}$ consist of the remaining lines of Z. By reversing the orientation of lines of M (or reversing those of $\bar{M}$) a cycle is formed. Thus by (2), M and $\bar{M}$ each have half as many lines as Z. Now $m(L_1, u, v) + m(L_2, v, u)$ is the number of lines of M minus the number in $\bar{M}$. Thus

$$m(L_1, u, v) + m(L_2, v, u) = 0$$

Since, as noted above,

$$m(L_2, u, v) = - m(L_2, v, u)$$

we see

$$m(L_1, u, v) = m(L_2, u, v)$$

The proof that (2) implies (3), in general, now proceeds by induction on the length of the shorter of L_1 and L_2. If this length is 1, then $L_1 \cup L_2$ is a semicycle, so that $m(L_1, u, v) = m(L_2, u, v)$ by the preceding paragraph. Starting with (2), suppose (3) has been proved for all pairs of semipaths for which the shorter has length at most $n - 1$, and L_1 and L_2 are semipaths joining u and v for which the shorter, say L_1, has length n. If $L_1 \cup L_2$ is a semicycle, then $m(L_1, u, v) = m(L_2, u, v)$ by the preceding paragraph. Otherwise, let w be any point other than u and v in both L_1 and L_2. Since the part of L_1 joining u and w has length less than n, it has the same orientation index from u to w as the corresponding part of L_2, by the induction hypothesis. Similarly, the parts of L_1 and L_2 joining w and v have the same orientation index from w to v. Piecing together the two parts of L_1 and the two parts of L_2 shows that L_1 and L_2 have the same orientation index from u to v.

(3) Implies (1). Assign to point v_1 the integer n_1. To each other point v_k, assign the integer $n_k = n_1 + m(L_1, v_1, v_k)$. We now show that this is a graded level assignment. To do this, it is sufficient to show that if $v_i v_j$ is a line of D, then $n_i = n_j - 1$. Let L_1 be any semipath joining v_1 and v_i. If v_j is not in L_1, then L_1 followed by $v_i v_j$ is a semipath joining v_1 and v_j and has one more line oriented from v_1 than L_1 has. Hence, $n_i + 1 = n_j$. On the other hand, if v_j is in L_1, let L_0 be the subpath joining v_1 and v_j. Adding the line $v_i v_j$ to L_0 forms a semipath joining v_1 and v_i which has one more line oriented to v_1 than L_0 has, so again $n_i = n_j - 1$. Thus, D is gradable, completing the proof.

Corollary 10.5a. No digraph containing an odd semicycle is gradable.

Let D be a digraph containing a semicycle Z of odd length. Then the cyclic orientation index of Z is an integer, but half its length is not. Thus statement (2) of the theorem does not hold, and so D is not gradable.

This theorem and its corollary may be illustrated by the digraphs of Figure 10.9. Consider the two semipaths of D_1 joining v_1 and v_5 : L_1 of length 4 and L_2 of length 1. We have already seen that $m(L_1, v_1, v_5) = 2$, and obviously $m(L_2, v_1, v_5) = 1$. From (3) it follows that D_1 is not gradable. However, Corollary 10.5a establishes this fact more simply since D_1 has a semicycle of odd length. In D_2, however, the only semicycle has length 6, and its cyclic orientation index is 3, proving that this digraph is gradable.

When we compare digraphs D_1 and D_2, we see that it may be possible to make certain modifications in an ungradable digraph so that it becomes gradable. Given a digraph D, a *one-step expansion* of D constructs a new digraph by deleting a line uv of D, adding a new point w, and adding the lines uw and wv. In this way it replaces a line by a path of length 2. A digraph E obtained from D by a succession of one-step expansions is called an *expansion* of D. Since the process of expansion introduces no additional cycles in a digraph, the following result is obvious.

Theorem 10.6. If D is acyclic, any expansion E of D is also acyclic.

We next show that every acyclic digraph has a gradable expansion.

Theorem 10.7. Let D be an acyclic digraph with a level assignment. Then there is an expansion E of D such that each point of D has the same level in E as in D, and E is gradable.

The proof of this theorem is quite simple. We replace each line $v_i v_j$ of D by a path of length $n_j - n_i$ and assign successively to the new points levels $n_i + 1$, $n_i + 2$, and so forth. The result is an expansion of D with a graded level assignment in which old points retain their levels.

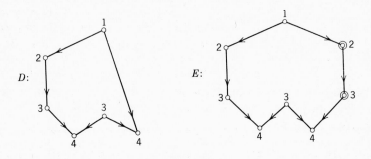

FIGURE 10.10

An illustration of this theorem is given by the digraphs of Figure 10.10. We see that digraph D has a level assignment but that it is not graded, since there is a line from a point of level 1 to one of level 4. Digraph E is an expansion of D, the new points being indicated by circles. Clearly, E is gradable.

MAXIMAL ACYCLIC DIGRAPHS

We are now in the position to consider an especially interesting class of acyclic digraphs, which will be studied in detail in the next chapter. Our present purpose is to provide an introductory exposition of their properties and to relate these to our preceding discussion. An acyclic digraph D is *maximal* if the addition of any line to D forms a cycle.

Theorem 10.8. Given an acyclic digraph D, there is a maximal acyclic digraph of which D is a spanning subgraph.

If D is an acyclic digraph that is not maximal, it must have a pair of points u and v such that $D \cup uv$ is acyclic. We then successively add lines to D as long as it is possible to do so without forming a cycle. This constructs a maximal acyclic digraph whose points are those of D.

Of course, a given acyclic digraph may be contained in more than one maximal acyclic digraph. The digraph D_1 shown in Figure 10.11 is acyclic. We can add lines to form a maximal acyclic digraph in several ways—for example, by adding v_1v_4, v_1v_5, v_3v_2, and v_3v_5. By doing this, we obtain the maximal acyclic digraph D_2. The next theorem states five equivalent conditions for a digraph to be maximal acyclic.

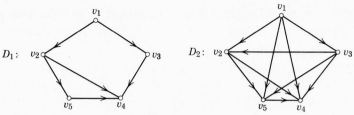

FIGURE 10.11

Theorem 10.9. The following statements for an acyclic digraph D with p points are equivalent:

(1) D is maximal.

(2) Given any three points of D, they can be labeled v_1, v_2, v_3 such that lines v_1v_2, v_2v_3, and v_1v_3 are in D.

(3) D has $p(p - 1)/2$ lines.

(4) D is complete.

(5) D is a complete order.

To prove this theorem, we show first the equivalence of (1), (4), and (5) in cyclic order and then show the equivalence of (2), (3), and (4).

(1) Implies (4). Let D be a maximal acyclic digraph. Suppose that two points u and v are not joined by a line. Since D is acyclic, there is no path in one direction, say from v to u. But then $D \cup uv$ is acyclic and this contradicts the maximality of D. Therefore, D must be complete.

(4) Implies (5). We take as given that D is complete. Since D is acyclic, it is asymmetric. We now show that D is transitive. Suppose that lines uv and uw are in D. Then since D is complete, uw or wu is in D. But wu cannot be in D, since it forms a cycle with uv and vw. Hence, uw is in D and D is transitive. Thus, D is asymmetric, transitive, and complete, that is, a complete order by definition.

(5) Implies (1). If D is a complete order, then the addition of any line to D forms a cycle of length 2, so that D is maximal.

(4) Implies (2). Let D be a complete acyclic digraph. Thus any subgraph spanned by three points of D has three lines. Two of these lines form a path; call them v_1v_2 and v_2v_3. For D to be acyclic, the third line must be v_1v_3, so that the points can be labeled as specified.

(2) Implies (3). We now assume that any three points of D can be labeled such that v_1v_2, v_2v_3, and v_1v_3 are in D. Thus, there is a line joining every pair of points. Since D is acyclic, there is exactly one. The number of pairs of points in D is $p(p - 1)/2$. Hence D has this many lines.

(3) Implies (4). Let D have $p(p - 1)/2$ lines. Since D has $p(p - 1)/2$ pairs of points and no pair can be joined by two lines, every pair must

be joined by exactly one. Thus D is complete, and the theorem is proved.

From Theorem 10.9, we see that a complete order is a complete acyclic digraph. Hence a complete order is unilateral, since every two points are 2-joined by a line. It follows then from Corollary 10.2a that in a complete order with p points the integers 1 through p provide a level assignment with fewest levels. These observations are illustrated by digraph D_2 of Figure 10.11, whose unique complete path is $v_1v_3v_2v_5v_4$. If these points are successively assigned levels 1 through 5, the result is a level assignment.

In view of Theorem 10.9, every maximal acyclic digraph is complete. For this reason, the process described in the proof of Theorem 10.8 whereby we start with an acyclic digraph and form a maximal one is called a *completion*. The next theorems relate the concepts of completion and transitive closure.

Theorem 10.10. The transitive closure of any acyclic digraph is contained in each of its completions.

If D is not transitive, then there exist points u, v, and w in D such that lines uv and vw are in D but uw is not. Since uw is in the transitive closure of D, we must show that it is in every completion of D. By Theorem 10.9 either uw or wu must be present in any completion of D. But if wu is present, it forms a cycle with lines of D. Thus uw is in every completion, proving the theorem.

Theorem 10.11. A digraph D is unilateral if and only if its transitive closure D^t is complete.

For any two points u and v, there is a line from u to v in D^t if and only if there is a path from u to v in D. Thus two points are joined by a line in D^t if and only if they are joined by a path in D. In other words, D^t is complete if and only if D is unilateral.

The same argument verifies the next statement.

Corollary 10.11a. A digraph D is strong if and only if its transitive closure D^t is complete symmetric.

If an acyclic digraph has two points u and v that are 1-connected, then it has more than one completion, since either uv or vu can be added in completing it. However, this cannot happen if the digraph is unilateral.

Corollary 10.11b. An acyclic digraph D is unilateral if and only if it has a unique completion.

Let D be unilateral and acyclic. Then its transitive closure D^t is complete, by Theorem 10.11. And by Theorem 10.10, D^t is in every completion. Hence D^t is its only completion.

To prove the converse, let u and v be points of an acyclic digraph D with only one completion. If u and v are not 2-joined, then adding either uv or vu results in an acyclic digraph, and so D has more than one completion. Therefore, D is unilateral since every two points of D must be 2-joined.

A TREE FROM A POINT

In this final section, we consider a special class of digraphs having a variety of realizations. A *tree from a point* is a digraph with a source but with no semicycles. In Figure 10.12, digraph D_1 is a tree from a point whereas D_2 is not, even though each digraph has a unique source. We note that in D_1, all other points have indegree 1, but this is not true for D_2. The next theorem characterizes a tree from a point in these terms.

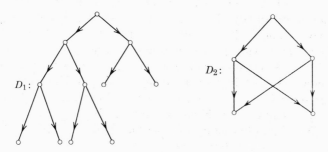

FIGURE 10.12

Theorem 10.12. A weak digraph is a tree from a point if and only if exactly one point has indegree 0 and every other point has indegree 1.

Let D be a tree from a point v. Then by definition $\mathrm{id}(v) = 0$ and all points are reachable from v. Obviously, since D has no semicycles, it is unipathic. Suppose that u is a point with indegree exceeding 1. Then there are two points adjacent to u and hence two paths from the source v to u, which is a contradiction.

For the converse, let v be the point of indegree 0, and let u be any other point of D. Since D is weak, there is a semipath L joining u and v. Suppose that L is not a path, that is, L is a strict semipath. Then by Corollary 2.3a, L has an r_2-point, in other words a receiver with indegree

2, contradicting the hypothesis. Thus it follows that L is a path, and v is a source of D. There can be no strict semicycles in D, since then there would be a point having indegree at least 2. Moreover, if D has a cycle Z, some point would have indegree greater than 1, because v has indegree 0 and can reach every point of Z. Therefore, D has no semicycles at all.

Certain conclusions may now be drawn concerning level assignments in a tree D from a point. Since D has no semicycles, it has no cycles. Hence, by Theorem 10.1, it has a level assignment. By definition, D has a source w and since it has no semicycles, it is unipathic. Therefore, we can assign level m to point w and level $m + n$ to each point at distance n from w, thereby assigning levels to every point of D. In particular, if we let $m = 0$, we can assign to each point v of D a level which is its distance from the source of D. Clearly, this level assignment is graded.

It is immediately evident that every line of a tree from a point is a bridge and hence basic. Moreover, every point other than the transmitter and receivers is a cut point. These observations have certain implications for organization theory. It is sometimes argued that an organization should have a single "ultimate source of authority" (less elegantly known as the top boss), with each subordinate having only one immediate supervisor. The digraph of authority in such an organization is a tree from a point. Since this structure is unipathic, it avoids the possibility that a person will receive conflicting orders. But since every line is a bridge, the organization is highly vulnerable. In this type of structure, any person who fails to pass on an order thereby prevents its transmission to all persons reachable from him.

Status in an Organization

Earlier in this chapter, we discussed two formulas for status in an organization. According to one of these, the status of a person is the sum of the distances from him to all of his subordinates. In the other, the status of a person is the sum of the differences in level between him and all of his subordinates. The first, by employing distances, makes use of shortest paths; the second, by employing differences in level, makes use of longest paths. We saw that these two definitions may not only give different status to an individual but may give different relative status to two different individuals. In an organization whose supervisory structure is a tree from a point, the two definitions must give the same status assignment, since every tree from a point is unipathic. Indeed, the two measures are equal in any equipathic digraph, because the lengths of all paths from one point to another are the same.

Game Trees

In the theory of games,[2] a move is described as a situation confronting a player when he must exercise a choice among a set of alternatives. Interspersed in the sequence of moves of a game there may occur certain events determined by chance, as the draw of a card or the toss of a die. These may be thought of as "chance moves." We can identify where we are in a game if we know what choices have been made at each move and what alternatives are available to each player (or to chance) at each possible future move. The entire set of future choices at some move, together with the choices already made, constitutes a state of the game. The game can be represented as a tree from a point, where the points are states and the lines from a point are the choices of succeeding states at this move. In such a tree, the fact that there is only one path from the start to each point means that if we know that a point represents a move in the game, we know exactly which choices have been made at each previous move. By using the distance from the source to assign levels, if v is reachable from u, then the difference between their levels is $d(u, v)$, and represents the number of choices made from u to v. The set of points reachable from u generates a tree from u and represents the game as it would be played if u were the starting point.

As a relatively simple illustration, let us consider the game of tic-tac-toe with two players, O and X. Suppose that on the first two moves choices have been made as shown in Figure 10.13. The choices are indicated in the game tree by labeled lines, so that X_i means that X puts his mark in square i. Only a fragment of the entire game tree is shown in the figure. At the indicated move of the game, X must choose among the seven possible alternatives. The fragment of the tree presented in the figure shows that if X plays X_7 and makes no subsequent mistakes, he can win. We see that after X_7 there is only one alternative for O, namely O_4, which will not result in a victory for X on the following move. Let us assume that X_7 is followed by O_4. If X_9 then follows, X must win whatever O plays. In principle, more complex games can be analyzed in this fashion. However, in a game as complex as chess, the game tree becomes so large that its use as described here is not practical even with the aid of a computer. Nonetheless, game trees provide a useful model for representing important features of decision making among a sequence of alternative choices.

[2] Game trees are discussed in Luce and Raiffa (1957, Ch. 3).

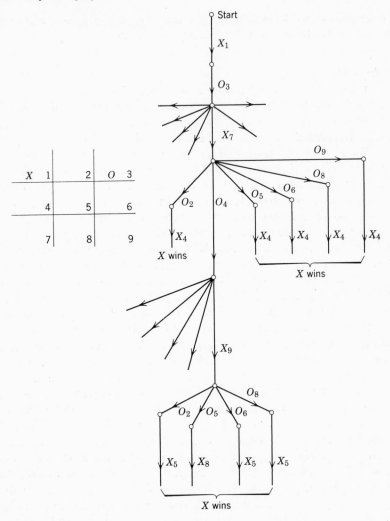

FIGURE 10.13

SUMMARY

Acyclic digraphs constitute the primary topic of this chapter. A basic finding is the equivalence of three statements: (1) D is acyclic, (2) D has a level assignment, and (3) the transitive closure D^t is a partial order. Since the condensation D^* of any digraph D is acyclic, this equivalence holds for all condensed digraphs.

Even though a digraph has a level assignment, it is possible that the differences in level between pairs of adjacent points are not all the same. For this reason, there is special interest in digraphs having a graded level assignment, that is, in which the difference in level between adjacent points is always 1. Such a digraph is equipathic, and each of its lines is basic. If D is acyclic, then there is an expansion E of D such that E is gradable.

For every acyclic digraph D, there is a maximal acyclic digraph of which D is a spanning subgraph. Moreover, an acyclic digraph is maximal if and only if it is a complete order. Thus, every complete acyclic digraph is transitive. Such digraphs are studied intensively in the next chapter.

The final section of the present chapter considers weak digraphs having a source but no semicycles. Such a digraph is known as a tree from a point. Being acyclic, a tree from a point has a level assignment. In fact, it has a graded level assignment. If we assign level 0 to the source, then we can assign to every other point a level which is its distance from the source. Such digraphs are encountered frequently in organization theory and in game theory.

EXERCISES

1. Let R be a quasi-order, that is, a relation which is reflexive and transitive. Let D be the digraph with the same set of points obtained from R by taking uv as a line of D if and only if uRv and not vRu. Show that D is a partial order.

2. Let R be a quasi-order. Show that R^* is a partial order.

3. In a summer camp for underprivileged children, it is found that boy u typically dominates boy v if and only if u weighs at least five pounds more than v; otherwise u and v simply ignore each other. Let D be the digraph of the camp's dominance structure. (a) Is D acyclic? (b) Is D a partial order? (c) Can the weight of each boy be used to form a level assignment for D? (d) Is it possible that D might be a complete order?

4. Consider the digraph D of an organization in which points correspond to people and a line uv means that person u directly supervises person v. What is the meaning of a line uv in the transitive closure D^t of D?

5. Prove: A digraph D has no semicycles if and only if every line of D is a bridge.

6. Prove: If D is weak and has a point v such that for every point u the orientation index from v to u of all semipaths joining them is the same, then D is acyclic.

7. Show that no complete order with more than two points has a graded level assignment.

8. Let D be an acyclic digraph with a single source. Show that D has a graded level assignment if and only if D is equipathic.

9. Show that if every line of a digraph D is basic, then every line in any expansion E of D is basic.

10. Let D be a partial order which is not complete. (a) Is there an expansion E of D such that E is a complete order? (b) Is there a completion of D which is a complete order? (c) If D has five points and five lines, how many lines must be added to obtain a complete order?

11. Consider the acyclic digraph shown in Figure 10.14. How many different sets of lines can be added to form a maximal acyclic digraph?

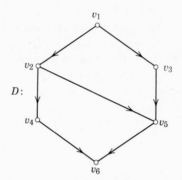

D:

FIGURE 10.14

12. Show that every completion of an acyclic digraph can be found by the following procedure: First, make a level assignment using the integers from 1 to p, and then draw all lines from each point to all points at higher level.

13. Prove: A partial order is an acyclic digraph.

14. Prove: D is a tree from a point if and only if it is unipathic and for every two points u and v, there is a point w such that both are reachable from w and no other point which can reach both is reachable from w.

15. Prove: Every digraph without any semicycles is gradable.

11 • Tournaments

> The more you read about Politics, you got to admit
> that each Party is worse than the other.
>
> WILL ROGERS

The purpose of this chapter is to investigate a restricted class of digraphs, known as tournaments.[1] The reason for the name is that such digraphs represent the structures of round-robin tournaments, in which players (or teams) engage in a game that cannot end in a tie and in which every player plays each other exactly once. Thus, if points represent players and each line represents the relationship "defeats," the digraph of a round-robin tournament is asymmetric and complete.

A great many empirical phenomena have asymmetric and complete structures and may, therefore, be represented graphically by tournaments. For example, it is known that many species of birds and mammals develop dominance relations so that for every pair of individuals, one dominates the other. Such a "pecking structure" is asymmetric and complete, and hence a tournament. Or, suppose that a committee is considering a set of alternative policies and engages in a series of votes in which each policy is paired against each other. The outcome of these votes can be represented by a tournament whose points are policies and whose lines indicate that one policy defeats the other.

Still another realization of tournaments arises in the method of scaling known as "paired comparisons." Suppose, for example, that someone wants to know the structure of a person's preferences among a collection of competing brands of a product. He can be asked to indicate for each pair of brands which one he prefers. If he is not allowed to indicate

---

[1] We are indebted to Leo Moser for many of the ideas in this chapter.

indifference, the structure of his stated preferences can be represented by a tournament.

In the first section of this chapter, we describe some of the more important properties displayed by all tournaments. We then turn to an important special class of tournaments, namely transitive ones. Such tournaments, as noted in the preceding chapter, are complete orders. Thus, for example, if a person's brand preferences correspond to a transitive tournament, they form a complete order. And since the relation "greater than" on the set of integers is also a complete order, each brand can be unambiguously assigned an integer indicating its ordinal position on a preference scale. However, in empirical research we often encounter tournaments that do not possess such a neat consistency. For this reason, it is useful to have a measure of how closely any given tournament approximates a transitive one. Such an index of the degree of consistency of a tournament is presented toward the end of the second section.

Finally, we consider strong tournaments. It is found that such tournaments are not transitive and hence are not complete orders. Despite this "unattractive" feature, strong tournaments have interesting properties in their own right.

SOME PROPERTIES OF TOURNAMENTS

A *tournament* is a nontrivial complete asymmetric digraph. It follows immediately from this definition that every tournament is unilateral and that every strong tournament has at least three points. Moreover, if U is any set of points of a tournament T such that U contains less than $p - 1$ points, then the subgraph $T - U$ is also a tournament. These observations may be verified in Figure 11.1, which shows all tournaments with 2, 3, and 4 points.

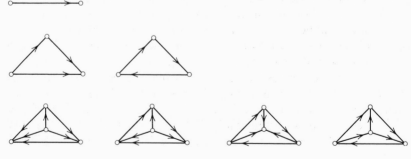

FIGURE 11.1

The adjacency matrix of a tournament T is easily described. Consider any two points v_i and v_j of T. Either line v_iv_j or v_jv_i is in T. Thus, we have that either $a_{ij} = 1$ or $a_{ji} = 1$. This information can be expressed succinctly by the equation

$$a_{ij} + a_{ji} = 1,$$

and constitutes the proof of the following statement.

Theorem 11.1.　A square binary matrix A is the adjacency matrix of a tournament if and only if $A + A' = J - I$.

Corollary 11.1a.　For any point v in a tournament with p points,

$$\operatorname{id}(v) + \operatorname{od}(v) = p - 1.$$

Corollary 11.1b.　The number of lines in a tournament with p points is $p(p - 1)/2$.

This last corollary follows at once upon applying Theorem 1.1 to Corollary 11.1a.

In the tournament of a round-robin competition, the outdegree of a point v_i is the number of victories won by player v_i. For this reason, in the remainder of this chapter we shall call the outdegree of a point v_i its *score*, denoted s_i. In view of Corollary 11.1a, the score of a point also determines its indegree.

The next theorem[2] gives a necessary and sufficient condition for a sequence of nonnegative integers to be the scores of some tournament with p points. Let T be any tournament and let s_i be the score of v_i. The *score sequence* of T is the ordered sequence of integers $(s_1, s_2, \ldots, s_p)$. We assume without loss of generality that the points v_i have been ordered in such a way that $s_1 \leq s_2 \leq \ldots \leq s_p$.

Theorem 11.2.　A sequence of nonnegative integers $s_1 \leq s_2 \leq \ldots \leq s_p$ is a score sequence if and only if their sum satisfies the equation:

I.
$$\sum_{i=1}^{p} s_i = \frac{p(p - 1)}{2}$$

and the following inequalities hold for every positive integer $k < p$:

II.
$$\sum_{i=1}^{k} s_i \geq \frac{k(k - 1)}{2}$$

We prove the necessity of conditions I and II by taking

$$s_1 \leq s_2 \leq \ldots \leq s_p$$

---

[2] This theorem is due to Landau (1953).

as the score sequence of a tournament T. By Theorem 1.1 the sum of the scores of T is the number q of lines, and by Corollary 11.1b, $q = p(p - 1)/2$, verifying equation I. To establish the inequalities II, we note that, for any integer k such that $k < p$, the subtournament generated by v_1, $v_2, \ldots, v_k$ contains exactly $k(k - 1)/2$ lines, by Corollary 11.1b. Hence in the entire tournament T,

$$\sum_{i=1}^{k} s_i \geq \frac{k(k - 1)}{2}$$

since there may occur in T a line from one of these points to one of the other $p - k$ points.

The proof of the converse is considerably more involved, and is omitted.

Theorem 11.2 is illustrated by the tournament with five points shown in Figure 11.2. The score of each point is indicated beside the point. Clearly, the score sequence of this tournament is $(1, 1, 2, 3, 3,)$. It is immediately apparent that equation I is satisfied, for the sum of scores is 10. The inequalities of II are satisfied as follows:

$$k = 1, \quad 1 \geq 0$$
$$k = 2, \quad 1 + 1 \geq 1$$
$$k = 3, \quad 1 + 1 + 2 \geq 3$$
$$k = 4, \quad 1 + 1 + 2 + 3 \geq 6$$

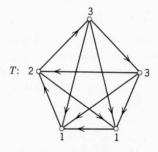

FIGURE 11.2

Consider a basketball league consisting of ten teams in which each team plays every other team once. Since no game can end in a tie, the digraph of the outcomes of all games at the end of the season is a tournament. What are the possible distributions of the number of victories among the teams? Clearly, each distribution must satisfy conditions

I and II of Theorem 11.2. This fact provides information concerning certain questions that may be asked about the final standings of the team. For example, what is the largest number of teams that can have a winning season? The answer is nine, since the sequence of integers $(0, 5, 5, 5, 5, 5, 5, 5, 5, 5)$ satisfies the conditions of Theorem 11.2 and no sequence containing ten integers, all greater than 4, does. Can the season end in a complete tie? Clearly not, since the average of the sum of the scores, $45/10$, is not an integer.

Theorem 11.3. A tournament has at most one transmitter.

To prove this theorem, we note that if v is a transmitter of a tournament, then v is adjacent to every other point, none of which can, therefore, be a transmitter.

Corollary 11.3a. If v is a transmitter of tournament T, then v is a unique 1-source, thus constituting the only point basis of T.

In other words, Corollary 11.3a states that if a tournament T has a transmitter v, then v is adjacent to every point of T. Thus, its distance to every other point is 1, and its score is $p - 1$. In terms of the above example, only one team in the basketball league can have an undefeated season and, by duality, only one team can have a season without any victories. If T does not have a transmitter, there will, of course, be at least one point with maximum score, which is less than $p - 1$. The next theorem provides information concerning the location of such points in T.

Theorem 11.4. In a tournament, the distance from a point with maximum score to any other point is 1 or 2.

To prove this theorem, let v be any point whose score s is maximum. Without loss of generality, we denote the points to which v is adjacent by $v_1, v_2, \ldots, v_s$. Since T is a tournament, v is adjacent from the remaining $p - 1 - s$ points $u_1, u_2, \ldots, u_{p-1-s}$, as in Figure 11.3. The proof will be completed if we show that each point u_k is adjacent from at least one point v_j, for then each distance $d(v, v_j) = 1$ and $d(v, u_k) = 2$. Assume that this is not the case for the point u_1. Then u_1 is adjacent to every point $v_1, v_2, \ldots, v_s$ as well as to v itself. Hence, its score is $od(u_1) \geq s + 1$. This contradicts the hypothesis that s is the largest score of any point, proving the theorem.

An interesting consequence of Theorem 11.4 follows when it is applied to a round-robin competition. Let v be a player with maximum score in such a competition consisting of at least three players. Then any player who defeats v is himself defeated by another player defeated by v.

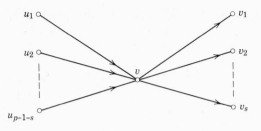

FIGURE 11.3

The directional dual of this conclusion says that if v is a player with minimum score, then any player defeated by v defeats another player who defeats v. In this chapter the directional duals of theorems will not be given, but the reader is urged to develop them for himself.

It should be noted in passing that every complete digraph contains a spanning subgraph that is a tournament. Theorem 11.4, therefore, holds also for any complete digraph.

Theorem 11.5.   If a tournament T has no transmitter, it contains at least three points—each of which can reach every point in at most two steps.[3]

Let u be a point of T with maximum score. By Theorem 11.4, u can reach every point in at most 2 steps. Since T has no transmitter, there is at least one point adjacent to u. Among all such points, let v have maximum score. Suppose there is a point v_0 not reachable from v within 2 steps. It follows that v_0 is necessarily adjacent to v and to every point which is adjacent from v, in particular, the point u. But then $s(v_0) \geq s(v) + 1$, contradicting the choice of v. Therefore, every point is reachable from v in at most 2 steps. By the same argument, if w has greatest score among the points adjacent to v, then w can reach every point within 2 steps. Since T is asymmetric and lines wv and vu are in T, necessarily u, v, and w are distinct points. Since every point is within distance 2 from each of these, the theorem is proved.

Another way of looking at this theorem is that if T has no 1-basis, then there are at least three points each of which constitutes a 2-basis.

---

[3] The directional dual of this theorem was stated by Silverman (1962) in the following picturesque terminology: Consider a club in which among any two members, one is a creditor of the other. A "bum" is defined as a member who is in debt to everyone else, and a "deadbeat" is one who is either in debt to every other member or else owes someone who owes the other members. Then, if the club has no bums, it has at least three deadbeats.

The next theorem[4] is certainly the best known result concerning tournaments. It also holds for any complete digraph.

Theorem 11.6.   Every tournament has a complete path.

The proof is given by induction on the number p of points. Referring to Figure 11.1, we see that every tournament with 2, 3, or 4 points has a complete path. As the inductive hypothesis, let the theorem hold for all tournaments with n points. Let T be any tournament with $n + 1$ points. To complete the proof of the theorem, it is necessary to show that T has a complete path.

Let v_0 be any point of T. Then $T - v_0$ is a tournament with n points. Thus the inductive hypothesis applies to $T - v_0$, so that it has a complete path which may be denoted without loss of generality by $P = v_1 v_2 v_3 \ldots v_n$. Let us return to T and show that the point v_0 can be added to P in order to obtain a complete path of T. Consider the two points v_0 and v_1 of T. There are two possibilities: Either line $v_0 v_1$ or $v_1 v_0$ is in T. If $v_0 v_1$ is a line of T, then $v_0 v_1 v_2 v_3 \ldots v_n$ is a complete path of T. On the other hand, if $v_1 v_0$ is in T, then let v_i be the first point of P, if any, for which the line $v_0 v_i$ is in T. Then necessarily line $v_{i-1} v_0$ is in T. Therefore,

$$v_1 v_2 \ldots v_{i-1} v_0 v_i \ldots v_n$$

is a complete path of T as shown in Figure 11.4. But there may not be any such first point v_i, since v_0 might be a receiver of T. In that case, $v_1 v_2 v_3 \ldots v_n v_0$ is a complete path of T, completing the proof.

Since every tournament has a complete path, it is possible to order all the players in a round-robin competition so that each defeats the

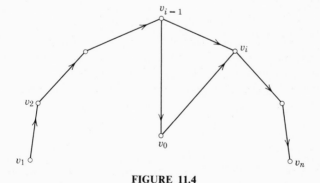

FIGURE 11.4

[4] This theorem is due to Rédei (1934). See König, (1936, p. 253).

succeeding one. And the integers 1, 2, ..., p can be assigned to the players to indicate their rank in this order. There are, however, two serious difficulties in such a procedure. First, there is no necessary relation, in general, between such a ranking of players and their scores. Second, a tournament may have more than one complete path, so that several different rankings may be possible. Figure 11.2 illustrates these observations. For example, there is a complete path from one of the two points with lowest score to the other one. In fact, each point has every possible rank in some complete path of this tournament.

Another way of stating these difficulties is to say that a tournament need not be a complete order. For we saw in Chapter 10 that if there is a complete order on a set of p points, then there exists a one-to-one correspondence between these points and the integers 1, 2, ..., p, in their natural order. Thus, whenever there is a complete order on a set of points, each point can be assigned a distinct rank. We have also seen that a complete order is defined as a relation that is irreflexive, asymmetric, complete, and transitive. Since every tournament has the first three of these properties, a transitive tournament is a complete order. There is considerable interest, therefore, in knowing the properties of transitive tournaments and, for any particular tournament, how much transitivity it displays.

HOW TRANSITIVE IS A TOURNAMENT?

In analyzing the degree of transitivity of a tournament, it is useful to refer to the subtournaments generated by any three of its points. A *triple* $\langle uvw \rangle$ of a tournament is the subtournament generated by the points u, v, and w. We saw in Figure 11.1 that there are only two tournaments with three points, and it can be readily verified that one of these is transitive and the other is cyclic. Thus, every triple is either transitive or cyclic. Obviously, every triple in a transitive tournament is transitive. Also, if a tournament is not transitive, it must contain at least one cyclic triple. It is possible, therefore, to quantify its degree of transitivity by using the number of its triples of each kind. It follows from well-known results in algebra that the total number of triples in a tournament with p points is

$$\binom{p}{3} = \frac{p(p-1)(p-2)}{6}$$

Before dealing directly with the question of the degree of transitivity of a tournament, we first need to have a structural characterization of a complete order (or transitive tournament). In order to do this, it is convenient to have some results concerning complete orders. These are presented in the next three theorems.

Theorem 11.7. If T is a complete order with at least three points, and if v is any point of T, then $T - v$ is also a complete order.

We already know that $T - v$ is itself a tournament. Since any three points of $T - v$ generate a transitive triple in T, they also generate a transitive triple in $T - v$. Hence $T - v$ is a complete order.

Theorem 11.8. Every complete order has a unique transmitter and a unique receiver.

It was shown in Chapter 10 that every complete order is acyclic. Since every tournament is unilateral, by Corollary 3.8a every complete order has a unique transmitter and receiver.

It should be noted that the converse of Theorem 11.8 is not true in general, since a tournament with a unique transmitter need not be a complete order.

The next corollary follows immediately, since no strong digraph has a transmitter.

Corollary 11.8a. No strong tournament is a complete order.

The transitive tournaments with 2, 3, and 4 points are shown in Figure 11.5.

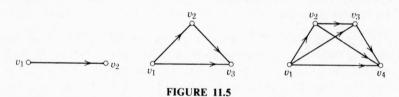

FIGURE 11.5

Theorem 11.9. If T is a complete order with p points, then T is isomorphic with the tournament T_p whose points are $v_1, v_2, \ldots, v_p$ in which v_i is adjacent to v_j if and only if $i < j$.

We prove the theorem using mathematical induction. If T has two points, the result is obviously true; see Figure 11.5. As the inductive hypothesis, we take the result as true when $p = n$. Let T be a complete order with $n + 1$ points. Let v_{n+1} be the unique receiver, guaranteed by Theorem 11.8. Then $T - v_{n+1}$ is a complete order, by Theorem 11.7, and has n points. Therefore, by the inductive hypothesis, $T - v_{n+1}$ is isomorphic with the tournament T_n with points $v_1, v_2, \ldots, v_n$ in which

v_i is adjacent to v_j if and only if $i < j$. Add to T_n the point v_{n+1} and the lines $v_i v_{n+1}$ for all $i \le n$. Clearly the result is the tournament T_{n+1}, which is isomorphic to T by this construction. Therefore, the result is true for $p = n + 1$. By the principle of mathematical induction, the theorem is true for every integer $p > 1$.

The first corollary of this theorem lists the major equivalent characterizations of a complete order.

Corollary 11.9a. The following statements are equivalent for any tournament T with p points.
(1) T is transitive, that is, T is a complete order.
(2) T is the transitive closure of a digraph consisting of a single path.
(3) T is acyclic.
(4) T has a unique complete path.
(5) The score sequence of T is $(0, 1, 2, \ldots, p - 1)$.

(6) T has $\binom{p}{3} = p(p - 1)(p - 2)/6$ transitive triples.

The detailed proof of the equivalence of these statements is omitted. The equivalences among the first five statements may be derived by exploiting the canonical form T_p of a complete order as given in Theorem 11.9. The equivalence of (6) and the others follows from the fact that every triple of a tournament T is transitive if and only if T is transitive.

Corollary 11.9b. The condensation of a tournament is a complete order or a single point.

If T is strong, then T^* is a single point. Therefore, take T as not strong. Obviously, the condensation of a complete digraph is itself complete. And since T^* is acyclic, it is asymmetric; so T^* is a tournament. Therefore, by statement (3) of Corollary 11.9a, T^* is a complete order.

Figure 11.6 shows a tournament T and its condensation T^*. Clearly, T is not transitive but T^* is. We can see that T is not transitive by examining the triple $\langle v_2 v_3 v_4 \rangle$, which is cyclic.

Suppose that a researcher has a collection of paintings and wants to order them according to judged beauty. He has a judge compare each with every other and indicate which of each pair is more beautiful. If the resulting tournament is not transitive, he cannot arrange the entire collection of paintings in a complete order. By judicious use of the "data suppression method," however, he can remove some of the paintings from the study and obtain a complete order among the remaining ones. This is guaranteed by Corollary 11.9b. For, if he keeps exactly

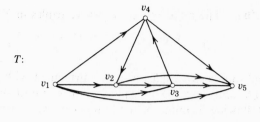

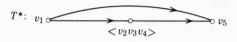

FIGURE 11.6

one painting from each strong component, the subtournament generated by these paintings will be a complete order (unless the entire tournament is strong). But he need not be so drastic, since if he removes just enough paintings from each strong component to render it acyclic, the resulting subtournament will be transitive.

If a tournament is not transitive, then it is often useful to know how many transitive triples it has. The next theorem shows that the number of transitive triples in any tournament may be easily calculated from the score sequence of the tournament.

Theorem 11.10. The number b of transitive triples in a tournament T with score sequence $(s_1, s_2, \ldots, s_p)$ is

$$b = \sum_{i=1}^{p} \frac{s_i(s_i - 1)}{2}$$

To prove this formula, let $b_i = s_i(s_i - 1)/2$. Then b_i is the number of combinations of s_i objects taken two at a time. But s_i is the number of points adjacent from v_i. Therefore, b_i is the number of pairs of points adjacent from v_i. But any transitive triple in the tournament T has a unique transmitter within it. Hence b_i is the number of transitive triples whose transmitter is v_i. Clearly, the number b of transitive triples in T is obtained by adding these numbers b_i for all the points. Thus

$$b = \sum_{i=1}^{p} b_i = \sum_{i=1}^{p} \frac{s_i(s_i - 1)}{2}$$

proving the theorem.

A little algebraic manipulation transforms the equation of Theorem 11.10 into the following equivalent form.

Corollary 11.10a. The number b of transitive triples in T is

$$b = \frac{1}{2} \sum_{i=1}^{p} s_i^2 - \frac{p(p-1)}{4}$$

Since the total number of triples in any tournament with p points is $p(p-1)(p-2)/6$, and since each triple is either transitive or cyclic, we obtain the following formula for the number of cyclic triples.

Corollary 11.10b. The number c of cyclic triples in a tournament satisfies the equation

$$c = \frac{p(p-1)(p-2)}{6} - \sum_{i=1}^{p} \frac{s_i(s_i-1)}{2}$$

The next corollary gives the maximum number of cyclic triples that may occur in any tournament. Its proof is omitted.[5]

Corollary 11.10c. Among all the tournaments with p points, the maximum number of cyclic triples is

$$c_{max}(p) = \begin{cases} \dfrac{p^3 - p}{24} & \text{if } p \text{ is odd, and} \\ \dfrac{p^3 - 4p}{24} & \text{if } p \text{ is even} \end{cases}$$

Coefficient of Consistency

In research employing paired comparisons, it is usually assumed that if a judge is entirely "consistent" in his decisions, the result will be a complete order, which therefore has no cyclic triples. Since in actual practice judges are seldom completely consistent, it is useful to have a coefficient indicative of the degree of consistency among the comparisons. Such a coefficient has been proposed by Kendall and Smith (1940). They wanted their coefficient of consistency to be normalized in such a way that its value is 1 when the tournament of comparisons is transitive and 0 when the tournament contains as many cyclic triples as possible, i.e., when it is as inconsistent as possible. Making use of the results in Corollary 11.10c, they define a coefficient of consistency ζ by the following equation in which c is the number of cyclic triples of a given tournament T with p points:

$$\zeta = 1 - \frac{c}{c_{max}(p)}$$

[5] This theorem is due to Kendall and Smith (1940), although it has been independently rediscovered many times subsequently.

Thus, we see that $0 \le \zeta \le 1$ for any tournament T. On substituting the result of Corollary 11.10c, this equation becomes:

$$\zeta = 1 - \frac{24c}{p^3 - p} \qquad \text{when } p \text{ is odd, and}$$

$$\zeta = 1 - \frac{24c}{p^3 - 4p} \qquad \text{when } p \text{ is even}$$

Use of the coefficient of consistency ζ may be illustrated by an investigation concerning the riskiness of certain securities. For simplicity, this example is developed for a study involving only six securities. The fifteen possible pairings of these securities may be partitioned into five sets of three pairs so that each set contains all six securities, for example, $\{AB, CD, EF\}$, $\{AC, BE, DF\}$, and so forth. Five investment counselors are each given one of the sets and asked to indicate for each pair which security is riskier. The combined judgments thus form a tournament in which a point represents a security and a line represents a judgment of "riskier than." We wish to calculate the coefficient of consistency ζ in order to estimate the degree of consistency of these pooled judgments.

First, we construct the adjacency matrix of this tournament and find the row sums, which are the scores of the securities. Let us assume that we obtain the following matrix:

$$A(T) = \begin{array}{c} \\ A \\ B \\ C \\ D \\ E \\ F \end{array} \begin{array}{c} \begin{array}{cccccc} A & B & C & D & E & F \end{array} \quad \text{sum} \\ \left[\begin{array}{cccccc} 0 & 0 & 0 & 0 & 0 & 0 \\ 1 & 0 & 1 & 0 & 0 & 0 \\ 1 & 0 & 0 & 1 & 0 & 0 \\ 1 & 1 & 0 & 0 & 1 & 0 \\ 1 & 1 & 1 & 0 & 0 & 0 \\ 1 & 1 & 1 & 1 & 1 & 0 \end{array} \right] \begin{array}{c} 0 \\ 2 \\ 2 \\ 3 \\ 3 \\ 5 \end{array} \end{array}$$

We next calculate the number of triples in this tournament:

$$\binom{p}{3} = \frac{6 \cdot 5 \cdot 4}{6} = 20$$

To find the number of cyclic triples we make use of Corollary 11.10b. To do so, we write the tournament's score sequence $(0, 2, 2, 3, 3, 5)$ and calculate

$$\sum_{i=1}^{6} \frac{s_i(s_i - 1)}{2}$$

as follows:

$$\frac{0 \cdot (-1)}{2} + \frac{2 \cdot 1}{2} + \frac{2 \cdot 1}{2} + \frac{3 \cdot 2}{2} + \frac{3 \cdot 2}{2} + \frac{5 \cdot 4}{2} = 18$$

Substituting into the equation of Corollary 11.10b, we obtain

$$c = 20 - 18 = 2$$

By Corollary 11.10c, the maximum number of cyclic triples in any tournament with six points is $c_{max}(6) = 192/24 = 8$. Since $c = 2$ in this tournament, the coefficient of consistency $\zeta = 1 - 2/8 = 0.75$.

Another coefficient of consistency has been proposed by Berge (1958). His ratio for measuring consistency is $b / \binom{p}{3}$, where b is the number of transitive triples of a tournament T, and the denominator $\binom{p}{3}$ is the total number of triples. This ratio will take on the value 1 if and only if T is transitive. But it will never have the value 0 when $p > 3$, since such a tournament must contain at least one transitive triple.

The Case of the Diabolical Subject[6]

Suppose that an experimenter employs the method of paired comparisons on p objects with a hostile subject who wishes to spoil the research by being as inconsistent as possible. What is the largest proportion of cyclic triples that this diabolical subject can produce? Since a tournament with p points has $\binom{p}{3}$ triples in all, the largest possible proportion of cyclic triples is $c_{max} / \binom{p}{3}$. By using Corollary 11.10c, we see that if p is odd,

$$\frac{c_{max}}{\binom{p}{3}} = \frac{\dfrac{p^3 - p}{24}}{\dfrac{p(p-1)(p-2)}{6}} = \frac{p+1}{4(p-2)} = \frac{1}{4}\left(1 + \frac{3}{p-2}\right) = \frac{1}{4} + \frac{3}{4p-8}$$

and similarly, if p is even,

$$\frac{c_{max}}{\binom{p}{3}} = \frac{1}{4}\left(1 + \frac{3}{p-1}\right) = \frac{1}{4} + \frac{3}{4p-4}$$

[6] The material in this section was suggested by some similar observations of Morrison (1962).

These results show that for large p, the maximum possible proportion of cyclic triples is only slightly more than 1/4 and approaches a limit of 1/4 as p approaches ∞. In fact, this maximum proportion in any tournament with p points differs from 1/4 by only $3/(4p - 8)$ or $3/(4p - 4)$.

In order to determine whether a particular subject is intentionally being inconsistent, the experimenter decides to compare the obtained proportion of cyclic triples with the proportion that he would get under the null hypothesis that all paired comparisons are random. What is the expected proportion of cyclic triples in a random tournament T on p points, that is, one in which for every pair of points v_i, v_j, the decision as to whether v_iv_j or v_jv_i is a line of T is determined by the toss of a coin? In view of the preceding results, the answer is striking: If $p \geq 3$, the mean or expected proportion of cyclic triples is 1/4, and thus does not depend on p. The proof of this assertion will be given shortly.

These results, taken together, show that if a large number of objects are compared, a maximally inconsistent subject will give nearly the same proportion of cyclic triples as would arise by chance! Even in a tournament with as few as ten points, the maximum proportion of cyclic triples deviates from the proportion expected by chance only by 1/12. Clearly, it will be difficult to distinguish a diabolical subject from one who behaves in a purely random fashion.

We now prove that if a tournament with p points, $p \geq 3$, is constructed by having the directions of its lines decided at random, the expected proportion of cyclic triples is 1/4. The proof proceeds by induction. There are two ways in which each line can be directed, and hence in a three point tournament there are eight ways that the three lines can be directed. Two of these ways result in cyclic triples, namely, v_1v_2, v_2v_3, v_3v_1, and v_2v_1, v_3v_2, v_1v_3. The other six triples are transitive. Thus the mean number of cyclic triples, where $p = 3$, is $2/8 = 1/4$.

As the induction hypothesis we assume the assertion proved for tournaments with p points and examine tournaments with $p + 1$ points. We consider all $(p + 1)$-point tournaments constructed by starting with a p-point tournament and then adjoining one new point v and p lines incident with it in all possible ways. Since the mean proportion of cycles using only the p initial points is 1/4 by the induction hypothesis, we need only to prove that the mean proportion of cycles containing v is 1/4.

Now for each initial underlying tournament of p points, we can adjoin the new lines in 2^p different ways varying from all toward v to all away from v. If there are k directed toward v and $p - k$ away from v, then there are $\binom{k}{2} + \binom{p-k}{2}$ pairs of new lines directed in the same direction (both toward or both away from v) and $k(p - k)$ in opposite directions. All triples formed with two lines both directed toward or away from v are transitive. With one line uv toward and one line vw away from v, a cyclic triple is formed if wu is present and not if uw is. By our assumption of randomness, wu is present in half the underlying p-point tournaments. Thus the proportion of cyclic triples containing v is one-half the proportion of pairs of lines incident with v, having one line directed toward v and one away from v. If we show that this proportion of pairs of lines is one-half, it follows that the mean number of cyclic triples is 1/4.

Each tournament contains $\binom{p}{2}$ lines incident with v. For a given underlying p-point tournament T there are 2^p ways of forming a larger tournament containing v. Thus there are altogether

$$2^p \binom{p}{2} = p(p - 1)2^{p-1}$$

triples containing v. Consider the tournaments formed from T by adjoining k lines toward v and $p - k$ lines from v. There are $\binom{p}{k}$ such tournaments. Each contains $k(p - k)$ pairs of lines, one of which is directed toward and one directed away from v, for a total of $\binom{p}{k} k(p - k)$ cyclic triples. We must add such numbers for all k, $0 \le k \le p$. It can be shown by algebraic manipulation that this sum is $p(p - 1)2^{p-2}$, which is half the total number, as was to be demonstrated.

We have shown, then, that in all tournaments, large or small, the proportion of cyclic triples to be expected by chance is exactly 1/4. This means, of course, that the expected proportion of transitive triples is 3/4. Thus, it should not be surprising to find that such empirical structures as pecking orders, athletic tournaments, and sets of paired comparisons show a rather high degree of consistency.

STRONG TOURNAMENTS

In Corollary 11.9b, we saw that the condensation of any tournament is a complete order or a single point. Thus if a tournament is not transitive, one may wish to focus attention upon its strong components.

For this reason, there is considerable interest in investigating the properties of strong tournaments. In this section, we present two criteria for a tournament to be strong as well as several conditions which are sufficient but not necessary.

Theorem 11.11. If a tournament T is strong, then it contains a cycle of each length $k = 3, 4, \ldots, p$.

This theorem is proved by induction. First we observe by Corollary 11.8a that since T is not transitive, it has a cyclic triple. We now take as our inductive hypothesis the statement that T has a cycle Z of length $k < p$. We will show that T must have a cycle of length $k + 1$. Let us label the cycle Z as $v_1v_2v_3 \ldots v_kv_1$. There are just two possibilities. Either there is a point u not in Z such that u is adjacent to some point of Z and adjacent from another point of Z, or there is no such point u.

Case 1. There is a point u not in Z such that for some points v and w in Z, lines uv and wu occur in T. The proof for this case is illustrated in Figure 11.7. Let us assume that the line v_1u is in T. Let v_i be the first point, going around the cycle from v_1, such that the line uv_i is in T. Then line $v_{i-1}u$ must be in T. Thus we see that T contains a cycle of length $k + 1$, namely $v_1v_2v_3 \ldots v_{i-1}uv_i \ldots v_kv_1$.

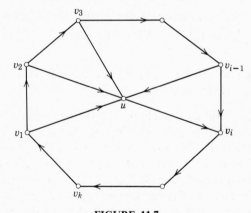

FIGURE 11.7

Case 2. There is no point u as in Case 1. Here, all points of T which are not in Z can be partitioned into two subsets U_1 and U_2, where U_1 is the set of all points not in Z adjacent to (every point of) Z, and U_2 is the set of all points not in Z adjacent from (every point of) Z. The sets U_1 and U_2 are not empty, since T is strong by hypothesis, and they are disjoint by the hypothesis of Case 2. Since T is strong, there exist a point u_1 in U_1 and a point u_2 in U_2 such that line u_2u_1 is in T. Then we may again construct a cycle of length $k + 1$ in T, namely:

$$u_1v_1v_2 \ldots v_{k-1}u_2u_1$$

To show that this cycle is of length $k + 1$, we count the number of distinct points in it. There are $k - 1$ points v_i and the two points u_1 and u_2, making a total of $k + 1$.

Since we have shown for each of these two cases that if T has a cycle of length k, it has a cycle of length $k + 1$, we have completed the proof of the theorem.

By Corollary 11.9a, one criterion for a tournament to be transitive is that it have a unique complete path. The first corollary of Theorem 11.11 provides an analogous criterion for a tournament to be strong.

Corollary 11.11a. A tournament is strong if and only if it has a complete cycle.

By Theorem 11.11, every strong tournament with p points has a cycle of length p, which is a complete cycle. And if a digraph has a complete cycle, it is strong, by Theorem 3.9.

Corollary 11.11b. Every strong tournament with at least four points has a neutral point.

Let T be a strong tournament with p points, $p \geq 4$. By Theorem 11.12, T has a cycle of length $p - 1$, say $v_1 v_2 \ldots v_{p-1} v_1$. Therefore, $T - v_p$ is strong, so that v_p is a neutral point of T.

Corollary 11.11c. If T is a strong tournament with p points, it has at least $p - 2$ cyclic triples.

We prove the result by induction. If a strong tournament has exactly 3 points, it clearly has $p - 2$ cyclic triples. As the inductive hypothesis, we take the result as true when $p = n$. Let T be strong with $n + 1$ points. By Corollaries 11.11b and 11.11a, T has a neutral point v_0 and $T - v_0$ has a complete cycle $Z = v_1 v_2 \ldots v_n v_1$. Since v_0 has score at least 1, without loss of generality we take the line $v_0 v_1$ in T. Since v_0 has indegree at least 1, we let v_i be the first point, going around the cycle Z from v_1, such that the line $v_i v_0$ is in T. Then $v_i v_0 v_{i-1} v_i$ is a cycle so that T has at least one more cyclic triple than does $T - v_0$. But by the inductive hypothesis, $T - v_0$, having n points and being strong, has at least $n - 2$ cyclic triples. Hence T has at least $n - 1$, and by the principle of induction, this proves the corollary.

Corollary 11.11d. There exists a strong tournament with p points and $p - 2$ cyclic triples.

That no strong tournament can have fewer cyclic triples is shown in the preceding corollary. We now show that a tournament with this few number of cyclic triples can be constructed. After starting with a transitive tournament with p points, we replace the line from its transmitter u to its receiver v by vu. We then have a strong tournament T, as shown in Figure 11.10. Since $T - u$ and $T - v$ are transitive and therefore contain no cyclic triples, every cyclic triple of T contains both u and v and hence also vu. Every point of T other than u and v forms a cycle with vu. There are $p - 2$ such points and hence $p - 2$ cyclic triples in T.

The preceding corollaries give the number of cyclic triples necessary for a tournament to be strong. The next theorem gives a sufficient condition, in terms of the maximum number of cyclic triples in tournaments with p points, as in Corollary 11.10c.

Theorem 11.12.   If T is a tournament with p points in which there are more cyclic triples than can occur in any tournament with $p - 1$ points, then T is strong.

Let T be a tournament with p points having more than $c_{max}(p - 1)$ cyclic triples. Suppose T is not strong, thus having at least two strong components. Clearly, all points of a cyclic triple lie in the same strong component. Hence if one strong component of T has k points, the number c of cyclic triples in T is no greater than the sum of the maximum numbers in tournaments with k and $p - k$ points:

$$c \le c_{max}(k) + c_{max}(p - k)$$

However, it can be verified algebraically that if $0 < k < p$, then

$$c_{max}(p - 1) \ge c_{max}(k) + c_{max}(p - k)$$

But this contradicts the assumption that $c > c_{max}(p - 1)$, thereby proving the theorem.

Corollary 11.12a.   Every tournament having a maximum number of cyclic triples is strong.

It will be recalled that formulas I and II of Theorem 11.2 provide a necessary and sufficient condition for a sequence of nonnegative integers to be the scores of some tournament with p points. Formulas I and III of the next theorem give the corresponding criterion for a strong tournament.

Theorem 11.13.   Let T be a tournament with score sequence

$$s_1 \le s_2 \le \ldots \le s_p$$

Then T is strong if and only if the equation

I. $$\sum_{i=1}^{p} s_i = \frac{p(p-1)}{2}$$

and the following inequalities hold for every positive integer $k < p$:

III. $$\sum_{i=1}^{k} s_i > \frac{k(k-1)}{2}$$

Before proving this theorem, we note that equation I is the same in Theorems 11.2 and 11.13 and that the only difference between the inequalities II and III is that the latter are strict.

We first show that if T is a strong tournament, then conditions I and III hold. But we already know that condition I holds, since Theorem 11.2 has established it for any tournament. To verify the inequalities III, we note that for any integer $k < p$, the subtournament generated by $\{v_1, v_2, \ldots, v_k\}$ contains exactly $k(k-1)/2$ lines, by Corollary 11.1b. But since T is strong, there must be a line from at least one of these points to one of the other $p - k$ points. Hence, in the entire tournament,

$$\sum_{i=1}^{k} s_i > \frac{k(k-1)}{2}$$

To prove the converse, consider conditions I and III as given. We know by Theorem 11.2 that there exists a tournament T with these scores. Assume that such a tournament T is not strong. Then it has exactly one strong component S which is a receiver of T^*. Obviously, the points in S have the smallest scores among all the points of T. If m is the number of points in S, then $m < p$, and the following equation holds:

$$\sum_{i=1}^{m} s_i = \frac{m(m-1)}{2}$$

since there are no lines in T from a point in S to a point not in S. But one of the inequalities of the given condition III is:

$$\sum_{i=1}^{m} s_i > \frac{m(m-1)}{2}$$

This contradiction establishes the converse part of the proof.

In Figure 11.8, tournament T_1 is strong and T_2 is not. It can be seen that T_1 has five points and that every score s_i is 2. Thus, $\sum_{i=1}^{5} s_i = 10$, meeting condition I of Theorem 11.13. That condition III is also satisfied may be seen from the following strict inequalities:

$$s_1 > 0, \qquad s_1 + s_2 > 1, \qquad s_1 + s_2 + s_3 > 3,$$

and

$$s_1 + s_2 + s_3 + s_4 > 6$$

Tournament T_2 has four points, and it can be readily seen that its score sequence is $(1, 1, 1, 3)$. Thus, $\sum_{i=1}^{4} s_i = 6$, satisfying condition I of Theorem 11.2. By checking the inequalities, we find that condition II of Theorem 11.2 is satisfied, but that condition III of Theorem 11.13 is not:

$$s_1 > 0, \qquad s_1 + s_2 > 1, \qquad \text{and} \qquad s_1 + s_2 + s_3 = 3$$

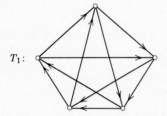

$T_1:$ $\qquad\qquad\qquad\qquad\qquad$ $T_2:$

FIGURE 11.8

We next give lower and upper bounds for the scores of a tournament.

Theorem 11.14. Let T be a tournament with score sequence $s_1 \leq s_2 \leq \ldots \leq s_p$. Then every score satisfies the inequalities:

$$\frac{k-1}{2} \leq s_k \leq \frac{p+k-2}{2}$$

First, we suppose that

$$s_k < \frac{k-1}{2}$$

Then, for every $i < k$,

$$s_i \leq s_k < \frac{k-1}{2}$$

so that

$$\sum_{i=1}^{k} s_i < \frac{k(k-1)}{2}$$

But by Theorem 11.2,

$$\sum_{i=1}^{k} s_i \geq \frac{k(k-1)}{2}$$

which is a contradiction. Hence,

$$\frac{k-1}{2} \leq s_k$$

The second inequality is dual to the first. In the converse tournament T' with score sequence $t_1 \leq t_2 \leq \ldots \leq t_p$,

$$t_{p-k+1} \geq \frac{(p-k+1)-1}{2} = \frac{p-k}{2}$$

by the first inequality of the theorem. But, $s_k = (p-1) - t_{p-k+1}$, so

$$s_k \leq (p-1) - \frac{p-k}{2} = \frac{p+k-2}{2}$$

proving the result.

The next theorems and their corollaries provide information regarding the scores of points and strong components of tournaments.

Theorem 11.15.   Let v_i and v_j be points in different strong components of a tournament T. Then the line $v_i v_j$ is in T if and only if $s_i > s_j$.

Let v_i and v_j be points in different strong components of T. Let the line $v_i v_j$ be in T. There is no cycle containing them. Every point adjacent from v_j is also adjacent from v_i, for otherwise we have a cycle containing v_i and v_j. In addition, v_j is adjacent from v_i, so $s_i > s_j$.

Conversely, if $s_i > s_j$, the line $v_j v_i$ cannot occur in T by this same argument. Hence, since T is complete, the line $v_i v_j$ is in T.

Corollary 11.15a.   In a tournament, any two points with the same score are in the same strong component.

This result follows immediately from Theorem 11.15. Both the corollary and the theorem are illustrated in Figure 11.9, which shows a tournament T having two strong components S_1 and S_2; the dashed arrow means that every point of S_1 is adjacent to every point of S_2. From the adjacency matrix $A(T)$, it can be ascertained that the score sequence of T is (1, 1, 1, 4, 4, 5, 5). By an inspection of T, we see that the three points with score 1 generate S_2, while the remaining points generate S_1. Moreover, the score of each point in S_1 is greater than the score of each point in S_2.

The next theorem gives a sufficient condition for points with unequal scores, such as those in S_1, to be in the same strong component. Although it is not a necessary condition, it may often be used in determining the strong components of a tournament.

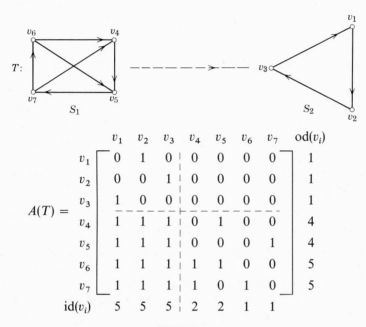

FIGURE 11.9

Theorem 11.16.   Let T be a tournament with score sequence $s_1 \leq s_2 \leq \ldots \leq s_p$. If $0 \leq s_n - s_m < (n - m + 1)/2$, then v_m and v_n are in the same strong component.

Suppose that there are points v_m and v_n with $0 \leq s_n - s_m < (n - m + 1)/2$ but they are not in the same strong component. Let j be the greatest integer less than n such that v_j is not in $S(v_n)$. By Theorem 11.14 we know that the score of v_n in the subtournament $S(v_n)$ is not less than $(n - j - 1)/2$. Also, by Theorem 11.15, there is a line from v_n to each of the j points v_i with $s_i \leq s_j$. Therefore,

$$s_n \geq j + \frac{n - j - 1}{2} = \frac{n + j - 1}{2}$$

We can use Theorem 11.15 again to see that every point adjacent from v_m is in the set $\{v_1, v_2, \ldots, v_j\}$.

If we apply Theorem 11.14 to the subtournament $\langle v_1 v_2 \ldots v_j \rangle$, it then follows that $s_m \leq (j + m - 2)/2$. By combining these results with our assumption, we have

$$\frac{n - m + 1}{2} > s_n - s_m \geq \frac{n + j - 1}{2} - \frac{j + m - 2}{2} = \frac{n - m + 1}{2}$$

which is a contradiction.

We may illustrate Theorem 11.16 by referring again to Figure 11.9. From Corollary 11.15a we were able to conclude that v_1, v_2, v_3 all lie in the same strong component since the scores of these points are all 1. We see that $s_7 = 5$ and $s_4 = 4$. Substituting into the inequality of Theorem 11.16, we obtain $0 \leq 5 - 4 = 1 < (7 - 4 + 1)/2 = 2$. Therefore, we conclude that v_4 and v_7 are in the strong component $S(v_4)$ and, *a fortiori*, so are v_5 and v_6.

The next two corollaries give sufficient conditions for a tournament to be strong.

Corollary 11.16a. If the difference between every two scores in a tournament T is less than $p/2$, then T is strong.

Since the scores are $s_1 \leq s_2 \leq \ldots \leq s_p$, the greatest difference between any two scores is $s_p - s_1$. By hypothesis, $s_p - s_1 < p/2$ so that s_p and s_1 are in the same strong component by Theorem 11.16. Similarly for any other point s_i, it follows from the theorem that s_i and s_1 are in the same strong component. Thus, the entire tournament is strong.

Corollary 11.16b. If both the outdegree and indegree of each point of a tournament T are at least $(p - 1)/4$, then T is strong.

If $\text{id}(v) \geq (p - 1)/4$, then

$$\text{od}(v) = (p - 1) - \text{id}(v) \leq p - 1 - \frac{p - 1}{4} = \frac{3(p - 1)}{4}$$

Thus, in particular, $s_p \leq 3(p - 1)/4$, and by hypothesis $s_1 \geq (p - 1)/4$. Hence,

$$s_p - s_1 \leq \frac{3(p - 1)}{4} - \frac{p - 1}{4} = \frac{2p - 2}{4} < \frac{p}{2}$$

Therefore, by the preceding corollary, T is strong.

The strong tournament T displayed in Figure 11.10 shows that the conditions of these corollaries are not necessary for a tournament to be strong. In T, the greatest and least scores are 4 and 1, so that $s_p - s_1 = 3 = p/2$. Also, the least score is less than $(p - 1)/4$. Nevertheless, the criteria are so simple that they are of considerable value in identifying strong tournaments.

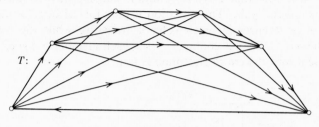

FIGURE 11.10

The Voting Paradox

Consider an electorate which, by majority vote, is to choose among a set of motions or candidates. Assume that the chairman casts a deciding vote in case of a tie. The possible outcomes resulting from the pairing of each motion against each other can be represented by a tournament in which each motion corresponds to a point and the fact that motion v_i can defeat motion v_j corresponds to a line v_iv_j. It has long been known that such a tournament may contain a cycle. In fact, the term "cyclical majorities" was employed by the Rev. C. L. Dodgson[7] (Lewis Carroll) to describe this kind of situation.

A simple example illustrates how a cyclic majority may arise. An eccentric alumnus of Carefree College has made a gift of \$100,000 to his alma mater with the stipulation that its use shall be determined by a three-man committee of the faculty. The committee consists of Professors B. Vivant, F. Fauna, and X. Starr. After months of thoughtful deliberation, the committee has reduced the possibilities to four alternatives: (1) faculty club, (2) botanical garden, (3) athletic scholarships, and (4) parking structure. Each member of the committee has a consistent set of preferences, as shown by the appropriate tournaments in Figure 11.11. Thus, B. Vivant most prefers the faculty club, F. Fauna ardently desires the botanical garden, and X. Starr puts athletic scholarships at the top of his list.

From the three tournaments of member preferences, we may construct a tournament representing the outcomes of committee balloting which would result if each member votes in accordance with his preferences. In tournament T of Figure 11.11, each line v_iv_j indicates that alternative

---

[7] An interesting discussion of this topic, together with an historical account of Dodgson's interest in the problem, is presented in Black (1958).

v_i can defeat alternative v_j. Thus, for example, there is a line from Club to Garden since this line appears in two of the three preference tournaments. It is clear that T is strong, and in keeping with Corollary 11.11a, has a complete cycle. This situation is paradoxical because the tournament of preferences for each voter is transitive while the tournament T of the majority votes contains cycles; each member of the electorate is consistent, but the entire electorate is not.

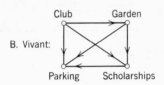

B. Vivant:

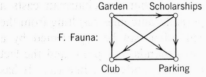

F. Fauna:

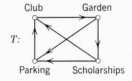

T:

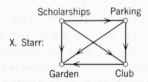

X. Starr:

FIGURE 11.11

Let us assume that the balloting proceeds as follows: The first vote is between the botanical garden and athletic scholarships, with the botanical garden the winner. Next, the botanical garden is pitted against the faculty club, and the faculty club wins. In the remaining vote, the parking structure defeats the faculty club. Thus, the committee selects an alternative which no member most prefers!

It is clear from the structure of T that the order in which the alternatives are voted upon is decisive. In fact, whenever a cyclical majority exists, the later an alternative in the cycle enters the voting the better its chance of adoption. Let us make the unlikely assumption that B. Vivant knows about these matters and persuades the committee to vote on his favorite, the faculty club, last. Clearly, no matter what the sequence of earlier votes, the final one will be between the faculty club and the botanical garden, with the faculty club victorious.

The voting paradox has stimulated a considerable literature concerning which procedure of voting is "best," but no completely satisfactory method has been devised. Arrow (1951) has considered the more general problem of finding a "social welfare function," whereby the preferences of individuals are equitably combined into a preference ordering by society. He has shown that it is impossible to satisfy one set of five plausible conditions for an equitable welfare function.[8]

SUMMARY

The restricted class of digraphs known as tournaments provides the topic of this chapter. A tournament is defined as a nontrivial complete asymmetric digraph. Thus, every tournament with p points has $p(p-1)/2$ lines. Since the number of lines in a tournament equals the sum of its scores (outdegrees of its points), every tournament satisfies the condition

$$\sum_{i=1}^{p} s_i = \frac{p(p-1)}{2}, \qquad \text{where } s_i \text{ is the score of } v_i$$

The points of a tournament may be arranged so that their scores form a nondecreasing order. Then the following inequalities also hold for every tournament, where $k < p$:

$$\sum_{i=1}^{k} s_i \geq \frac{k(k-1)}{2}$$

A tournament is strong if and only if these inequalities are strict, that is,

$$\sum_{i=1}^{k} s_i > \frac{k(k-1)}{2}$$

and it is transitive if and only if

$$\sum_{i=1}^{k} s_i = \frac{k(k-1)}{2}$$

Thus, the score sequence of every transitive tournament is $(0, 1, 2, \ldots, p-1)$.

[8] A useful discussion of Arrow's Impossibility Theorem is provided by Luce and Raiffa (1957). For a discussion of these matters, see Coombs (1964).

The following results are basic to the study of tournaments: (1) every tournament has a complete path; (2) a tournament is strong if and only if it has a complete cycle; and (3) a tournament is transitive, that is, a complete order, if and only if it has a unique complete path. Thus, it is possible to rank the points of any tournament T in accordance with a complete path, but such a ranking is unique if and only if T is transitive. In a complete order, there is a one-to-one correspondence between the ranking of its points given by its complete path and its score sequence. Since a tournament is a complete order if and only if it is acyclic, the condensation T^* of any tournament T is a complete order.

We saw that in a tournament any distance from a point with maximum score is 1 or 2. Every tournament has at most one transmitter, and if it has a transmitter v, the distance to every point from v is 1. If a tournament has no transmitter, then it contains at least three points each of which can reach every point in at most two steps.

In the study of tournaments, triples play a crucial role. The number of triples in a tournament with p points is

$$\binom{p}{3} = \frac{p(p-1)(p-2)}{6}$$

Every triple of a tournament is either transitive or cyclic. Clearly, a tournament is a complete order if and only if all of its triples are transitive. Thus, the more cyclic triples there are in a tournament, the less consistent is the tournament. This fact gives rise to a coefficient of consistency for a tournament with p points, which is stated in terms of the number of cyclic triples it has.

Finally, we found that there is a relationship between the score sequence of a tournament and the number of its triples that are transitive or cyclic.

In this chapter we are concerned with digraphs in which exactly one line joins each pair of points. In the next chapter, we consider a variety of other restrictions that may be placed upon digraphs to yield various kinds of interesting specialized digraphs.

EXERCISES

1. In the tournament shown in Figure 11.12, find all the points with minimum score and verify that the directional dual of Theorem 11.4 is satisfied.

2. (a) In a round-robin competition, is it possible for exactly one team to finish at the top of the standings even though no team wins all its games? (b) Construct a tournament with no transmitter but having a unique point with maximum score.

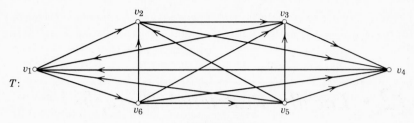

FIGURE 11.12

3. Let T be a tournament whose strong components are $T_1, T_2, \ldots, T_k$. Let h be the number of complete paths of T and let h_i be the number of complete paths of the subtournament T_i. Show that $h = h_1 h_2 \ldots h_k$.

4. Prove: If a committee employs the procedure of successively pairing alternative motions and selecting one by majority vote, the later a motion enters the voting the greater its chance of adoption.

5. Show that in no tournament with 4 points does every point constitute a 2-basis. Then construct such a tournament with 5 points.

6. Let a score sequence be called *simple* if it belongs to exactly one tournament. Show that every score sequence of tournaments with fewer than 5 points is simple, but that this is not so for $p = 5$.

7. Use Theorem 11.2 and show that the sequence of integers $(2, 2, 3, 3, 3, 4, 4)$ is a score sequence of a tournament T and construct such a tournament.

8. Show that the sufficient condition of Corollary 11.16a is also necessary for all tournaments with less than 6 points.

9. Construct a tournament whose score sequence is $(0, 5, 5, 5, 5, 5, 5, 5, 5, 5)$.

10. Show that every tournament with more than 3 points has at least one transitive triple.

11. Calculate the coefficient of consistency ζ for each tournament with 4 points shown in Figure 11.1.

12. Construct a tournament with 5 points which has the greatest possible number of cyclic triples.

13. Show that in any complete order with more than two points, every point is 2, 2. To disprove the converse, construct a tournament which is not a complete order but has every point 2, 2.

14. Show that in any complete order with more than two points, the following statements are equivalent for any line x: (a) x is on the unique complete path. (b) x is basic. (c) x is 2, 1.

15. Prove: Let the points of a tournament have outdegree s_i and indegree t_i. Then

$$\sum_{i=1}^{p} s_i^2 = \sum_{i=1}^{p} t_i^2$$

16. Construct a sequence of integers $r_1 \le r_2 \le \ldots \le r_p$ which satisfies the inequalities of Theorem 11.14 but is not the score sequence of a tournament.

12 • Locally Restricted Digraphs

We cannot do with more than four,
To give a hand to each.

LEWIS CARROLL
Through the Looking Glass

By a locally restricted digraph we shall mean one in which the indegree or outdegree of every point satisfies certain restrictive conditions. One purpose of this chapter is to characterize some of the local restrictions that can occur in a digraph. Certainly a random choice of numbers will not necessarily serve as the indegrees and outdegrees of a digraph. The first theorem provides specifications that determine when such an assignment of numbers to a digraph can be made.

The next section considers the structures and properties of the digraphs in which every point has outdegree 1. Such structures occur, for example, when each person makes exactly one sociometric choice within a group. The directional dual is illustrated by an organization chart in which each person has exactly one boss, except perhaps the top boss.[1]

Another interesting class of locally restricted digraphs consists of those in which the indegree and outdegree of every point are the same. Digraphs with this property have special traversibility properties, which serve to characterize them and also to solve a variety of puzzles and problems.

A carrier is a special kind of point with equal outdegree and indegree, namely 1. Sometimes such points may be suppressed from a digraph without any significant modification of the structural properties of the digraph containing the remaining points. The chapter concludes with a study of the effect on connectedness of suppressing carriers.

[1] His wife is not a member of the organization.

LOCAL RESTRICTIONS

The purpose of this section is to describe some local restrictions that can occur in a digraph. In order to state this question precisely, we call the *degree of a point* v the ordered pair (od(v), id(v)). For brevity of notation, let $s_i = $ od(v_i) and $t_i = $ id(v_i). For a digraph D with p points, the sequence of ordered pairs (s_1, t_1), (s_2, t_2), ..., (s_p, t_p) is a *degree sequence* of D. A given sequence of ordered pairs of nonnegative integers is called *graphical* if there exists a digraph D with points v_i such that the given sequence belongs to D. The first theorem sets a criterion for a given sequence to be graphical.

The fact that not all sequences of ordered pairs are graphical may be seen by considering the sequence (0, 0), (1, 1). As noted in Chapter 1, a point with degree (0, 0) is an isolate and one with (1, 1) is a carrier. Thus the above sequence will be graphical only if there exists a digraph with two points, one an isolate and the other a carrier. Obviously, this is impossible. All of the degree sequences of digraphs with two points are given by

$$(0, 0), (0, 0)$$

$$(1, 0), (0, 1)$$

$$(1, 1), (1, 1)$$

Other examples of degree sequences were given in Chapter 2. There it was observed, in different notation, that the digraph consisting of a single path has the degree sequence (1, 0), (1, 1), ..., (1, 1), (0, 1). Also, the complete symmetric digraph K_p is the only digraph with p points in which every point v has id(v) = od(v) = $p - 1$. The preceding chapter was devoted to a study of tournaments, which satisfy the condition that every point has total degree $p - 1$. The purpose of all these examples is to show that the idea of a locally restricted digraph is not entirely new.

A degree sequence is called *simple* if it belongs to exactly one digraph. For example, we have just seen that (3, 3), (3, 3), (3, 3), (3, 3) is a simple degree sequence belonging only to K_4. On the other hand, (1, 1), (1, 1), (1, 1), (1, 1) is not a simple degree sequence, since it belongs to each of the two digraphs of Figure 12.1.

In a sociometric setting, if a list of the number of choices made and received by each member of the group can only be realized by one group structure, the corresponding "group synthesis problem" is uniquely solvable since the given degree sequence is simple.

We now present a criterion for a degree sequence to be graphical. First we make an observation establishing an upper bound to the sum

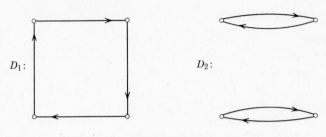

$D_1:$ $D_2:$

FIGURE 12.1

of the outdegrees of a set U consisting of k points of a digraph D. Let Y be the lines of D incident from points of U. Where do they go? A point v in U can receive at most $k - 1$ of them because $U - v$ has $k - 1$ points. Since the total number of lines received by v altogether is $\text{id}(v)$, it cannot receive more than $\text{id}(v)$ from U. Thus v receives at most $\min\{k - 1, \text{id}(v)\}$ lines of Y. Suppose, on the other hand, v is not in U. Then it receives at most k lines of Y. It also receives no more than $\text{id}(v)$ lines of Y. Hence v is the second point of at most $\min\{k, \text{id}(v)\}$ lines of Y. Since Y has $\sum_{v \in U} \text{od}(v)$ lines, we see that the number of lines from points of U satisfies

$$\sum_{v \in U} \text{od}(v) \le \sum_{v \in U} \min\{k - 1, \text{id}(v)\} + \sum_{v \notin U} \min\{k, \text{id}(v)\}$$

This assertion is a necessary, but not a sufficient, condition for a degree sequence to be graphical.

Now we are ready to consider a criterion for a given sequence to be graphical.[2] It is convenient to order the points so that the outdegrees are monincreasing, opposite to the usual ordering of the scores for tournaments.

Theorem 12.1. Consider a given sequence of ordered pairs of nonnegative integers $(s_1, t_1), (s_2, t_2), \ldots, (s_p, t_p)$, where $s_1 \ge s_2 \ge \ldots \ge s_p$, $0 \le s_i \le p - 1$, and $0 \le t_i \le p - 1$. This sequence is graphical if and only if the equation

Ia. $$\sum_{i=1}^{p} s_i = \sum_{i=1}^{p} t_i$$

and the following inequalities hold for every integer $k < p$:

IIa. $$\sum_{i=1}^{k} s_i \le \sum_{i=1}^{k} \min\{k - 1, t_i\} + \sum_{i=k+1}^{p} \min\{k, t_i\}$$

[2] This result was given by Fulkerson (1960).

The necessity of these two conditions is easy to establish. By Theorem 1.1, the sums of the outdegrees and indegrees are equal, so Ia holds. And for each integer k, $1 \leq k \leq p - 1$, IIa follows from the inequalities preceding Theorem 12.1 by taking U to be the set consisting of the first k points, and recognizing that $s_i = \mathrm{od}(v_i)$ and $t_i = \mathrm{id}(v_i)$.

The proof of the sufficiency of these two conditions is much more involved and will not be given here.

We illustrate this theorem with the digraph of Figure 12.2, where the points v_i have been numbered so that $s_1 \geq s_2 \geq \ldots \geq s_p$. Here the outdegrees of D are $(4, 3, 3, 1, 1)$ and its indegrees are $(2, 1, 2, 3, 4)$. Thus condition Ia of the theorem is verified at once. The second condition is verified for this digraph D by the following inequalities:

$$k = 1:\ s_1 = 4 \leq 0 + \sum_{i=2}^{5} \min\{1, t_i\} = 4$$

$$k = 2:\ s_1 + s_2 = 7 \leq \sum_{i=1}^{2} \min\{1, t_i\} + \sum_{i=3}^{5} \min\{2, t_i\} = 2 + 6 = 8$$

$$k = 3:\ s_1 + s_2 + s_3 = 10 \leq 5 + 6 = 11$$

$$k = 4:\ s_1 + s_2 + s_3 + s_4 = 11 \leq 8 + 4 = 12$$

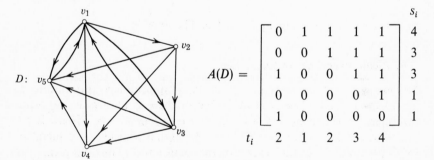

FIGURE 12.2

It is interesting to note that conditions I and II of Theorem 11.2 are but a special case of these conditions Ia and IIa. To prove this assertion, we show that when $s_i = p - 1 - t_i$, then I and II follow from Ia and IIa, respectively. Since the order of outdegrees is opposite to that used for tournaments, we use the directional dual of IIa. Thus, for every $k < p$,

$$\sum_{i=1}^{k} (p - 1 - s_i) \leq \sum_{i=1}^{k} \min\{k - 1, s_i\} + \sum_{i=k+1}^{p} \min\{k, s_i\}$$

Therefore, since $s_i \geq \min\{k - 1, s_i\}$ and $k \geq \min\{k, s_i\}$,

$$\sum_{i=1}^{k} (p - 1) - \sum_{i=1}^{k} s_i \leq \sum_{i=1}^{k} s_i + \sum_{i=k+1}^{p} k$$

Then,

$$k(p - 1) - \sum_{i=1}^{k} s_i \leq \sum_{i=1}^{k} s_i + (p - k)k$$

and transposing,

$$\sum_{i=1}^{k} s_i \geq \frac{1}{2}k(k - 1)$$

proving the inequalities II of Theorem 11.2.

Since we now have $s_i + t_i = p - 1$, and by Ia,

$$\sum_{i=1}^{p} s_i = \sum_{i=1}^{p} t_i$$

the equality

$$\sum_{i=1}^{p} s_i = \frac{p(p - 1)}{2}$$

follows at once, proving equation I of Theorem 11.2.

The Picnic Problem: An Excursion

This criterion for a sequence to be graphical has applications in problems involving assignments. One of these is known as the picnic problem, in which m families want to travel in n cars. There is the auxiliary condition (not entirely unrealistic) that whenever two members of one family are in the same car, they will fight! Thus the picnic can be held only if there is a seating arrangement in which no two members of a family are together. It is easy to verify that three families having 4, 4, and 3 members cannot be seated in this way in four cars with capacities 5, 2, 2, and 2 seats.

A solution to a picnic problem may be represented by a digraph in which every point is either a transmitter or a receiver. The transmitters are families and the receivers are vehicles; a line means that a member of the corresponding family is assigned to that particular car. Of course there cannot be lines joining two families or two cars, or a line from a car to a family since every line must necessarily go from a transmitter to a receiver. Also, because there cannot be more than one person of a given family in each automobile, the result is a digraph. The outdegree of a transmitter is then the number of members of that family and the indegree of a receiver is the capacity of the corresponding car.

Any assignment problem such as a picnic problem has associated with it a sequence of ordered pairs $(s_1, 0), (s_2, 0), \ldots, (s_m, 0), (0, t_1), (0, t_2), \ldots,$ $(0, t_n)$, where s_i is the size of the ith largest family and t_j is the capacity of the jth car. The solvability of the problem is then equivalent to the question of whether its sequence is graphical.

As a simple illustration of a picnic problem and its solution, consider three small families whose sizes are 4, 3, and 3 who want to go on a picnic in five sport cars, each a two-seater. Thus the three transmitters have outdegree 4, 3, and 3, and there are five receivers, each with indegree 2. Such a digraph is shown in Figure 12.3.

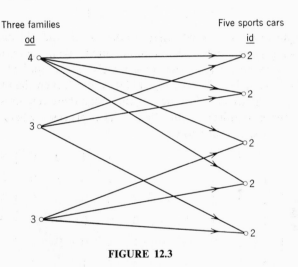

FIGURE 12.3

Since the only lines of this digraph go from families to cars, its adjacency matrix consists mainly of 0's. In fact, all its nonzero entries lie in the submatrix whose rows correspond to families and whose columns correspond to cars. Thus, to represent the digraph of Figure 12.3, we need only consider the 3×5 matrix

$$
\begin{array}{cccccc}
& c_1 & c_2 & c_3 & c_4 & c_5 & s_i \\
f_1 & \begin{bmatrix} 1 & 1 & 1 & 1 & 0 \end{bmatrix} & & & & & 4 \\
f_2 & \begin{bmatrix} 1 & 1 & 0 & 0 & 1 \end{bmatrix} & & & & & 3 \\
f_3 & \begin{bmatrix} 0 & 0 & 1 & 1 & 1 \end{bmatrix} & & & & & 3 \\
t_j & 2 & 2 & 2 & 2 & 2 & \\
\end{array}
$$

Here, of course, the rows represent the families f_i, the columns the cars c_j, and an i, j entry of 1 indicates that someone in the ith family is assigned to the jth car.

Even if one knows that a particular picnic problem has a solution, the problem of finding a satisfactory assignment still remains. Gale (1957) shows that "The m families should be seated in m stages according to the following simple rule: at each stage distribute the largest unseated family among those buses having the greatest number of vacant seats."

To illustrate this, we take as a final example of the picnic problem one whose solution may not be entirely obvious. Consider a proposed picnic for five families in ten vehicles, the last three of which are single-seater motorcycles:

$$s_i: \ 8, 8, 5, 5, 4$$

$$t_j: \ 5, 5, 4, 4, 4, 3, 2, 1, 1, 1$$

It is straightforward to verify that conditions Ia and IIa are satisfied. The following matrix (whose rows and columns again represent families and vehicles, respectively) shows how Gale's rule is applied. First one family of 8 is seated in the largest cars as in row 1, then the other family of 8 is assigned places by the rule. At this stage there remain six unfilled cars and three families to fill them. The process, when continued results in the assignment shown.

$$
\begin{bmatrix}
1 & 1 & 1 & 1 & 1 & 1 & 1 & 1 & 0 & 0 \\
1 & 1 & 1 & 1 & 1 & 1 & 1 & 0 & 1 & 0 \\
1 & 1 & 1 & 1 & 1 & 0 & 0 & 0 & 0 & 0 \\
1 & 1 & 1 & 1 & 1 & 0 & 0 & 0 & 0 & 0 \\
1 & 1 & 0 & 0 & 0 & 1 & 0 & 0 & 0 & 1
\end{bmatrix}
\begin{matrix}
8 \\ 8 \\ 5 \\ 5 \\ 4
\end{matrix}
$$
$$\ \ \ 5 \ \ 5 \ \ 4 \ \ 4 \ \ 4 \ \ 3 \ \ 2 \ \ 1 \ \ 1 \ \ 1$$

FUNCTIONAL DIGRAPHS

A *function* is conventionally defined as a relation whose ordered pairs (u, v) have the property that for each first element u, there corresponds a unique second element v. Since there is no restriction in this definition which prohibits the possibility of ordered pairs of the form (v, v), a function may be regarded as a relation in which every point has outdegree 1. Comparing this with the definitions in Chapter 1, we see that whenever there is a loop at a point v, this loop is the only line from v. A *functional digraph* is a digraph in which every point has outdegree 1. Thus a functional digraph is a function with no loops.

A small summer camp has four cabins each housing eight boys. In a research project each boy is asked to indicate the one boy in his cabin whom he most admires. Since every boy is required to make exactly one choice, the choices for each cabin form a functional digraph. Fortunately, for our purposes, each of these four digraphs is in a different category of connectedness, as shown in Figure 12.4, where the category of D_i is i.

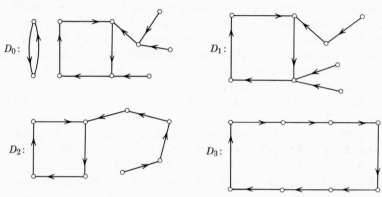

FIGURE 12.4

We see that each cabin contains at least one "cycle of admiration" and that any additional choices are directed toward that cycle. Apparently, then, there is a tendency in this camp for the admiration structure to be organized around an "in-group" whose choices form a cycle. We may ask whether this tendency is peculiar to this camp, or whether it will be found more generally. The answer to this question does not require further empirical research, for it can be obtained from an examination of the structural properties of functional digraphs.

Theorem 12.2 provides a structural characterization of functional digraphs.[3] In order to state it, we require the dual of a concept studied in Chapter 10. A *tree toward a point* v is a weak digraph with no semicycles in which v is the only sink.

Theorem 12.2. The following statements are equivalent for a weak digraph D.

(1) D is functional.

(2) There is a cyclic line x such that $D - x$ is a tree toward fx.

(3) D has exactly one cycle Z, and after deleting its lines each weak component of the resulting digraph consists of a tree toward a point of Z.

---

[3] For a discussion of this theorem and its corollaries, see Harary (1959*d*).

(*1*) *Implies* (*2*). By definition every point of a functional digraph has outdegree 1. By Corollary 3.8c, D has a cycle. Let x be any line of this cycle. Then in $D - x$ every point has outdegree 1 except fx, which has outdegree 0. By the directional dual of Theorem 10.12, it follows that $D - x$ is a tree toward fx.

(*2*) *Implies* (*3*). Let x be a line of a weak digraph D for which $D - x$ is a tree toward fx. By the directional dual of Theorem 10.12, D contains a unique cycle consisting of the unique path of $D - x$ from sx to fx together with x. Since x is in this cycle, deleting its lines from D amounts to deleting lines of $D - x$. But when a line y is deleted from a tree to a point, the result is two weak components, one of which is a tree toward fy. Hence the result of deleting lines of the cycle is a digraph whose weak components are trees toward points of the cycle.

(*3*) *Implies* (*1*). First it is clear that every point not in Z has outdegree 1, since it is in a tree toward a point but is not its sink. Also, each point of Z has outdegree at least 1, and if any point u has outdegree at least 2, then D must have more than one cycle. To see this, note that there are but two possibilities: D contains a line not in Z from u either to a point of Z, or to a point not in Z. In either case, it follows that D contains a cycle other than Z.

Because a digraph is functional if and only if each of its weak components is functional, the preceding theorem serves to characterize the structure of all functional digraphs. It follows at once from the theorem that the number of cycles of a functional digraph is equal to the number of its weak components. Therefore, a functional digraph is disconnected if and only if it has more than one cycle.

Theorem 12.2, then, settles our question about the admiration structure of groups. If any structure corresponds to a functional digraph, it must resemble one of the digraphs shown in Figure 12.4. The empirical possibilities are limited by the nature of functional digraphs.

The next corollary characterizes the structure of a weak functional digraph in each category.

Corollary 12.2a. A functional digraph D is strong if and only if it consists of one cycle; D is strictly unilateral if and only if it consists of a cycle and a path toward a point of that cycle; D is strictly weak if and only if it contains exactly one cycle and has at least two transmitters.

The sufficiency of these conditions is immediate.

Let D be a weak functional digraph. By Theorem 12.2 it has a unique cycle Z. It follows from (3) of that theorem that its condensation D^* is a tree toward the point S_0 corresponding to Z in D. By Corollary

3.4a, D and D^* have the same category of connectedness. Now if D^* is strong, it consists of a single point—that is, D consists of the cycle Z. Moreover, if D^* is strictly unilateral, it contains a nontrivial complete open sequence L, and since D^* is a tree to S_0 it has no semicycles. Thus L is a complete path to S_0. Since D^* is a tree toward a point, it is unipathic. Therefore, L is D^*. Thus, D consists of Z together with a path toward a point of Z. Finally, if D^* is strictly weak it contains two points joined only by strict semipaths, that is, D contains a single cycle and two points which are transmitters and thus 1-connected.

Corollary 12.2b. Let D be a functional digraph.
(1) If D is strong, every point has indegree 1.
(2) If D is strictly unilateral, exactly one point has indegree 0.
(3) If D is strictly weak, at least two points have indegree 0.
(4) The number of weak components of D is its number of cycles.

The first two statements follow immediately from Corollary 12.2a, and together they imply the third. Since each weak component has exactly one cycle, the fourth statement follows.

Theorem 12.2 and its corollaries are illustrated by Figure 12.4. Each of the weak digraphs shown there contains exactly one cycle, whereas the disconnected digraph contains more than one. The removal of any cyclic line x from one of the weak digraphs results in a tree toward fx, and the deletion of all lines of the cycle leaves a digraph in which each weak component consists of a tree toward a point of the cycle. The three weak digraphs illustrate the characterizations provided in Corollary 12.2a. In each digraph, the indegrees conform to the statements of Corollary 12.2b.

We now consider briefly digraphs in which every point has outdegree n. If D is a digraph in which every point has outdegree 2, then D is the union of two spanning functional subgraphs. These subgraphs may be constructed in the following manner. Call x_i and y_i the two lines from point v_i. Let D_1 be the spanning subgraph of D in which each point v_i has only line x_i from it, and similarly let D_2 have the lines y_i. Then D_1 and D_2 are functional digraphs and D is the union of D_1 and D_2. This observation may be generalized at once to obtain the following result.

Theorem 12.3. Let D be a digraph in which every point has outdegree n. Then D is the union of n spanning functional subgraphs, no two of which have a common line.

If a sociometric test is given to a group in which each person is required to make a fixed number of choices (3, for example), in the resulting digraph every point has outdegree 3. This digraph is clearly the union 3 spanning functional subgraphs, no two of which have a line in common. Of course, each of these subgraphs has the properties described in Theorem 12.2.

If we reverse the directions of the lines of a functional digraph, we obtain its converse. A *contrafunctional digraph* is one in which every point has indegree 1. The directional dual of Theorem 12.2, which involves trees from points of the cycle, is easily formulated and is omitted.

In Chapter 6 we described a procedure used by a research organization to select an administrative committee. It will be recalled that each staff member voted for the one person who, in his oponion, would best represent his viewpoint. In the digraph of the votes, shown in Figure 6.12, each line vu indicates that "v best represents the viewpoint of u." The committee was to be formed from a 2-basis, or from a minimal 2-cover, of this digraph. We may now observe that the digraph of votes is contrafunctional since each point has indegree 1. From the directional dual of Theorem 12.2, then, we know that every weak component of the resulting digraph consists of a tree from a point of Z. It follows that every point lying on a cycle of the digraph is a source of its weak component. Thus, any committee formed by this procedure will contain a member from each cycle of the digraph.

It is possible for a digraph to be both functional and contrafunctional. The next theorem characterizes such digraphs.

Theorem 12.4. The following conditions are equivalent for any digraph D.
(1) D is both functional and contrafunctional.
(2) Every point of D is a carrier.
(3) Every weak component of D is a cycle.

The equivalence of the first two of these conditions is given by the definition of a carrier. The third condition immediately implies the second, since any point v of a cycle has $\mathrm{id}(v) = \mathrm{od}(v) = 1$. Finally, the third condition follows from the first on applying both Theorem 12.2 and its dual. For the only way each point v of a cycle can have both a tree toward v and a tree from v is for v to be adjacent with points on the cycle only.

An elementary-school Christmas party provides an illustration of Theorem 12.4. The names of the children are put in a hat, and each child draws one. The drawing is managed so that no child draws his own name. Each child gives a present to the child whose name he draws. Regarding the children as points, let there be a line uv if child u draws the name of child v. The resulting digraph is functional, since each child draws one name. It is contrafunctional since each name is drawn once. Thus, by Theorem 12.4, every weak component of the digraph is a cycle.

A one-to-one correspondence of a set V of points assigns to each point v of V some point u in such a way that no other point is assigned to u. That is, given a point v, we know what point is assigned to it; and given that u is assigned to some point, we can find what point is assigned to u. If we designate the assignment of u to v by the line vu, then a one-to-one correspondence gives rise to a digraph that is both functional and contrafunctional. In the setting of the Christmas party, the one-to-one correspondence is that set up between the giver and the recipient.

The Umbrella Problem

Consider the following problem.[4] "Six men, A, B, C, D, E, F, of negligible honesty, met on a perfectly rough day, each carrying a light inextensible umbrella. Each man brought his own umbrella, and took away—let us say 'borrowed'—another's. The umbrella borrowed by A belonged to the borrower of B's umbrella. The owner of the umbrella borrowed by C borrowed the umbrella belonging to the borrower of D's umbrella. If the borrower of E's umbrella was not the owner of that borrowed by F, who borrowed A's umbrella?"

The solution can be represented by a digraph in which a line means "borrowed the umbrella of." Such a digraph is both functional and contrafunctional, so each weak component is a cycle. There are four possibilities:

$\qquad$ 3 cycles of length 2: $- - -, - - -, - - -$.

$\qquad$ cycles of length 2 and 4: $- - -, - - - - -$.

$\qquad$ 2 cycles of length 3: $- - - -, - - - -$.

$\qquad$ a cycle of length 6: $- - - - - - -$.

We have this information: (i) there is a sequence of length 2 from A to B, (ii) there is a sequence of length 3 from C to D, (iii) there is no sequence of length 2 from F to E. From (i), we have these possibilities: $- - -$, $A-B-A$; $A-B A, - - - -$; or $A-B - - - A$. By using (ii) we have the alternatives: $C D C, A-B-A$; $A C B-D-A$; and $A D B-C-A$. The first of these cannot occur, since then (iii) would be violated. Thus, the digraph

[4] This problem is quoted from *Eureka*, 1947 (April), **9**, 22. Its solution, stated in a different terminology, was given in *Eureka*, 1948 (March), **10**, 25.

must consist of either $A\ C\ B\ E\ D\ F\ A$ or $A\ D\ B\ E\ C\ F\ A$. In either case, F borrowed A's umbrella.

TRAVERSABLE DIGRAPHS

In this section, we study digraphs with the particular local restriction that every point has equal outdegree and indegree. This numerical property will be seen to have an interesting structural implication. We shall find, following Euler (1707–1783), that every such digraph which is weakly connected is traversable in the following sense: It is possible to start at any point v, travel along each line exactly once, and return to v.

Isographs

A digraph is called an *isograph* if for every point v, $\text{id}(v) = \text{od}(v)$. Clearly, every symmetric digraph is an isograph. That there are also isographs which are not symmetric is shown by any cycle of length greater than 2. We have already studied one kind of isograph, namely one that is both functional and contrafunctional. The next theorem provides a structural characterization of isographs. A collection of cycles is said to be *line-disjoint* if no two of the cycles have a line in common. Two line-disjoint cycles may of course have points in common.

Theorem 12.5. A nontrivial weak digraph is an isograph if and only if it is the union of line-disjoint cycles.

First consider a weak digraph D which is the union of line-disjoint cycles. Since each cycle contributes exactly 1 to both the outdegree and indegree of each of its points, it follows that D is an isograph.

For the converse, let D be a nontrivial weak isograph. Then every point has positive total degree, and hence positive outdegree. By Corollary 3.8c, D contains a cycle Z. The process of removing the lines of Z results in a digraph in which each weak component is an isograph. The same procedure is then applied to the nontrivial weak components. Repeating this process until no cycles remain gives a collection of line disjoint cycles. Every line of D occurs in this collection, since otherwise the weak component containing it, being an isograph, would contain a cycle.

We illustrate, using Figure 12.5, the fact that the collection of line-disjoint cycles may not be unique. Here one such collection is given by the cycles $v_2 v_5 v_2$ and $v_1 v_2 v_3 v_4 v_5 v_1$, while another such collection contains the cycles $v_1 v_2 v_5 v_1$ and $v_2 v_3 v_4 v_5 v_2$.

Isographs are a special case of digraphs in which every point has even total degree. Just as Theorem 12.5 characterizes isographs, the broader class of locally restricted digraphs can also be similarly characterized. This is done in the following result, whose proof, being analogous to that of the theorem, is omitted.

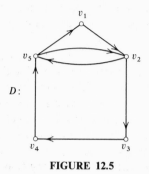

FIGURE 12.5

Corollary 12.5a.   Every point of a nontrivial weak digraph D has even total degree if and only if D is the union of line-disjoint semicycles.

Finally, we note that the connectedness category of an isograph is somewhat restricted.

Corollary 12.5b.   Every weak isograph is strong.

Let u and v be two points of a weak isograph D, and let L be a semipath joining them. By Theorem 12.5, each line of L lies in a cycle. Together these cycles form a closed sequence containing u and v. Hence u and v are mutually reachable, and D is strong.

Traversability

In addition to paths and cycles, there is another special type of sequence which is of interest. A *trajectory* is defined as a sequence in which no line occurs more than once. Just as for sequences, we may speak of closed, open, and complete trajectories. It is also convenient to call a trajectory which contains every line of a digraph *line-complete*. Clearly, except for digraphs with isolated points, a line-complete trajectory is complete!

A nontrivial weak digraph is called *traversable* if it has a line-complete closed trajectory. The digraph of Figure 12.5 happens to be traversable; one line-complete closed trajectory is $v_1v_2v_3v_4v_5v_2v_5v_1$. The next theorem relates the concepts of traversable digraphs and isographs.

Theorem 12.6. A weak digraph is traversable if and only if it is an isograph.

First, let L be a line-complete closed trajectory of a traversable digraph D. Then, considering the first and last point of L as one occurrence of that point, each occurrence in L of a point contributes 1 to both the outdegree and indegree of that point. Since every line of D occurs exactly once in L, it follows that each point has equal outdegree and indegree. Hence D is an isograph.

For the converse we are given that D is a weak isograph. By Theorem 12.5, D can be expressed as the union of line-disjoint cycles. Let Z_1 be any of these cycles. If $D = Z_1$, it is, of course, traversable. Otherwise, since D is weak, there is some other cycle Z_2 having a point v in common with Z_1. The sequence which starts at v and consists of the cycles Z_1 and Z_2 in succession is a closed trajectory containing all the lines of Z_1 and Z_2. By repeating this process, we construct a closed trajectory containing the lines of all the cycles, proving that D is traversable.

The Frustrated Milkman. A milkman has to cover an area of a city in which all streets are one-way. To save time and money he wants a route that will go along each street exactly once. Figure 12.6 shows a digraph of the streets of this area in which each point represents an intersection and each line indicates the direction of traffic. After several days of trial-and-error, he gives up in utter frustration. Had he been a graph theorist, he could have used Theorem 12.6 to discover immediately that there can be no route meeting his requirements.

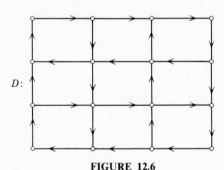

D:

FIGURE 12.6

SUPPRESSED DIGRAPHS

We have already encountered the suppression of carrier points in one kind of digraph, namely a semipath (Chapter 2). In this section, the concept of suppression of a carrier is generalized to arbitrary digraphs.

In doing so, however, we must be careful that the result is not pointless. For instance, if a digraph consists of a cycle, all points are carriers, so that "to suppress all carriers" would leave us with nothing to talk about.

A point v is *suppressible* if there are points u and w such that uv and vw are the only lines incident with v and $d(u, w) = 2$. The *suppression* of the suppressible point v results in the digraph obtained by adding the line uw to $D - v$; that is, it is the digraph $D - v \cup uw$. Figure 12.7 illustrates these concepts: v_1 and v_2, although they are carriers, are not suppressible points of D, whereas v_3 and v_4 are. Digraph E is the result of suppressing v_4, and we see that it has no suppressible points.

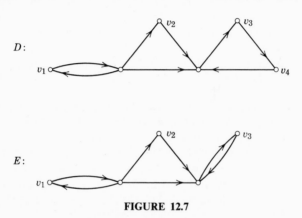

FIGURE 12.7

The suppression of a point is seen to be opposite to the operation of expansion studied in Chapter 10. Here we remove a carrier and add a new line, whereas in expansion we delete a line and add a new point v and two lines so that v becomes a carrier.

A *suppressed digraph* of a digraph D is obtained from D by suppressing one suppressible point at a time until no more remain. We note that since a suppressed digraph has, by definition, no suppressible points, it is its own suppression. In Figure 12.8 both D_1 and D_2 are suppressions of D, showing that the order of suppression of points affects which points remain after suppression. We shall see later that this is the only way in which two suppressions of a given digraph differ. But first we study some other aspects of suppressed digraphs.

Theorem 12.7. A point v occurring in a suppression D_0 of a digraph D retains its identification from D; that is, v is a receiver, transmitter, carrier, ordinary point, or isolate of D_0 if and only if it has the same character in D.

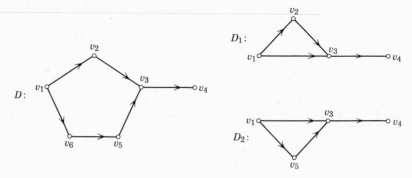

FIGURE 12.8

This result follows from the fact that when a point of a digraph is suppressed, the outdegrees and indegrees of all other points remain the same.

In the next theorem, we find that the reachability relation among surviving points is not changed by suppression.

Theorem 12.8.   Let u and v be points in a suppression D_0 of a digraph D. Then v is reachable from u in D_0 if and only if it is reachable from u in D.

To prove this theorem it is sufficient to show that when one point of digraph D is suppressed, reachability among the remaining points is preserved. Let D_1 be the result of suppressing a point w of D, and let $u'w$ and wv' be the lines of D incident with w. Then $u'v'$ is the new line in D_1 replacing the path $u'wv'$. Let u and v be points of D_1, and assume L is a path in D from u to v. If L does not contain w, then it also appears in D_1; otherwise replacing the subpath $u'wv'$ of L by the new line $u'v'$ results in a path from u to v in D_1. On the other hand, if L_1 is a path in D_1 from u to v which does not contain $u'v'$, it is also in D; otherwise replacing the line $u'v'$ in L_1 by the path $u'wv'$ results in a path from u to v in D.

An equivalent formulation of Theorem 12.8 is that the connectedness matrix of a suppressed digraph is obtained from that of the original digraph by deleting the rows and columns corresponding to the suppressed points.

In general, as shown in Figure 12.8, a digraph may have more than one suppression. The next theorem shows that two suppressions can differ only in the labels indicating which points survive.

Theorem 12.9. Any two suppressed digraphs of a given digraph are isomorphic.

Let D_1 and D_2 be suppressions of a digraph D. Label all noncarriers of D. Then all noncarriers of D_1 and D_2 have the same labels. Let u_0 and v_0 be noncarriers of D, and hence of D_1 and D_2. A necessary and sufficient condition that $u_0 v_0$ be in D_1 is that there be a path in D from u_0 to v_0 whose other points are all carriers. But this is also a necessary and sufficient condition for $u_0 v_0$ to be in D_2. Therefore, any line joining two noncarriers in one suppressed digraph appears in the other.

We now consider carriers in the suppressed digraphs. Each carrier w in D_1 is adjacent from a point u and to a point v. We first take $u \neq v$. Since w is not suppressible in D_1, the line uv must be in D_1, so u and v are noncarriers. If there are n paths in D from u to v containing no other noncarriers, there must be n such paths in both D_1 and D_2. One of these is the line uv, and the other $n - 1$ paths contain exactly one carrier, for otherwise there would still be a suppressible point in a suppressed digraph. By labeling these $n - 1$ carriers $w_1, w_2, \ldots, w_{n-1}$ in both D_1 and D_2, we see that uw_i and $w_i v$ are in both suppressed digraphs. From this it follows that there is a one-to-one correspondence between the carriers in D_1 and D_2 which are adjacent from one point to another.

By the same sort of argument, it can be shown that if the carrier w is adjacent to and from the same noncarrier, $u = v$, there is also a one-to-one correspondence between all such carriers adjacent with that noncarrier in both D_1 and D_2.

The only remaining case is that in which $u = v$ is a carrier. Then in D_1, uvu is a weak component, and it necessarily resulted from the suppression of all but two points in a cycle constituting a weak component in D. Thus, both D_1 and D_2 must have the same number of such cycles of length 2.

By considering all possible cases, we have shown that there is a one-to-one correspondence between the points of D_1 and of D_2 which preserves adjacency. Hence by definition, D_1 and D_2 are isomorphic, completing the proof.

From this theorem we know that, ignoring labels indicating which points survive, a digraph D has a unique suppression which we may denote by D^o and call *the suppression* of D. The next theorem relates the connectedness categories of D and D^o.

Theorem 12.10. If D is not a strictly weak digraph, then $c(D^o) = c(D)$. If D is strictly weak, then $c(D^o) = 1$ or 2.

To prove this theorem it is sufficient to show that if E is obtained from D by suppressing one point v, then the above equalities hold for $c(E)$. From Theorem 12.8 it follows that the reachability relation among the points of E is the same as in D, so that $c(E) \geq c(D)$. Now if $c(E) > c(D)$, v must be a weakening point. But a strong digraph has no weakening point, and if D is disconnected, v is an isolate, and hence not suppressible. Furthermore, in a unilateral digraph, a weakening point must, by Corollary 8.10b, be a transmitter or a receiver, and hence not suppressible. Thus the first statement is proved. If D is in C_1, then $D - v$ is in C_1 or C_2, since by Theorem 8.6 there are not any 1, 3 points. It follows that E is in either C_1 or C_2, proving the second statement.

We illustrate this theorem using Figure 12.9. Digraphs D_1 and D_1^o are both strictly unilateral. In contrast, D_2 and D_3 are both strictly weak, but D_3^o is unilateral while D_2^o is not.

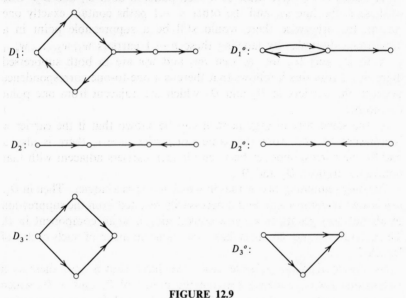

FIGURE 12.9

SUMMARY

In a locally restricted digraph, the indegree or outdegree of every point satisfies certain restrictive conditions. Such digraphs have been studied in this chapter. The first theorem presented a criterion for a sequence of ordered pairs of nonnegative integers to be graphical, that is, a degree sequence of some digraph.

An interesting special class of locally restricted digraphs is given by those in which the outdegree of every point is 1. These are called functional digraphs. Their directional duals are known as contrafunctional digraphs. Some digraphs are both functional and contrafunctional. We found that these various kinds of digraphs display certain striking structural characteristics; in particular, each weak component is a cycle.

We then turned to the study of traversable digraphs. From the viewpoint developed in this chapter, these are weakly connected digraphs whose local restriction is defined by the equality of the outdegree and indegree of each point. They have the property that it is possible to start from any point, travel along each line exactly once, and return to the starting point.

The chapter concluded with a study of suppressed digraphs. The suppression of a point v of a digraph is permitted if v is a carrier and the distance from the point adjacent to v to the point adjacent from v is 2. A suppressed digraph of D is obtained by suppressing one suppressible point at a time until none is left. It was shown that every digraph has a unique suppressed digraph. The connectedness category of the suppressed digraph bears a special relationship to the category of the original digraph.

EXERCISES

1. Determine whether the following sequences of ordered pairs are graphical: (a) (3, 2), (2, 0), (1, 2), (1, 3). (b) (1, 0), (1, 0), (1, 2), (1, 2). (c) (3, 1), (3, 3), (2, 2), (0, 2).

2. Construct a graphical sequence which belongs to an isograph, but does not belong to any symmetric digraph.

3. Characterize contrafunctional digraphs by stating the dual of Theorem 12.2.

4. Condense the cycle of a weak functional digraph to a single point u. Prove that the resulting digraph is a tree toward u.

5. Construct a traversable digraph having $3, j$ points for $j = 0, 1, 2, 3$.

6. Prove that no traversable digraph has a 3, 1 line.

7. Prove: If D is a unipathic digraph, then D is traversable if and only if every line is 3, 2.

8. Construct the implication digraph of the following statements, where D is a weak digraph which is not traversable. (a) D has a line-complete open trajectory. (b) D can be made traversable by the addition of one line. (c) There are two points u and v such that $od(u) - id(u) = id(v) - od(v) = 1$ and for all other points w, $id(w) = od(w)$.

9. Let a digraph be called *semitraversable* if it has a line-complete closed semi-trajectory. Prove or disprove: A strong digraph is traversable if it is semi-traversable.

10. Prove or disprove: A digraph D is traversable if and only if its suppression D^0 is.

11. Show that every carrier of a suppressed digraph lies on a transitive triple or a cycle of length 2.

12. Draw all suppressed digraphs with three points.

13. Prove: Every new point introduced in the expansion of a digraph is suppressible in the resulting digraph.

14. Prove: If E is an expansion of D, then E^0 and D^0 are isomorphic.

15. Construct a suppression of the digraph D in Figure 12.10 and show how its connectedness matrix is obtained from $C(D)$.

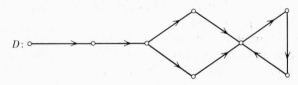

FIGURE 12.10

16. If a digraph has three carriers, none of which is suppressible, what is the fewest number of points it can have? What if the number of carriers is 2?

13 · Balance in Structures

Heaven has no rage like love to hatred turned
Nor hell a fury like a woman scorned.

WILLIAM CONGREVE
The Mourning Bride

In discussing realizations of digraph theory, we have let the lines of a digraph represent some empirical relation on a set of elements. Thus, for example, the points of a digraph D may stand for the members of a group and the lines may indicate interpersonal relationships of liking. In this case, the presence of a line uv in D means that person u likes person v, and the absence of this line means that u does not like v. It must be noted, however, that if line uv is not in D we cannot safely conclude that u is indifferent to v, for u may actively dislike v. If we are to represent the affective relation, then, we must distinguish between positive and negative relationships, that is, between liking and disliking. In this chapter, we consider how digraph theory may be extended so as to deal with signed relationships.

Many empirical relations require the designation of signs. Thompson (1963) has observed that "typical examples of psychological data, especially those concerning human relationships, involve an antithesis which requires both plus *and* minus signs to express it adequately. This kind of polarity is inconvertible, that is, cannot be fully expressed if the signs are left out." Such relations as loves, supports, tells truth to, associates with, and makes happy are intrinsically positive, in the sense of accepted cultural values, and their opposites—hates, threatens, lies to, avoids, and makes unhappy—are intrinsically negative. Each pair of opposites, taken together, may be considered a signed relation and represented by a signed digraph whose lines are either positive or negative. The positive and negative lines represent relationships which are intrinsically positive and negative respectively.

CRITERIA FOR BALANCE

We say that S is a *signed digraph*, whose underlying digraph is D, if S is obtained from D by designating each line as being either positive or negative. Figure 13.1 shows a digraph D together with a signed digraph S whose underlying digraph is D. We adopt the convention that solid lines are positive and dashed lines are negative.

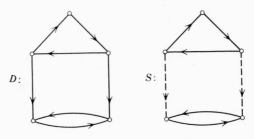

FIGURE 13.1

Interest in signed digraphs has been stimulated by a theory of cognitive balance advanced by Heider (1946). He was primarily concerned with three entities as cognized by an individual—P, the person under study; O, another person; and X, an impersonal entity—and relations on these entities. Thus, in dealing with the signed relation of evaluating, Heider focused attention on three relationships: P's evaluation of O, P's evaluation of X, and O's evaluation of X (as seen by P). Two examples of such a P–O–X unit might be: (1) P likes O, P dislikes X, and O dislikes X; (2) P likes O, P dislikes X, and O likes X. According to Heider, the first of these is balanced, whereas the second is not. Stated more generally, a P–O–X unit is balanced if all three relationships are positive or if two are negative and one is positive. Heider proposed that balanced triads are associated with a state of equilibrium and that unbalance is accompanied by psychological tension.

Cartwright and Harary (1956) have shown how Heider's conception of cognitive balance can be treated in terms of signed digraphs and generalized to an arbitrary number of elements.[1] In the following discussion, we employ the approach advanced by them.

---

[1] For further discussions of the use of signed digraphs in empirical research, see the following: Berger, *et al.* (1962), Cartwright and Harary (1956), Davis (1963), Flament (1963), Morrissette (1958), Rosenberg *et al.* (1960), and Zajonc (1960).

By the *sign of a semicycle* is meant the product of the signs of its lines. A signed digraph S is called *balanced* if every semicycle of S is positive. In other words, S is balanced if every semicycle has an even number of negative lines. It is clear that Heider's specification for balanced P–O–X units is a particular instance of this definition. Figure 13.2 shows four signed digraphs, each of which has as its underlying digraph a transitive triple. Clearly, S_1 and S_3 are balanced, but S_2 and S_4 are not. We readily see that S_1 and S_2 correspond to the first and second P–O–X units discussed above.

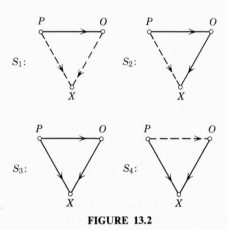

FIGURE 13.2

By carefully ascertaining the sign of each semicycle in the signed digraph S of Figure 13.1, it can be shown that S is balanced. But even in so simple a structure, the process is tedious. It is, therefore, desirable to have additional criteria for balance. Their development, however, requires some preliminary discussion.

To generalize from the sign of a semicycle, the *sign of a set Y of lines* is the product of the signs of its lines and is denoted $s(Y)$. Thus, we can also speak of positive and negative semipaths, paths, and cycles.

Obviously, if Y_1 and Y_2 are line-disjoint sets, the sign of the union of Y_1 and Y_2 is the product of the signs of the two sets:

$$s(Y_1 \cup Y_2) = s(Y_1) \cdot s(Y_2)$$

The next theorem gives a similar result about the symmetric difference of two sets of lines.

Theorem 13.1. If Y_1 and Y_2 are two sets of lines of a signed digraph, then $s(Y_1 \oplus Y_2) = s(Y_1) \cdot s(Y_2)$.

The proof of this theorem is essentially set-theoretic. We know that:

$$Y_1 = (Y_1 - Y_2) \cup (Y_1 \cap Y_2)$$

and

$$Y_2 = (Y_2 - Y_1) \cup (Y_1 \cap Y_2)$$

Since each of these is a union of disjoint sets,

$$s(Y_1) = s(Y_1 - Y_2) \cdot s(Y_1 \cap Y_2)$$

and

$$s(Y_2) = s(Y_2 - Y_1) \cdot s(Y_1 \cap Y_2)$$

Multiplying these equations, we get:

$$s(Y_1) \cdot s(Y_2) = s(Y_1 - Y_2) \cdot s(Y_2 - Y_1) \cdot s(Y_1 \cap Y_2) \cdot s(Y_1 \cap Y_2)$$

Since $s(Y_1 \cap Y_2) \cdot s(Y_1 \cap Y_2)$ is always positive, and since $Y_1 - Y_2$ and $Y_2 - Y_1$ are disjoint,

$$s(Y_1) \cdot s(Y_2) = s[(Y_1 - Y_2) \cup (Y_2 - Y_1)]$$

Thus, $s(Y_1) \cdot s(Y_2) = s(Y_1 \oplus Y_2)$, as was to be shown.

The following corollary restates the theorem in another form.

Corollary 13.1a.   Two sets of lines Y_1 and Y_2 have the same sign if and only if their symmetric difference $Y_1 \oplus Y_2$ is positive.

We now state three criteria for balance.[2]

Theorem 13.2.   The following statements are equivalent for any signed digraph S.

(1) S is balanced, that is, every semicycle of S is positive.

(2) For every pair of points, all semipaths joining them have the same sign.

(3) The set V of points of S can be partitioned into two subsets (one of which may be empty) such that each positive line joins two points of the same subset and each negative line joins two points of different subsets.

This theorem is proved in cyclic order.

(*1*) *Implies* (*2*). Let u and v be any two points of a balanced signed digraph S and let L_1 and L_2 be any two semipaths joining them. It is easy to show that in the subgraph generated by $L_1 \oplus L_2$ every point has even total degree. By Corollary 12.5a, $L_1 \oplus L_2$ can be expressed

---

[2] Theorems 13.2–13.7 appeared in Harary (1954, 1955a, 1959b).

as the union of a collection of line-disjoint semicycles. Since every semicycle of S is positive, the set of lines in $L_1 \oplus L_2$ is positive. By Corollary 13.1a, then, the semipaths L_1 and L_2 have the same sign, as was to be shown.

(2) *Implies* (3). Without loss of generality, we may consider S as weakly connected. If S has no negative lines, the implication holds by taking one of the sets to be all of V and the other set to be empty. Otherwise, let v be a point incident with a negative line. We construct a partition of V into sets U and W and show that they satisfy the condition in (3). Let U be the set of points which are joined to v by negative semipaths and let W be the remaining points (including v). By (2) all semipaths from v to points of U are negative and to points of W are positive.

Let x be a negative line. Then there are semipaths joining v with fx and joining v with sx having opposite signs. Thus, one of the points, fx or sx, is in U and the other is in W. On the other hand, if x is positive, there are semipaths joining v with fx and joining v with sx having the same sign. Thus both fx and sx are in U or both are in W.

(3) *Implies* (1). Let V_1 and V_2 be a partition of the points of S which satisfies (3). Let Z be any semicycle of S and let u be any point of Z. By beginning at u and following Z back to u, we must go from V_2 to V_1 as many times as from V_1 to V_2. Therefore, Z has an even number of negative lines, so it is positive. This completes the proof of the theorem.

We now have three criteria for determining whether a signed digraph is balanced. These may be called the "semicycle," the "semipath," and the "partition" criterion, respectively. We illustrate them, using Figure 13.3. First, we can locate all six semicycles of S and observe that each is positive. Alternatively, we can take all 28 pairs of distinct

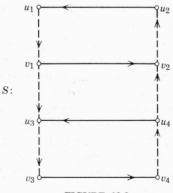

FIGURE 13.3

points and verify that all semipaths joining the same pair have the same sign. Third, we can partition the set of points of S into the two subsets, $V_1 = \{u_1, u_2, u_3, u_4\}$ and $V_2 = \{v_1, v_2, v_3, v_4\}$, and then observe that each positive line joins two points of the same set and each negative line joins points of different sets. This partition criterion is especially convenient when it can be verified readily by visual inspection, as for example in Figure 13.1.

An interesting result concerning partitioning points in digraphs follows as a corollary of the preceding theorem.[3]

Corollary 13.2a. Every semicycle of a digraph has even length if and only if the set of points can be partitioned into two sets such that every line joins two points of different sets.

Let D be any digraph and form the signed digraph S by taking every line negative. Then D has no odd semicycles if and only if S is balanced, that is, there is a partition of the points of S into two sets such that no line joins two points of the same set.

Local Balance

By definition, a signed digraph S is balanced if every semicycle of S is positive. Thus, for any point v of S, it follows that every semicycle containing v is positive. We say that a signed digraph S is *locally balanced at v*, or more briefly, S is *balanced at v*, if every semicycle containing v is positive. Obviously, S is balanced if and only if it is balanced at each of its points. The next theorem and its corollary show that useful information about a signed digraph S can be derived from knowing that S is balanced at one of its points.

Theorem 13.3. Let S be a signed digraph which is locally balanced at a point v. If u and v lie on a common block and u is not a cut point, then S is locally balanced at u.

To prove this theorem, we must show that every semicycle containing the point u is positive. Let Z be any such semicycle. Since u is not a cut point, Z lies in the block containing u and v. If v is in Z, then Z is positive since S is balanced at v. Therefore, consider v as not in Z. Let x be a line of Z incident with u. From the equivalence of (1) and (2) of Theorem 9.6, it follows that there is a semicycle Z_0 containing point v and line x. Then Z_0 consists of two semipaths L_1 and L_2 joining v and u, as shown in Figure 13.4(a). Proceeding from v along L_1, let v_1 be the first point of Z encountered, and similarly let v_2 be the first point of L_2

[3] This result is given in König (1936, p. 151).

from v which is on Z, as in Figure 13.4(b). Then $v_1 \neq v_2$. Let L_3 be the semipath of Z_0 joining v_1 and v_2 which contains v; L_4 that containing u; and L_5 the semipath joining v_1 and v_2 which together with L_4 form Z, as in the figure. Then $L_3 \cup L_4$ and $L_3 \cup L_5$ are semicycles, and they are both positive since they contain v. Therefore, L_4 and L_5 have the same sign, so that $Z = L_4 \cup L_5$ is positive. This establishes the theorem.

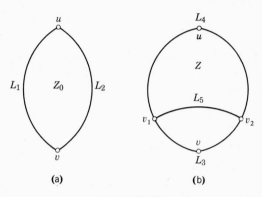

(a)   (b)

FIGURE 13.4

As a consequence of this theorem we have the following result, which simplifies some of the criteria for structural balance presented in Theorem 13.2. The result follows from Theorem 13.3, and the fact that S is balanced if and only if it is balanced at each of its points.

Corollary 13.3a. A signed block is balanced if and only if it is balanced at any one point. A weak signed digraph with cut points is balanced if and only if it is balanced at each of its cut points.

In Figure 13.3 it is clear that S is weak and contains no cut points, that is, it is a weak block. Corollary 13.3a asserts that to check whether or not S is balanced we need consider only the semicycles containing one point. Thus, for example, we can show that S is balanced simply by showing that the three semicycles containing u_1 are all positive.

The signed digraph S of Figure 13.5 is weak but contains a cut point v_3. It is readily verified that S is not balanced at v_3, and hence S is not balanced. On the other hand, S is balanced at v_1 and, in keeping with Theorem 13.3, it is also balanced at v_2.

In some empirical interpretations of a signed digraph, we may be interested only in balance at a particular point. Suppose, for example, that Figure 13.5 represents an affective relation on a set of people as perceived by person v_1. It may turn out that v_1 is sensitive only to the

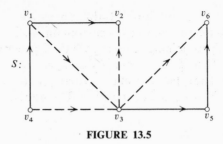

FIGURE 13.5

signs of semicycles that contain him; he is indifferent to the semicycle $v_3v_5v_6v_3$. Here, we would expect the structure to be in a state of equilibrium, even though it is not balanced, since it is locally balanced at v_1.

MEASURES OF STRUCTURAL BALANCE

If two signed digraphs are not balanced, it is natural to ask whether one is more balanced than the other. For such a question to be meaningful, one needs a measure of the amount of balance. We now consider two indexes for structural balance.

Degree of Balance

The degree of balance of a signed digraph, denoted β, is the ratio of the number of positive semicycles b^+ to the total number of semicycles b in the digraph; that is $\beta = b^+/b$. If S has no semicycles, we define $\beta(S) = 1$ and say that S is vacuously balanced. The degree of balance always lies between 0 and 1, and when S is balanced, $\beta = 1$. The greater the value of β, the "more balanced" is S. We may regard β as the probability that a randomly chosen semicycle of S is positive.

Theorem 13.4. Let $B_1, B_2, \ldots, B_k$ be the distinct blocks of a signed digraph S, and let b_i^+ and b_i be the number of positive semicycles and the total number of semicycles in B_i. Then the degree of balance of S is given by

$$\beta = \frac{b_1^+ + b_2^+ + \ldots + b_k^+}{b_1 + b_2 + \ldots + b_k}$$

This theorem is immediate, since the lines of any semicycle all lie within a single block. Clearly, S is balanced if and only if each of its blocks is balanced.

The degree of balance of the signed digraph of Figure 13.6 can be calculated using this theorem. The first (left) block has three semicycles,

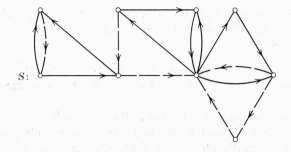

FIGURE 13.6

only one of which is positive; the second has six, all positive; and the third has three negative and three positive semicycles. Therefore,

$$\beta(S) = \frac{1 + 6 + 3}{3 + 6 + 6} = \frac{2}{3}$$

We have already noted that a signed digraph is balanced if and only if $\beta = 1$. We now wish to characterize those that are as unbalanced as possible, that is, those with zero degree of balance. To do this, we first establish the following interesting result.

Theorem 13.5. A signed block with more than one semicycle has a positive semicycle.

It is evident that any block having two semicycles has at least three. We first show that there is a positive semicycle in every signed block with exactly three semicycles. Let S be a signed block with three semi-cycles Z_1, Z_2, and Z_3 such that Z_1 and Z_2 are negative. It is easily verified that in the subgraph generated by $Z_1 \oplus Z_2$, every point has even total degree. By Corollary 12.5a, the lines of $Z_1 \oplus Z_2$ form a collection of semicycles. Since S has only three semicycles and there is at least one line in $Z_1 \oplus Z_2$, the lines of $Z_1 \oplus Z_2$ must form Z_3. There-fore, by Theorem 13.1, Z_3 is positive, so that every signed block with exactly three semicycles has a positive one. But every block with more than three semicycles has a subgraph which is a block with exactly three. This completes the proof of the theorem.

Theorem 13.6. A weak signed digraph S has degree of balance equal to zero if and only if it has a semicycle and every block consists of a negative semicycle or just one line.

First, if S has zero degree of balance, it must have at least one semi-cycle, and all of them must be negative. Thus by Theorem 13.5, no block of S can have more than one semicycle. Conversely, by Theorem 13.4, if no block of S has a positive semicycle and S has at least one semicycle, then $\beta(S) = 0$.

A Drama at the Gaiety Theater. A spectacularly successful play in four scenes was staged at the Gaiety Theater. We give a synopsis of its plot.

Scene 1: Hero discovers that his friend Buddy likes Blackheart whom Hero believes to be a despicable character. As the scene ends, a stranger Goodman encounters Blackheart and displays instant dislike for him.

Commentary: The signed digraph S_1, shown in Figure 13.7, represents the situation at this time. S_1 has two blocks, both of which satisfy Theorem 13.6, and $\beta(S_1) = 0$. Clearly, this is a "bad scene."

Scene 2: As the curtain rises, Hero meets Goodman and finds him to be a most attractive fellow. In a dramatic finale, Hero tries without success to change Buddy's attitude toward Blackheart.

Commentary: The signed digraph S_2 consists of a single block containing three semicycles. It is readily seen that $\beta(S_2) = \frac{1}{3}$. Thus, S_2 is more balanced than S_1, but its degree of balance is still small. It is interesting to note that, in keeping with Theorem 13.5, the addition of either a positive or negative line from Hero to Goodman in S would produce a positive semicycle so that $\beta(S_2) = \frac{1}{3}$.

Scene 3: The principal development of this scene consists of interaction between Goodman and Buddy. By the end of the scene it has become apparent that Goodman cannot tolerate Buddy.

Commentary: We now have S_3, which contains six semicycles, three of which are positive. Hence, $\beta(S_3) = \frac{3}{6}$. The situation has now become more balanced than before, but it is still not balanced.

Scene 4: In the final scene, it develops that Buddy is really the son of Goodman. There follows an emotion-packed episode in which Goodman is reconciled with Buddy who, in turn, renounces Blackheart. Hero's original judgment of Blackheart is justified, and all ends well. The audience streams out into the street exuding a grand peace of mind.

Commentary: The final structure is represented by S_4, which clearly satisfies the criteria of Theorem 13.2. Thus, $\beta(S_4) = 1$. We note that balance was finally attained by changing the signs of two lines.

Line-Index for Balance

The amount of balance in a signed digraph can also be measured by the number of lines that must be removed or whose sign must be changed in order to achieve balance. The *negation* of a collection of lines of a signed digraph is obtained when the sign of each line is changed. It is

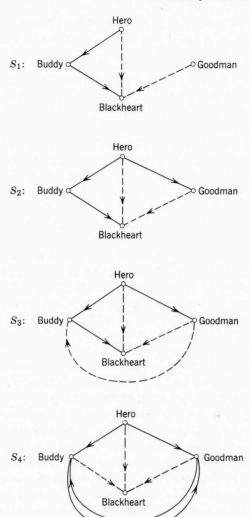

FIGURE 13.7

obvious that any signed digraph has one set of lines whose negation
results in balance, namely the set of all negative lines. A collection Y
of lines is called *negation-minimal* if its negation results in balance, but
the negation of any proper subset of Y does not. In Figure 13.8 we have
a signed digraph S which is not balanced. One negation-minimal
set of lines consists of all three negative lines. The negation of any
proper subset of this collection does not result in balance. However,

there are negation-minimal sets having fewer lines. For example, the negation of x_1 and x_2 produces balance.

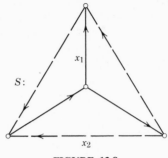

FIGURE 13.8

In an analogous way, we define a *deletion-minimal* set Y of lines of a signed digraph S as a set whose removal leaves a balanced structure, but the removal of any proper subset of Y does not. The next theorem relates the negation-minimal and the deletion-minimal sets of any signed digraph.

Theorem 13.7.   Any deletion-minimal set of lines of a signed digraph is negation-minimal, and conversely.

To prove this theorem, we show first that every deletion-minimal set contains a negation-minimal set, and then that the converse is also true. The first result is proved by induction. Let Y be a deletion-minimal set of lines of S. Obviously if Y is empty, S is balanced, so Y is also negation-minimal. Now suppose Y consists of a single line x. Thus, $D - x$ is balanced whereas D is not. Hence D has a negative semicycle Z_1 containing x. Suppose that D also has a positive semicycle Z_2 containing x. Then one of the semipaths $Z_1 - x$ and $Z_2 - x$ is positive and the other is negative. By Theorem 13.2, it follows that $D - x$ is not balanced. This contradiction shows that x lies in no positive semi-cycle. Since $D - x$ is balanced, every negative semicycle of D contains x. Therefore, the negation of x results in balance, so Y is negation-minimal.

Now as the inductive hypothesis, we assume that for any signed digraph, every deletion-minimal set of n lines contains a negation-minimal set. Let Y be a deletion-minimal set of $n + 1$ lines of S, and let x be any line of Y. Clearly, $S - x$ has $Y - x$ as a deletion-minimal set. Hence by the inductive hypothesis, $Y - x$ contains a negation-minimal set Y_0 of lines for $S - x$. Let S_0 be the signed digraph resulting from S by the negation of the set Y_0. There are two cases to consider. First, if S_0 is balanced, then clearly Y contains a negation-minimal set. Now suppose S_0 is not balanced. Then $S_0 - x$ is balanced, so that x constitutes a deletion-minimal set of one line for S_0. We have already shown that such a set is also negation-minimal. Therefore, the negation of $Y_0 \cup x$ produces balance. Thus, in either case Y contains a negation-minimal set for S. By the principle of induction, every deletion-minimal set contains a negation-minimal one.

For the converse, let Y be a negation-minimal set of lines of S. Thus, every negative semicycle of S contains a line of Y, so that $S - Y$ has no negative semicycles. Hence Y contains a deletion-minimal set.

We have proved that every deletion-minimal set of lines contains a negation-minimal set, which in turn contains a deletion-minimal set. Therefore, every deletion-minimal set is negation-minimal, and conversely.

Figure 13.8 illustrates this theorem. It has been established that lines x_1 and x_2 form a negation-minimal set. Their removal also produces balance. In view of Theorem 13.7, we define, more generally, an *alteration-minimal* set of lines as one which is deletion-minimal or negation-minimal. Thus, in Figure 13.8, $\{x_1, x_2\}$ is an alteration-minimal set. It can readily be verified that the deletion of one of these lines and the negation of the other produces balance. This observation is an illustration of the following corollary.

Corollary 13.7a. Given an alteration-minimal set of lines for a signed digraph, balance is achieved when any subset of these lines is deleted and the remaining lines are negated.

Let Y be an alteration-minimal set for S, and let Y_0 be any subset of Y. The set of lines $Y - Y_0$ is clearly both a deletion-minimal and negation-minimal set for $S - Y_0$. Therefore, the deletion of Y_0 together with the negation of $Y - Y_0$, or the negation of Y_0 together with the deletion of $Y - Y_0$, results in balance, proving the corollary.

Among all alteration-minimal sets of lines for a signed digraph, one with the smallest number of lines is called *alteration-minimum*. By the *line-index* $\lambda(S)$ of a signed digraph S we mean the number of lines in an alteration-minimum set of S. The line-index of S tells us the smallest number of lines that must be altered to attain balance. The lines that must be changed are all contained in an alteration-minimum set. Thus, if a principle of "least cost" governs balancing processes and if the change of each line requires the same amount of cost, then the lines of an alteration-minimum set will be most susceptible to change and $\lambda(S)$

is a measure of the amount of cost required to attain balance.[4] Unfortunately, no simple algorithm is known for finding alteration-minimum sets, but the task is not too difficult in small digraphs.

In discussing the drama at the Gaiety Theater, we noted that $\beta(S_3) = \frac{3}{6}$ and that changing the signs of two lines would produce balance. It can be verified that in Figure 13.7, $\lambda(S_3) = 2$. We might expect that the degree of balance and the line-index are negatively correlated. The two signed digraphs of Figure 13.9 show, however, that these two measures may order digraphs alike. Thus, $\lambda(S_1) = 2$ and $\beta(S_1) = \frac{3}{11}$ whereas $\lambda(S_2) = 3$ and $\beta(S_2) = \frac{4}{11}$.

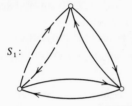   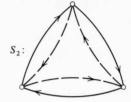

FIGURE 13.9

LIMITED BALANCE

Beyond a certain length, semicycles may be empirically unimportant in so far as balance is concerned. For instance, it may make little difference in an affective structure whether rather long semicycles are negative. A signed digraph S is *N-balanced* if every semicycle of length N or less is positive. In other words, S is N-balanced if every negative semicycle of S has length greater than N. Thus, N-balance may be regarded as limited balance in analogy with limited reachability.

The *adjacency matrix* $A(S)$ *of a signed digraph* S has entries $a_{ij} = 0$ if line $v_i v_j$ is not in S and $a_{ij} = +1$ or -1 if $v_i v_j$ is in S, depending on its sign. In Figure 13.10, we have a signed digraph S and its adjacency matrix $A(S)$.

$$
A(S) = \begin{bmatrix}
0 & 0 & 0 & 0 & +1 \\
-1 & 0 & -1 & 0 & -1 \\
0 & +1 & 0 & +1 & 0 \\
0 & -1 & 0 & 0 & +1 \\
+1 & -1 & 0 & -1 & 0
\end{bmatrix}
$$

FIGURE 13.10

[4] Rosenberg and Abelson have proposed a similar principle. See Rosenberg *et al.* (1960).

It is clear that any two points v_i and v_j may have two lines in common, only one, or none. We say that v_i and v_j are *o-adjacent* if they have no lines in common. Otherwise, they are *p-adjacent* if their common lines are positive, *n-adjacent* if their common lines are negative, and *a-adjacent* (ambivalent) if their common lines have different signs. We see in Figure 13.10 that v_1 and v_3 are *o*-adjacent; v_1 and v_5 are *p*-adjacent, as are v_3 and v_4; v_2 and v_5 are *n*-adjacent, as are v_2 and v_1; and v_2 and v_3 are *a*-adjacent.

The *valency matrix* $B = [b_{ij}]$ of a signed digraph has entries *o, p, n, a* to indicate the type of adjacency between each v_i and v_j. Thus, the valency matrix of a signed digraph S can be formed from its adjacency matrix $A(S)$ as follows:

$$b_{ij} = o \quad \text{if } a_{ij} = a_{ji} = 0$$

$$b_{ij} = p \quad \text{if } a_{ij} + a_{ji} > 0$$

$$b_{ij} = n \quad \text{if } a_{ij} + a_{ji} < 0 \text{ and}$$

$$b_{ij} = a \quad \text{otherwise}$$

It can be seen that the valency matrix $B(S)$ of the signed digraph of Figure 13.10 is:

$$B(S) = \begin{bmatrix} o & n & o & o & p \\ n & o & a & n & n \\ o & a & o & p & o \\ o & n & p & o & a \\ p & n & o & a & o \end{bmatrix}$$

Since $b_{23} = a$, we know that v_2 and v_3 lie on a negative cycle of length 2. Thus, in general a signed digraph is 2-balanced if and only if its valency matrix has no entry $b_{ij} = a$.

Figure 13.11 shows another signed digraph S and its valency matrix B.

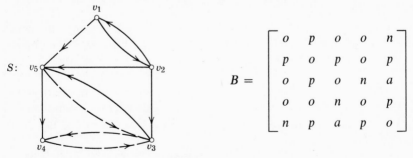

$$B = \begin{bmatrix} o & p & o & o & n \\ p & o & p & o & p \\ o & p & o & n & a \\ o & o & n & o & p \\ n & p & a & p & o \end{bmatrix}$$

FIGURE 13.11

For such a matrix to be of value, we must have rules for working with its elements. The addition and multiplication tables are defined to be the following:

+	o	p	n	a
o	o	p	n	a
p	p	p	a	a
n	n	a	n	a
a	a	a	a	a

·	o	p	n	a
o	o	o	o	o
p	o	p	n	a
n	o	n	p	a
a	o	a	a	a

With this arithmetic, one can perform the various matrix operations on matrices of this type. For example, the square of matrix B of Figure 13.11 is

$$B^2 = \begin{bmatrix} p & n & a & n & p \\ n & p & a & a & a \\ a & a & a & a & a \\ n & a & a & p & a \\ p & a & a & a & a \end{bmatrix}$$

As an illustration, the entry $b_{24}^{(2)}$ is calculated as follows:

$$p \cdot o + o \cdot o + p \cdot n + o \cdot o + p \cdot p = o + o + n + o + p = a$$

The next theorem describes the entries of powers B^k of B, and uses the usual notation $B^k = [b_{ij}^{(k)}]$.

Theorem 13.8. Let S be a signed digraph whose valency matrix is B. Then the entry $b_{ij}^{(k)}$ of B^k is o, p, n, or a in accordance with whether the semisequences of length k joining v_i and v_j are nonexistent, all positive, all negative, or have both signs, respectively.

We shall not prove this theorem, but illustrate it using the signed digraph of Figure 13.11. We have noted that $b_{24}^{(2)} = a$. Thus, by the theorem, there must be at least one positive and at least one negative semiquence joining v_2 and v_4. And we see that this is indeed the case: the path $v_2 v_5 v_4$ is positive whereas both semipaths $v_2 v_3 v_4$ are negative. Also, since $b_{33}^{(2)} = a$, there must be a negative closed semisequence containing v_3, namely the cycle $v_3 v_5 v_3$. Thus this signed digraph is not 2-balanced.

We are now in a position to give a matrix criterion for N-balance.

Theorem 13.9. A signed digraph S is N-balanced if and only if the diagonal entries of each matrix B^k, $k = 1, 2, \ldots, N$ are all o or p.

This result follows directly from the preceding theorem and the fact that if there is a negative closed semisequence of length k, then there is a negative semicycle of length less than or equal to k.

As a result of this theorem, we have a matrix criterion for balance.

Corollary 13.9a. Let N be the length of a longest semicycle of a signed digraph S. Then S is balanced if and only if no matrix B^k, $k = 1, 2, \ldots, N$, has a diagonal entry of n or a.

CYCLE-BALANCE AND PATH-BALANCE

Thus far in discussing balance we have been concerned with the signs of semicycles. We have not distinguished between strict semicycles and cycles. In certain kinds of realizations, however, one may be interested only in cycles.

Consider, for example, the signed digraph shown in Figure 13.12. Here we let the points represent a group of employees of a firm. A positive line $v_i v_j$ means that v_i likes v_j and will tell him the truth; a negative line $v_i v_j$ means that v_i dislikes v_j and will lie to him; and the absence of a line means that v_i is indifferent to v_j and will not communicate to him. Let us assume that v_1 overhears something that

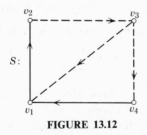

FIGURE 13.12

makes him believe that the firm's president is an alcoholic. He passes this item of gossip to v_2, who informs v_3 that the president definitely is not an alcoholic. Then v_3 tells v_1 and v_4 that he is. Finally, v_4 informs v_1 that the president is a lush. Since the signs of the cycles of S are all positive, v_1 hears from others only the same rumor that he started, thus confirming his original belief. Had one of the cycles been negative, v_1 would not have received such complete confirmation.

A signed digraph is said to be *cycle-balanced* if every cycle is positive. In Figure 13.13, S is cycle-balanced. But since S has a negative semicycle, it is not balanced. If this signed digraph is given the same interpretation as in Figure 13.12, we see that no person will receive disconfirmation of a rumor he starts even though some people will hear conflicting rumors.

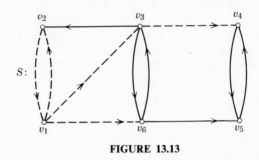

FIGURE 13.13

The following little result will be found useful in the treatment of cycle-balance.

Theorem 13.10. Every negative closed sequence in a signed digraph contains a negative cycle.

Let L be a negative closed sequence. By Theorem 2.7, it contains a cycle Z. If Z is negative, the theorem is verified. If it is positive, delete it from S, thereby obtaining a shorter negative closed sequence. When this process is repeated, we eventually find a negative cycle.

This result enables us to prove the following theorem.

Theorem 13.11. A signed digraph S is cycle-balanced if and only if each strong component of S is balanced.

First, if every strong component of S is balanced, then every cycle is positive, since each cycle lies within a single strong component.

For the converse, let S be cycle-balanced. Suppose that one of its strong components S_1 contains a negative semicycle Z, whose sequence of points and lines is $v_1, x_1, v_2, x_2, \ldots, v_n, x_n, v_1$. In general, depending on the orientation of x_i, sx_i may be v_i or v_{i+1}. Let Y be the set of those lines x such that $sx_i = v_i$. Since each line x_i of Y lies in the strong component S_1, there is a path from sx_i to fx_i. This path has the same sign as the line x_i since together they form a cycle which is positive by hypothesis. Therefore, when each line of Y is replaced by such a path, the result is a negative closed sequence. By Theorem 13.10, S therefore has a negative cycle, which is impossible. This contradiction completes the proof of the theorem.

We note that both of the strong components of Figure 13.13 are balanced and that, in accordance with Theorem 13.11, the entire signed digraph is cycle-balanced.

Corollary 13.11a. A strong signed digraph is balanced if and only if it is cycle-balanced.

This special case of the theorem is useful in testing a strong signed digraph for balance since it shows that it is only necessary to ascertain whether every cycle is positive. The next corollary follows from Theorem 13.11 in the same way that Corollary 13.2a follows from its theorem.

Corollary 13.11b. In a strong digraph, every semicycle is even if and only if every cycle is even.

Let us now consider another feature of the signed digraph of Figure 13.13. Suppose that v_1 tells v_6, contrary to his own belief, that the president is not an alcoholic. As noted above, he will eventually receive a rumor confirming his belief. We see, however, that v_4 will hear two conflicting versions of the rumor started by v_1, one traveling by the path $v_1 v_6 v_3 v_4$ and the other by $v_1 v_6 v_5 v_4$. The first of these is positive, whereas the second is negative.

A signed digraph is *path-balanced* if for every pair of points, all paths from one to the other have the same sign. It is easily seen that the signed digraph of Figure 13.14 is path-balanced. However, the existence of a negative cycle shows that it is not cycle-balanced and, of course, not balanced. If S is interpreted as a rumor network, everyone will hear a single version of any rumor started by v_1, but v_1 will receive only a version disconfirming his own belief.

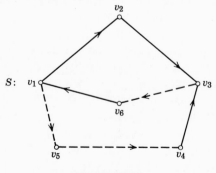

FIGURE 13.14

Since every pair of point-disjoint paths from u to v forms a semicycle, the next theorem shows that path-balance is a special case of balance.

Theorem 13.12.   A signed digraph S is path-balanced if and only if every two point-disjoint paths from one point to another have the same sign.

First, it is obvious that if S is path-balanced, then every two point-disjoint paths from one point to another have the same sign. For the converse, assume that every two point-disjoint paths from one point to another have the same sign. Now suppose that S is not path-balanced, i.e., there are two points u and v and paths of different sign from u to v. Among such pairs of points, take u_0 and v_0 so that $d(u_0, v_0)$ is minimal. Let L_1 and L_2 be paths from u_0 to v_0 so that L_1 has length $d(u_0, v_0)$ and $s(L_1) \neq s(L_2)$. Then L_1 and L_2 must have a third point w in common, since otherwise they are point disjoint and hence have the same sign. Let L_3 and L_4 be the subpaths of L_1 and L_2 from u_0 to w, and let L_5 and L_6 be the subpaths from w to v_0. Thus, $L_1 = L_3 \cup L_5$ and $L_2 = L_4 \cup L_6$. Therefore, either $s(L_3) \neq s(L_4)$ or $s(L_5) \neq s(L_6)$. Since both L_3 and L_5 are shorter than L_1, this contradicts the choice of u_0 and v_0, completing the proof of the theorem.

To recapitulate, we have seen that if a signed digraph is balanced, then it is cycle-balanced and path-balanced. Figures 13.13 and 13.14 show that the converse of this statement is not true in general. They also show that a signed digraph may be cycle-balanced but not path-balanced, and vice versa. Which of these concepts is appropriate for analyzing empirical balancing tendencies will depend upon the nature of the situation.

We have suggested that for certain purposes we may be primarily interested in whether a signed digraph S is locally balanced at a point v and whether S is N-balanced. In the first case, we are concerned only with semicycles containing v; in the second, only with semicycles in S of length N or less. Clearly the concepts of balance, local balance, N-balance, cycle-balance, and path-balance can be combined in various ways. Thus, for example, we can say that S is N-*balanced at point* v if all semicycles of length N or less containing v are positive. We leave to the reader the interesting occupation of forming other combinations of concepts of balance.

SUMMARY

In this chapter, we have concentrated on various kinds of balance in signed digraphs. Criteria for balance and its different special cases were developed. In the first section, three criteria for balance were presented. The first is definitional: every semicycle is positive. The second criterion concerns semipaths: for every pair of points, all semipaths joining them have the same sign. The third, or "partition" criterion, states that the set of points of the signed digraph can be partitioned into two sets such that each negative line and no positive line joins two points of different sets.

We then considered a special case of balance, that is, local balance at a point v, which means that every semicycle containing the distinguished point v is positive. It was shown that if a signed digraph is locally balanced at a point v, then every block containing v is balanced. This result simplifies certain of the previously developed criteria for balance. For instance, if S is a block, then we need only verify that all semicycles through any one point are positive.

Two measures for the amount of balance in a signed digraph were then studied. The degree of balance is the proportion of positive semicycles, whereas the line index is the minimum number of lines whose alteration balances the signed digraph. Each of these measures has its particular advantages and disadvantages.

In the study of limited balance, that is, the case in which all semicycles of length N or less are positive, we developed a matrix criterion, using the valency matrix $B(S)$. A signed digraph S is N-balanced if $b_{ii}^{(k)} = o$ or p, for all $k \le N$. A signed digraph whose longest semicycle has length N is then balanced if it is N-balanced.

We then examined the special case, cycle-balance, meaning that every cycle is positive. It was found that a strong signed digraph is cycle-balanced if and only if it is balanced. Therefore, we have another criterion for balance in strong signed digraphs: every cycle is positive.

Finally, we dwelt briefly on another special case: path-balance. Here, for every pair of points, all paths from one point to another have the same sign. This is similar to the semipath criterion for balance.

In a manner of speaking, one could say that signed digraphs form an extension of digraphs. In the next chapter, we shall consider other extensions of digraph theory.

EXERCISES

1. Consider the signed digraph S in Figure 13.15. (a) Is S balanced? (b) What is its degree of balance? (c) What is the smallest value of N for which S is N-balanced? (d) Is S cycle-balanced? (e) Is S path-balanced? (f) At which points is S locally balanced? (g) What is the line-index for S? (h) Identify all alteration-minimal sets in S.

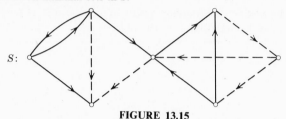

S:

FIGURE 13.15

2. Construct a signed digraph S such that S is 3-balanced but not 4-balanced.

3. Consider the following adjacency matrix of a signed digraph S.

$$A(S) = \begin{bmatrix} 0 & -1 & 0 & 0 & 0 & -1 \\ 0 & 0 & +1 & 0 & 0 & +1 \\ 0 & 0 & 0 & -1 & -1 & 0 \\ 0 & 0 & 0 & 0 & 0 & 0 \\ 0 & 0 & 0 & +1 & 0 & 0 \\ 0 & 0 & 0 & 0 & +1 & 0 \end{bmatrix}$$

(a) Draw S and ascertain whether it is balanced. (b) What are the values of N such that S is N-balanced? (c) For what values of N is S N-path-balanced? (d) Is S cycle-balanced? (e) What is the degree of balance of S? (f) What is its line-index?

4. Imitating Theorem 13.2, find criteria for local balance.

5. By making the digraph in Figure 13.16 into a signed digraph, disprove the following statement: If every negative cycle of a strong signed digraph has length greater than N, then S is N-balanced.

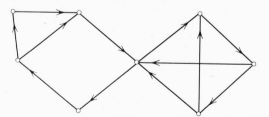

FIGURE 13.16

6. Let A be the adjacency matrix of a signed digraph S, and let the matrix $P(S)$ be obtained from A by replacing each $+1$ by p, each -1 by n, and each 0 by o. Use the appropriate arithmetic to prove that $B = P + P'$, where B is the valency matrix.

7. Formulate results for sequences and N-cycle-balance similar to Theorem 13.9 using the matrix P of Exercise 6.

8. Determine using matrices for what values of N a structure with the following valency matrix is N-balanced.

$$
B = \begin{bmatrix}
o & n & o & n & n \\
n & o & p & o & p \\
o & p & o & n & o \\
n & o & n & o & p \\
n & p & o & p & o
\end{bmatrix}
$$

Verify this by constructing a signed digraph with this valency matrix.

9. Construct a signed digraph which is path-balanced but has both positive and negative sequences from one point to another.

10. Prove or disprove: S is 2-balanced if and only if $B(S)$ has no entry of a.

11. Prove or disprove: If S is weak and the subgraph generated by its positive lines is disconnected, then S is balanced.

12. Prove: If S is a weak balanced signed digraph, the partition of Theorem 13.2 is unique.

13. Let the point-index of a signed digraph S be defined as the minimum number of points whose removal makes S balanced. Prove: The point-index of S is never greater than the line-index.

14 · Networks

And finds, with keen, discriminating sight,
Black's not so black;—nor white so *very* white.

GEORGE CANNING
New Morality

In the first twelve chapters of this book, we have developed the elements of a formal theory of digraphs. It will be recalled from Chapter 1 that the axiom system for digraphs permits no loops and no parallel lines. Although these restrictions have the positive advantage of allowing us to concentrate on strictly structural issues, they also impose severe limitations upon the properties of empirical systems which can be represented by means of digraphs. In a digraph, a line uv is either present or absent. But as we saw in Chapter 13, it is sometimes useful to be able to distinguish between positive and negative lines, and we showed how digraph theory can be extended to encompass signed digraphs.

In this chapter, we consider other useful ways in which digraph theory may be extended. First, we relax the requirement that there be no loops, permitting us to give a natural representation of such relationships as self-evaluation. Then, by assigning "values" to lines we provide a basis for distinguishing between lines which represent relationships of different strength or type. We are thereby able to deal with such varying factors as the intensity of affection, the frequency of communication, the probability that one event follows another, or the cost of transportation, and to handle in one representation combinations of different kinds of empirical relations.

This extension of digraph theory leads to the study of abstract systems called networks. We begin by discussing certain properties of networks that are analogous to those of digraphs considered in preceding chapters.

We then indicate how matrices can be associated with networks in a manner similar to that for digraphs. Next, we show that a markov chain is a special case of a network, and provide a brief discussion relating concepts of digraph theory to those in the theory of markov chains. Finally, we describe certain ways in which costs and flow can be treated by means of networks. Since a complete study of networks would require a book in itself, our purpose in this chapter is merely to indicate the nature of this extension of digraph theory and to provide references for further study.

NETWORKS

A *network* consists of a relation on a finite set V of points, with its set of lines denoted as usual by X, but also including a "value" assigned to each line. If this value is always 1, we still have a relation. Thus, relations form a special class of networks. If the set of values consists of $+1$ and -1, then we have a signed relation. And if this relation is irreflexive, we have a signed digraph, as studied in the preceding chapter.

Many different kinds of "values" may be assigned to the lines of a network, and we shall consider here only a few of the more important possibilities. Although we shall deal primarily with numerical values, nonnumerical ones are also permitted.

Let us look first at a network with a nonnumerical set of values. Consider a finite set $S = \{a, b, c\}$, where each element of S stands for one of three different relations on a set V of points. We may then construct a network N on the set V in the following way. There is a line uv in N if and only if (u, v) is in at least one of the relations. The value assigned to line uv is a subset of S, indicating the relations in which (u, v) is found. Thus, for example, the assignment of $\{a, b\}$ to line uv would mean that this line is in the first two of these relations but not in the third.

To illustrate this value system, members of a small group might be asked to indicate from their group membership their first choices for work companion, leisure-time companion, and group leader. Digraphs for each of these kinds of sociometric choice are shown for a hypothetical example in Figure 14.1.

To see how the choices based on these three criteria are related to one another, it is convenient to portray the information as a network. We first form the union of the three digraphs of Figure 14.1, and then to the lines we assign as values some subset of the letters a, b, c, according to the digraphs of Figure 14.1 from which they arise. In Figure 14.2 is shown the network N which contains all of this information. Sometimes

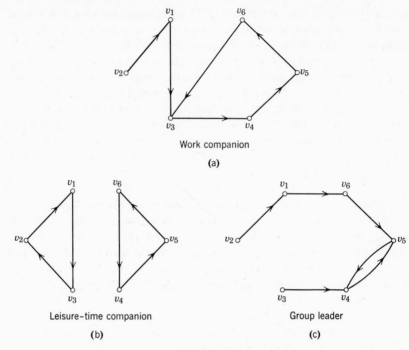

Work companion

(a)

Leisure-time companion

(b)

Group leader

(c)

FIGURE 14.1

the number of relations so depicted in one network is called the *type* of the network; here N is a network of type 3.

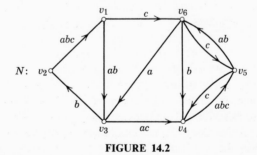

FIGURE 14.2

For many purposes, it is convenient to use the set of positive integers, or some subset of them, for assigning values to the lines of a network. As an example, consider a sociometric questionnaire in which each respondent indicates his three best friends in rank order. In the network of choices for a group of people, there is a line uv whenever person u

chooses person v. The set $S = \{1, 2, 3\}$ serves as a value system for the network, if we assign one of these integers to each line so as to indicate the rank of the corresponding choice.

The frequency with which certain events occur may also be represented by a network whose value system is a set of positive integers. Suppose that a car-rental company has three stations and allows a customer to rent a car at any station and return it to any. For each rental, we may think of a car as "going" from the station of rental to the station of return. The record of rentals, for a given period of time, may be represented by a network N with three points which correspond to the three stations. There is a line uv in N if and only if at least one rental goes from station u to station v, and the value assigned to line uv indicates the number of such rentals. Since a car may be returned to the station at which it was rented, this network may contain loops. Such a network is shown in Figure 14.3. When the value system of a network N is a set of positive integers, the *strength* of N is the maximum value on its lines; here N is a network of strength 30.

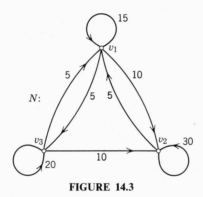

FIGURE 14.3

Many of the concepts of digraph theory can be modified so that they apply to networks. We shall not, of course, be able here to present all such modifications, but from the definitions and examples given, the general procedure should be clear. Each modification is a generalization in the sense that if 1 is the only value available, then the new concepts are identical with the corresponding ones for digraphs. However, a word of caution should be added: The formation of many concepts of digraph theory involves some arithmetical operation on other concepts. For example, the length of a path is the number of lines in it or, equivalently, the sum of the values of its lines. In extending concepts of digraph theory to networks, one must be careful to use an operation appropriate to the value system for the network and to the interpretation envisaged.

Let N be a network with points $v_1, v_2, \ldots, v_p$ and a numerical value system. The *outdegree value* of v_i in N is the sum of the values on the lines from v_i; the *indegree value* is the directional dual. In Figure 14.3 the outdegree values of v_1, v_2, v_3 are 30, 35, 35, respectively, and the indegree values are 25, 50, 25. Clearly, the sum of the outdegree values for all points of N and the sum of the indegree values are both equal to the sum of the values of all the lines (cf., Theorem 1.1). In the example, this sum is 100, indicating that there were 100 rentals during the period under consideration.

The frequencies represented by a network can be normalized in two meaningful ways. If the value of line uv is divided by the sum of the values of all lines of N, the obtained value is the probability that an event taken at random from N is of the form (u, v). Thus, in the example of Figure 14.3, the probability that a car is rented at station 1 and returned to station 2 is 0.10.

A second way of normalizing consists of dividing the value of each line uv by the outdegree value of u. The resulting value also represents a probability, namely the proportion of all events starting at u that go to v. In Figure 14.3, we see that of all cars rented at station 1, $\frac{1}{2}$ are returned to station 1, $\frac{1}{3}$ are returned to station 2, and $\frac{1}{6}$ are returned to station 3. It is clear that probabilities can be assigned in this way to all lines of a network. The resulting network illustrates a markov chain, a topic to be considered later.

A very useful interpretation of numerical values of a network, which sounds more special than it is, arises when we consider the value of each line as a "cost" of some sort. This cost may be measured in any of several empirically meaningful ways, such as the cost in money, time, or effort. As an example, the points of a network might represent cities with each line standing for the existence of a transportation facility going directly from one city to another. Depending on the terrain, there might be three different modes of transportation: rail, truck, or air. Then the value assigned to each line gives the cost per unit weight of shipping something from the first point of the line to the second. Such a network is given in Figure 14.4.

The *cost length* of a path is the sum of the cost values of its lines. In the network of Figure 14.4, the cost length of the path $v_3v_4v_2v_1$ is 12, and that of $v_3v_4v_1$ is 15. A *cost geodesic* from u to v is a path from u to v whose cost length is minimum. The *cost distance* from u to v is the cost length of a cost geodesic from u to v. It can be verified that the cost distance from v_3 to v_1 is 12, whereas that from v_1 to v_3 is 17. The reader will find it useful to ascertain the other cost distances in this network.

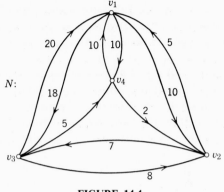

FIGURE 14.4

We have seen that distance is used in the definition of many concepts of digraph theory. It is a relatively straightforward matter to extend these to networks having cost values. Each of the concepts involving reachability within a given distance, discussed in Chapter 6, can be extended immediately to ones referring to reachability within a given cost distance. There should be no difficulty in defining the cost out-number of a point, its cost innumber, and related concepts referring to cost radii and cost centers, and so on.

THE MATRIX OF A NETWORK

With any network N, whose points are $v_1, v_2, \ldots, v_p$, we may associate a matrix M whose role is analogous with that of the adjacency matrix of a digraph. The matrix $M = [m_{ij}]$ has $m_{ij} = 0$ if the line v_iv_j does not appear in N; otherwise m_{ij} is the value of the line v_iv_j. For brevity we shall simply refer to M as the *value matrix* of N. Of course, nonzero entries are permitted on the diagonal of M since a network may contain loops.

As a first example of a network N and its value matrix M, let us consider a network whose value system is the set $S = \{+1, -1, \pm 1\}$. Such a network differs from the signed digraphs discussed in the preceding chapter in that the value ± 1 is now permitted. Here, a line uv indicates that person u has some evaluative feeling for v, and the values $+1 \ -1, \ \pm 1$, mean respectively that the feeling is positive, negative, or both, that is, ambivalent. We assume that a person can have evaluative feelings directed toward himself.

We now show how such a network may be derived from two opposite underlying relations on the same set of people. The relation R^+ shown in Figure 14.5 contains all positive relationships, and the relation R^- contains all negative ones. The network N is obtained from these in the following manner. There is a line uv in N if and only if there is a line uv in R^+ or R^-. The value of a line uv in N is $+1$ if uv is in R^+ only, it is -1 if it is in R^- only, and it is ±1 if it is in both. The value matrix M may be constructed immediately from N, with the result shown in Figure 14.5. Of course, if we are given a square matrix M with appropriate values, we can draw a corresponding network N and then break N down into its underlying positive and negative relations.

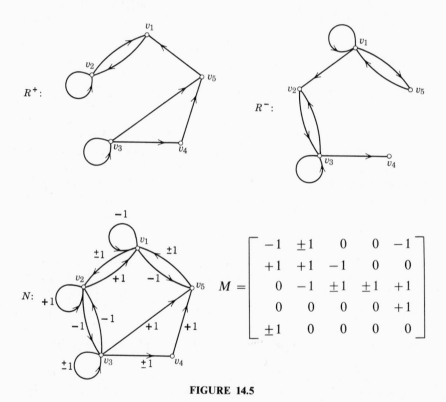

FIGURE 14.5

Another example of a network and its value matrix is provided by Berger and Snell (1957). They consider annual population movements in a hypothetical system consisting of three cities. Migration data are available showing for each city the number of people who move to each other city and the number who do not move away from the city. These data are presented in the value matrix shown in Figure 14.6. It is evident that the row sums give the population of each city at the beginning of the year, whereas the column sums indicate their populations one year later. The value in each cell gives the value of the corresponding line of the network shown in Figure 14.6.

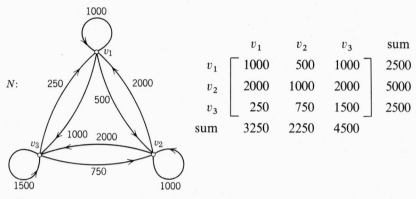

$$\begin{array}{ccccc}
 & v_1 & v_2 & v_3 & \text{sum} \\
v_1 & \begin{bmatrix} 1000 & 500 & 1000 \\ 2000 & 1000 & 2000 \\ 250 & 750 & 1500 \end{bmatrix} & & & \begin{matrix} 2500 \\ 5000 \\ 2500 \end{matrix} \\
\text{sum} & 3250 & 2250 & 4500 &
\end{array}$$

FIGURE 14.6

For many purposes, it is more convenient to normalize data of this sort and to form a new value matrix M in which the i, j entry gives the proportion of the initial population of city v_i which moves to city v_j during the year. The normalized data of Figure 14.6 are presented in Figure 14.7. Each row sum of this new matrix is, of course, 1.

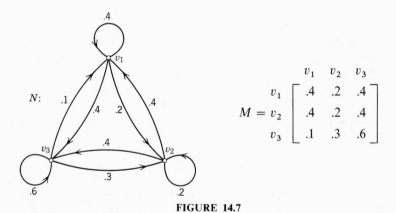

$$M = \begin{array}{c} v_1 \\ v_2 \\ v_3 \end{array}\begin{array}{ccc} v_1 & v_2 & v_3 \\ \begin{bmatrix} .4 & .2 & .4 \\ .4 & .2 & .4 \\ .1 & .3 & .6 \end{bmatrix} \end{array}$$

FIGURE 14.7

By a *probability matrix* we mean a square matrix in which there are no negative entries and the sum of the entries of every row is 1. Clearly, the matrix of Figure 14.7 is a probability matrix. The next theorem and corollary give an important property of probability matrices.

Theorem 14.1. If B and C are probability matrices, so is their product BC.

To prove this assertion, let $B = [b_{ij}]$ and $C = [c_{ij}]$. Then the i,j entry of the product BC is $\sum_{k=1}^{p} b_{ik}c_{kj}$. Therefore, the sum of the entries in the ith row of BC is

$$\sum_{j=1}^{p} \sum_{k=1}^{p} b_{ik}c_{kj}$$

Now $\sum_{j=1}^{p} \sum_{k=1}^{p} b_{ik}c_{kj} = \sum_{k=1}^{p} \sum_{j=1}^{p} b_{ik}c_{kj} = \sum_{k=1}^{p} b_{ik} \sum_{j=1}^{p} c_{kj} = \sum_{k=1}^{p} b_{ik} \cdot 1 = 1.$

The last two steps follow since B and C are probability matrices. Thus, BC is a probability matrix, as was to be shown.

The next corollary follows immediately and will not be proved.

Corollary 14.1a. If M is a probability matrix, then so is every power M^n, for any positive integer n.

Since the value matrix M shown in Figure 14.7 is a probability matrix, it follows from Theorem 14.1 that M^2 is also a probability matrix. This conclusion is verified by the square of M shown below.

$$M^2 = \begin{bmatrix} .28 & .24 & .48 \\ .28 & .24 & .48 \\ .22 & .26 & .52 \end{bmatrix}$$

The significance of Theorem 14.1 and its corollary will be discussed further in the next section. First, however, we show one use of these matrices in terms of the migration data considered above. A $1 \times n$ matrix is called a *vector of length n*. Let us represent the populations of the three cities at time t_i by a vector $P_i = [p_{i1}\ p_{i2}\ p_{i3}]$, where p_{ij} is the population of v_j at t_i. In accordance with the row sums given in Figure 14.6, we have

$$P_0 = [2500 \quad 5000 \quad 2500]$$

Now if we form the product of P_0 and the probability matrix $M(N)$ shown in Figure 14.7, we obtain a vector P_1 which gives the populations of the three cities after one year. The calculation $P_0M = P_1$ is as follows:

$$[2500 \quad 5000 \quad 2500] \cdot \begin{bmatrix} .4 & .2 & .4 \\ .4 & .2 & .4 \\ .1 & .3 & .6 \end{bmatrix} = [3250 \quad 2250 \quad 4500]$$

It can be seen that P_1 corresponds to the column sums shown in Figure 14.6, which as we saw above are the city populations after one year.

If we assume that the probability matrix M remains constant over time, then clearly we can form the product P_1M to obtain P_2, the distribution of population after two years. Since $P_2 = P_1M$ and $P_1 = P_0M$, it follows that $P_2 = P_0M^2$. The reader should verify for himself that $P_0M^2 = P_1M = P_2 = [2650 \quad 2450 \quad 4900]$. In general, the population matrix P_n, $n > 0$, is the product P_0M^n. Thus, if we know the initial population matrix P_0 and the probability matrix M, we can find the distribution at any subsequent time t_n by finding the nth power of M and then forming the product P_0M^n.

MARKOV CHAINS

A *markov chain*[1], or more briefly, a *chain*, is a network in which the value of each line is a positive number, and the outdegree value of each point is exactly 1. The value matrix of a chain, called its *transition matrix*, is clearly a probability matrix. The points of a chain are usually called states. The value of a line x is regarded as the conditional probability that if the state of a process represented by the chain is fx, then the next state will be sx. We have already encountered a chain in this chapter, for the network of Figure 14.7 satisfies the definition of a chain: Here the state v_i means "residing in city v_i" and the value of a line v_iv_j indicates the probability that a person residing in city v_i at the beginning of the year will reside in city v_j one year later.[2]

---

[1] Actually, we are dealing here with discrete stationary markov chains. As customarily conceived, such a chain represents some process which moves from one state to another through time (not continuous, but in discrete steps). The chain consists of a collection of states, which in our case is finite. At any time, each state has an assigned value indicating the probability that the process is in that state at that time. For each time and each pair of states v_i and v_j, there is also a probability that the process next goes to state v_j given that it is in state v_i, independent of the sequence used in reaching v_i. If these transition probabilities are the same at all times, we have a stationary markov chain.

The theory was initiated by A. A. Markov in his basic study of sequences of events with a given distribution of initial probabilities, which have the simple property that the probability of the next event in a successive sequence of trials depends on the present event and *not* on any of the preceding events. This property must be kept in mind when considering possible applications of chains. For a further discussion of chains, see Kemeny and Snell (1960) or Feller (1957).

[2] The functional digraphs discussed in Chapter 12 may also be regarded as chains by assigning to each line the value 1. Since every point of such a network has exactly one line going from it, this is an example of a "rendezvous with destiny." Once the initial state of a process is known, its state at any subsequent time can be calculated with complete certainty.

Applications of chains have been made to surprisingly diverse areas: learning theory, beginning with Estes (1950) and Bush and Mosteller (1955); information theory, Shannon (1948); changes in attitudes, Anderson (1954); labor and social mobility, Blumen, Kogan, and McCarthy (1955), and Berger and Snell (1957); epidemiology of mental disease, Marshall and Goldhammer (1955); brand loyalty and brand switching, Lipstein (1959), and Harary and Lipstein (1962); and many others.[3] It is our purpose here to provide only a brief introduction to the ideas of chains, emphasizing the role of the underlying digraphs.

To illustrate chains, we describe the "gambler's ruin," that is, two boys matching pennies. This situation is represented by the chain shown in Figure 14.8. The state v_i indicates that one of these two boys, hereafter known as "our hero," has i cents. We assume in this example that the total wealth of the two boys is 5 cents. The transition rules are given in the figure. Thus, for example, if our hero at any time has 2 cents, he is in state v_2. If he wins the toss (an alternative with probability $\frac{1}{2}$), he then proceeds to state v_3; and if he loses (also probability $\frac{1}{2}$), he goes to v_1. The only line from v_0 is a loop. Therefore, if he arrives at v_0 he has lost his fortune; he must stay in this state, and he has painfully learned why the game is known as "gambler's ruin." Another possible outcome is state v_5 which represents our hero as victor, and he has yet to see the error of his ways.

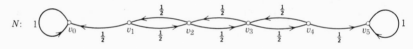

FIGURE 14.8

Let us now consider the transition matrix M of a chain. The entry m_{ij} is the probability of going from v_i to v_j in one step. Since the successive steps of a chain do not depend on previous steps, they are independent, and the product $m_{ik}m_{kj}$ can be interpreted as the probability that the process moves from v_i to v_k at one step and then in the next goes from v_k to v_j. In general, the probability of going from v_1 to v_n along a sequence $L = v_1v_2v_3 \ldots v_n$ in a chain is the product $m_{12}m_{23} \ldots m_{n-1,n}$ of the probabilities of the lines in L. Now, the probability of going from v_i to v_j in exactly n steps is the sum of the probabilities of going from v_i to v_j

[3] For further discussion of applications of chains, see Harary (1959a), Kemeny and Snell (1962), Berger, et al. (1962), and Luce, Bush, and Galanter (1963). Most applications have used only stationary markov chains, and some of these have been criticized, because in the process they describe the transition probabilities change with time. However, in spite of much effort, nonstationary chains remain mathematically intractable.

along all sequences of length n in the chain. This sum is given by the i, j entry of the matrix M^n and is between 0 and 1, in accordance with Corollary 14.1a. By the nth *transition probability* from v_i to v_j in a chain is meant the probability of going from v_i to v_j in exactly n steps. When we collect these observations, we have the following result. This theorem is the analogue for chains of Theorem 5.1, which gives the meaning for a digraph of the powers of its adjacency matrix.

Theorem 14.2. Let M be the transition matrix of a given chain. Then in M^n the i, j entry is the nth transition probability from v_i to v_j.

To illustrate this theorem, we return to the chain of the "gambler's ruin" shown in Figure 14.8. Its transition matrix M is as follows:

$$M = \begin{bmatrix} 1 & 0 & 0 & 0 & 0 & 0 \\ \frac{1}{2} & 0 & \frac{1}{2} & 0 & 0 & 0 \\ 0 & \frac{1}{2} & 0 & \frac{1}{2} & 0 & 0 \\ 0 & 0 & \frac{1}{2} & 0 & \frac{1}{2} & 0 \\ 0 & 0 & 0 & \frac{1}{2} & 0 & \frac{1}{2} \\ 0 & 0 & 0 & 0 & 0 & 1 \end{bmatrix}$$

Upon raising this matrix to its powers M^2 and M^3, we obtain the following results:

$$M^2 = \begin{bmatrix} 1 & 0 & 0 & 0 & 0 & 0 \\ \frac{1}{2} & \frac{1}{4} & 0 & \frac{1}{4} & 0 & 0 \\ \frac{1}{4} & 0 & \frac{1}{2} & 0 & \frac{1}{4} & 0 \\ 0 & \frac{1}{4} & 0 & \frac{1}{2} & 0 & \frac{1}{4} \\ 0 & 0 & \frac{1}{4} & 0 & \frac{1}{4} & \frac{1}{2} \\ 0 & 0 & 0 & 0 & 0 & 1 \end{bmatrix}$$

$$M^3 = \begin{bmatrix} 1 & 0 & 0 & 0 & 0 & 0 \\ \frac{5}{8} & 0 & \frac{1}{4} & 0 & \frac{1}{8} & 0 \\ \frac{1}{4} & \frac{1}{4} & 0 & \frac{3}{8} & 0 & \frac{1}{8} \\ \frac{1}{8} & 0 & \frac{3}{8} & 0 & \frac{1}{4} & \frac{1}{4} \\ 0 & \frac{1}{8} & 0 & \frac{1}{4} & 0 & \frac{5}{8} \\ 0 & 0 & 0 & 0 & 0 & 1 \end{bmatrix}$$

The i, j entry of M^3 is the probability of going from v_i to v_j in exactly 3 steps. Thus, if our hero starts his venture with 4 cents, the probabilities that after three tosses he will have 0, 1, 2, 3, 4, or 5 cents are given by the entries of the row of M^3 corresponding to v_4, that is,

$$(0, \tfrac{1}{8}, 0, \tfrac{1}{4}, 0, \tfrac{5}{8})$$

Clearly, there is only one sequence of length 3 from v_4 to v_1, namely $L = v_4 v_3 v_2 v_1$, whose probability is $\tfrac{1}{2} \cdot \tfrac{1}{2} \cdot \tfrac{1}{2} = \tfrac{1}{8}$. On the other hand, there are two such sequences from v_4 to v_3: $L = v_4 v_3 v_4 v_3$ and $L = v_4 v_3 v_2 v_3$. Since the probability of each sequence is $\tfrac{1}{8}$, the probability of going from v_4 to v_3 in exactly 3 steps is $\tfrac{1}{4}$.

Depending on the structure of a network which defines a chain, various properties of the chain can be determined which are independent of the magnitudes of the probabilities assigned to its lines. For example, in Figure 14.8 the points v_0 and v_5 are receivers, and are the only such points. The only possible outcomes of the chain are these two states. An *absorbing state* of a chain is a receiver of its network. An *absorbing chain* has an absorbing state and all such states form the unique point contrabasis. An *ergodic chain* is a strong chain. Of course not every chain is absorbing or ergodic.

We consider a particularly interesting type of ergodic chain. A *regular chain* has some power n of its transition matrix M positive, that is, M^n has no zero entries. Interpreted graphically, this means that for any two points v_i and v_j in the network, there is a sequence from v_i to v_j of length n. The underlying digraph of a regular chain is therefore strong, and so regular chains are ergodic. But not every ergodic chain is regular. The chain consisting of a single cycle is ergodic but not regular. For example, in Figure 14.9 we show the first three powers of the transition matrix of a cyclic triple. Since $M^3 = I$, we find $M^4 = M$, $M^5 = M^2$,

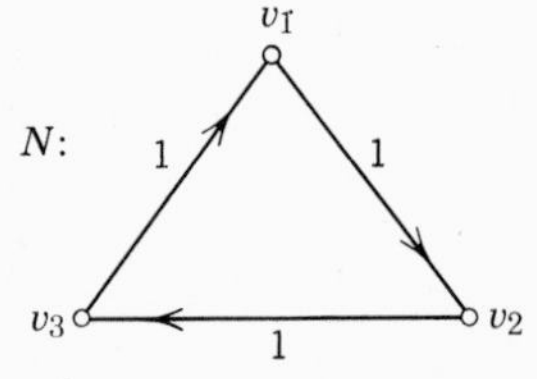

$$M = \begin{bmatrix} 0 & 1 & 0 \\ 0 & 0 & 1 \\ 1 & 0 & 0 \end{bmatrix} \quad M^2 = \begin{bmatrix} 0 & 0 & 1 \\ 1 & 0 & 0 \\ 0 & 1 & 0 \end{bmatrix} \quad M^3 = \begin{bmatrix} 1 & 0 & 0 \\ 0 & 1 & 0 \\ 0 & 0 & 1 \end{bmatrix}$$

FIGURE 14.9

and every power of M is one of M, M^2, or I. Thus, no power of M has all positive entries, and this ergodic chain is not regular.

To illustrate a regular chain, let us consider a hypothetical example involving the purchasing behavior of the consumers of some product. Assuming that we have sufficient information, we can construct a "brand chain" whose states represent the purchase of a brand of the product and whose transition probabilities are the relative frequency of consumers shifting from one brand to another on successive purchases. The value of the loop at each point indicates the degree of "brand loyalty," or the proportion of those purchasing a brand who buy it again next time. Automobiles and cosmetics afford examples of products for which there have been found high and low brand loyalties respectively.

Suppose that the brand chain for five brands of some product has the following transition matrix:

$$
M = \begin{bmatrix}
\frac{1}{2} & \frac{1}{12} & \frac{1}{12} & 0 & \frac{1}{3} \\
0 & \frac{2}{3} & 0 & 0 & \frac{1}{3} \\
\frac{1}{12} & \frac{1}{12} & \frac{1}{2} & 0 & \frac{1}{3} \\
\frac{1}{4} & \frac{1}{4} & \frac{1}{4} & \frac{1}{4} & 0 \\
\frac{1}{6} & 0 & 0 & \frac{1}{2} & \frac{1}{3}
\end{bmatrix}
$$

To discover whether this chain is regular, we raise M to higher powers. The result for M^3 and M^8 is given below.

$$
M^3 = \begin{bmatrix}
.260 & .144 & .109 & .208 & .277 \\
.125 & .342 & .046 & .208 & .277 \\
.188 & .141 & .182 & .208 & .277 \\
.179 & .231 & .137 & .140 & .312 \\
.244 & .199 & .164 & .156 & .236
\end{bmatrix}
$$

$$
M^8 = \begin{bmatrix}
.205 & .214 & .126 & .182 & .273 \\
.198 & .227 & .120 & .182 & .273 \\
.204 & .214 & .127 & .182 & .273 \\
.202 & .219 & .125 & .181 & .273 \\
.204 & .216 & .126 & .182 & .272
\end{bmatrix}
$$

Since M^3 is positive, we find that the chain is regular. Upon examining these matrices, we also see a tendency for the rows to become much alike.

This is not special to our example, but reflects a property of regular chains.

This property is specified in Theorem 14.3, but before stating it we need a preliminary definition. A *probability vector* $P = [p_1 p_2 \ldots p_s]$ has nonnegative entries and the sum of its entries is 1. When s equals the number of points in a chain, a probability vector may be used to indicate the likelihood that each point is the first state to occur in the chain. In this case it is known as the *initial probability vector* of the chain.

Theorem 14.3. For a regular chain, the powers of its transition matrix M approach a limit. This limit matrix has all rows alike, and each is equal to the unique probability vector P for which $PM = P$.

This theorem tells us that the rows of M^n are nearly alike when n is large. Since by Theorem 14.2 the i, j entry of M^n is the nth transition probability from v_i to v_j, the approximate equality of the rows of M^n means that the probability that the process is in a given state v_j after n steps is nearly independent of the beginning state. Thus, in our example the distribution of purchases after a large number of steps is nearly independent of the initial distribution, as seen in M^8 above.

Theorem 14.3 also states that the rows of the limit matrix, and hence the "final" distribution of purchases, are given by the probability vector for which $PM = P$. Since we know M, we can find the limit matrix by solving $PM = P$ for P. We know that $P = [p_1 p_2 \ldots p_s]$ and that M is an $s \times s$ matrix. Therefore, we have the following equations:

$$p_1 m_{11} + p_2 m_{21} + \ldots + p_s m_{s1} = p_1$$

$$p_1 m_{12} + p_2 m_{22} + \ldots + p_s m_{s2} = p_2$$

$$\vdots$$

$$p_1 m_{1s} + p_2 m_{2s} + \ldots + p_s m_{ss} = p_s$$

and since P is a probability vector, we have

$$p_1 + p_2 + \ldots + p_s = 1$$

This last equation, together with any $s - 1$ of the preceding ones, gives us a system of s equations with s unknowns. By solving these simultaneously, we obtain the values of P.

If we apply this procedure to the transition matrix M of our regular brand chain, we obtain $P = [.203 \quad .218 \quad .125 \quad .182 \quad .273]$, which is seen to be approximately the same as each row of M^8. In general, then, if we know the transition matrix of a regular brand chain, we can predict the "final" distribution of purchases simply by calculating P. Whenever a system of purchases corresponds to a regular brand chain, it will approach a steady distribution which is given by P and is nearly independent of the initial distribution of purchases.

Corollary 14.3a shows that additional information may be obtained from the probability vector P of Theorem 14.3.

Corollary 14.3a. For a regular chain with s states, matrix M, and probability vector P such that $PM = P$, the mean number of steps from an occurrence of state v_i to the next occurrence of this state is $1/p_i$.

From the fixed vector P of the brand chain given above, we see that the average number of steps between two consecutive purchases of the third brand is $1/.125 = 8$.

We now turn briefly to absorbing chains. Certain statistical information can readily be obtained for these chains, since an absorbing chain has the special property that all its absorbing states constitute its unique point contrabasis. For example, answers can be given to the following questions, worded in terms of the gambler's ruin. What is the probability that our hero will be ruined? How many times will he have a certain sum before the game ends? How long can the game be expected to last?

These questions can be answered by matrix methods that begin by finding the inverse of the submatrix of M determined by nonabsorbing states. We can find (a) the probability that an absorbing chain in a given state will end in a specified absorbing state, (b) the mean number of times before absorption that it will be in a particular nonabsorbing state, given its initial state, and (c) the mean number of steps to absorption from a given nonabsorbing state. For further information about absorbing and other markov chains consult the absorbing book of Kemeny and Snell (1960).

COST GEODESICS

We turn now to consideration of a network N in which the value of each line x is interpreted as the cost of going from fx to sx via x. We restrict our attention to irreflexive networks. In the *cost matrix* C of N, the diagonal entries c_{ii} are 0, the entry c_{ij} is ∞ if there is no line $v_i v_j$, and c_{ij} is the cost value of line $v_i v_j$ when this line is in N. Figure 14.10 shows a network N and its cost matrix C.

It will be recalled that the cost length of a path is the sum of the cost values of its lines, that a cost geodesic from u to v is a path from u to v with minimum cost length, and that this value is the cost distance from u to v. In other words, the cost distance from u to v is the minimum

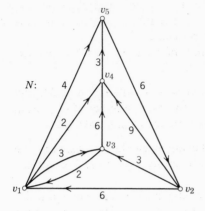

$$C = \begin{bmatrix} 0 & \infty & 3 & 2 & 4 \\ 6 & 0 & 3 & 9 & \infty \\ 2 & \infty & 0 & 6 & \infty \\ \infty & \infty & \infty & 0 & 3 \\ \infty & 6 & \infty & \infty & 0 \end{bmatrix}$$

FIGURE 14.10

cost among all paths from u to v. Observe that here the number associated with a path is the sum of the costs of its lines whereas in chains we used the products of the values of the lines. And here we use the minimum of the lengths of sequences from one point to another, whereas in chains we added the numbers for all such sequences. We now show how to find the cost distance from each point to every other in N by matrix operations analogous to those used in Chapter 5 for finding distances in a digraph. Let us denote by f_{ij} the cost distance from v_i to v_j. Then the *cost-distance matrix* F of a network N is a square matrix whose entries are the cost distances f_{ij}.

We begin with the cost matrix C of the network, but use a modified arithmetic[4] to obtain "powers" $C^{[2]}, C^{[3]}, \ldots$ of C. In this arithmetic, "modified multiplication" of numbers is given by $a \mathbin{\dot\times} b = a + b$ and "modified addition" by $a \mathbin{\dot+} b = \min(a, b)$. Thus, for example, $2 \mathbin{\dot\times} 3 = 5$ and $2 \mathbin{\dot+} 3 = 2$. To show how to obtain $C^{[2]}$ from the cost matrix C of Figure 14.10, we calculate $c_{24}^{[2]}$.

$$
\begin{aligned}
c_{24}^{[2]} &= (6 \mathbin{\dot\times} 2) \mathbin{\dot+} (0 \mathbin{\dot\times} 9) \mathbin{\dot+} (3 \mathbin{\dot\times} 6) \mathbin{\dot+} (9 \mathbin{\dot\times} 0) \mathbin{\dot+} (\infty \mathbin{\dot\times} \infty) \\
&= 8 \quad \mathbin{\dot+} \quad 9 \quad \mathbin{\dot+} \quad 9 \quad \mathbin{\dot+} \quad 9 \quad \mathbin{\dot+} \quad \infty \\
&= 8
\end{aligned}
$$

Each term of the equation, shown in parentheses, gives the cost length of a sequence from v_2 to v_4, whose length is at most 2, and the "modified product" of these is the minimum cost length among these sequences. Thus, $c_{ij}^{[2]}$ gives the minimum cost among all such sequences and hence all paths from v_i to v_j, and in general $c_{ij}^{[n]}$ is the minimum cost among all

[4] The procedure described here is due to Maria Hasse (1961).

paths from v_i to v_j whose length is at most n. The following theorem summarizes these observations and states the general procedure for finding the cost distance from v_i to v_j in any cost network.

Theorem 14.4. Let C be the cost matrix of a network N. Let n be a positive integer such that the "modified powers" $C^{[n]} = C^{[n+1]}$. Then $c_{ij}^{[n]}$ is the cost distance from v_i to v_j, and $C^{[n]} = F$, the cost-distance matrix of N.

By carrying through the calculation prescribed by this theorem for the cost matrix C for Figure 14.10, we find the cost-distance matrix of a network N as follows. Here we observe that $n = 4$ is the smallest positive integer such that $C^{[n]} = C^{[n+1]}$.

$$C^{[2]} = \begin{bmatrix} 0 & 10 & 3 & 2 & 4 \\ 5 & 0 & 3 & 8 & 10 \\ 2 & \infty & 0 & 4 & 6 \\ \infty & 9 & \infty & 0 & 3 \\ 12 & 6 & 9 & 15 & 0 \end{bmatrix} \qquad C^{[3]} = \begin{bmatrix} 0 & 10 & 3 & 2 & 4 \\ 5 & 0 & 3 & 7 & 9 \\ 2 & 12 & 0 & 4 & 6 \\ 15 & 9 & 12 & 0 & 3 \\ 11 & 6 & 9 & 14 & 0 \end{bmatrix}$$

$$C^{[4]} = C^{[5]} = F = \begin{bmatrix} 0 & 10 & 3 & 2 & 4 \\ 5 & 0 & 3 & 7 & 9 \\ 2 & 12 & 0 & 4 & 6 \\ 14 & 9 & 12 & 0 & 3 \\ 11 & 6 & 9 & 13 & 0 \end{bmatrix}$$

Theorem 14.4 provides a way of finding the distance matrix of a digraph which is often more economical than that given by Theorem 5.19.

Corollary 14.4a. Consider a digraph D as a network in which every line has value 1. The distance matrix of D is given by the cost-distance matrix F, as obtained by the method of Theorem 14.4.

The cost-distance matrix F of a network N tells us the minimum cost of going from v_i to v_j along some cost geodesic. It does not, however, identify the cost geodesics of N. The problem of finding the cost geodesics from v_i to v_j can be solved using the cost-distance matrix F in a manner analogous to the procedure presented in Theorem 5.25 for digraphs.[5] Given a network N, let us define the *cost-geodetic network* N_g *from* v_i *to* v_j

[5] This approach is presented in Flament (1963).

as the subnetwork of N containing those points and lines of N which lie on at least one cost geodesic from v_i to v_j. The following statements, which are analogues of Theorems 5.22 through 5.24, can be readily verified.

(1) Every subpath of a cost geodesic is a cost geodesic.
(2) A point v_k is on a cost geodesic from v_i to v_j if and only if $f_{ik} + f_{kj} = f_{ij}$.
(3) Let v_r and v_s be two points on a cost geodesic L from v_i to v_j and let N contain the line $v_r v_s$. Then $v_r v_s$ is on L if and only if $f_{ir} + c_{rs} = f_{is}$.

These results lead to the following theorem.

Theorem 14.5. Let v_j be reachable from v_i in N. The cost-geodetic network N_g from v_i to v_j consists of all points v_k in N such that $f_{ik} + f_{kj} = f_{ij}$ and all lines $v_r v_s$ of N from one of the points to another such that $f_{ir} + c_{rs} = f_{is}$.

To illustrate this theorem, we show how to obtain the cost-geodetic network N_g from v_5 to v_4 for the network N of Figure 14.10. The points of this cost-geodetic network are those points v_k such that $f_{5k} + f_{k4} = f_{54}$. By referring to the cost-distance matrix F of N, we see that $f_{54} = 13$ and that every point v_k of N satisfies the equation $f_{5k} + f_{k4} = 13$. We know, therefore, that all points of N are contained in the cost-geodetic network from v_5 to v_4. To obtain the lines of this cost-geodetic network, we use the equation $f_{5r} + c_{rs} = f_{5s}$ and find that it is satisfied for the following values:

$$f_{55} + c_{52} = f_{52} = 6$$
$$f_{52} + c_{23} = f_{53} = 9$$
$$f_{53} + c_{31} = f_{51} = 11$$
$$f_{51} + c_{14} = f_{54} = 13.$$

Thus, the only cost geodesic from v_5 to v_4 is $L = v_5 v_2 v_3 v_1 v_4$.

Suppose that the points of the network of Figure 14.10 represent five cities, and that the value of each line gives the unit cost of shipping a product directly from one city to another. The absence of a line $v_i v_j$ means that there is no direct transportation from city v_i to city v_j. The cost-distance matrix F tells us the minimum unit cost of shipping the product from each city to each other. If we wish to find a shipping route with minimum cost, we construct the cost-geodetic network N_g from v_i to v_j. Thus in our example, we see that the minimum unit cost of shipping the product from city v_5 to city v_4 is 13 and that the cheapest route is $v_5 v_2 v_3 v_1 v_4$. The same procedures can, of course, be used for other interpretations of cost networks.

FLOWS IN NETWORKS

In this section we interpret a network as a system of "channels" capable of carrying a "flow" of such things as commodities, messages, or traffic of various sorts. Each line $v_i v_j$ of the network represents a channel capable of carrying a flow directly from v_i to v_j. By the *capacity of a line* $v_i v_j$ we mean the largest number of units that can flow along $v_i v_j$. We assume that the flow through a network begins at a transmitter and terminates at a receiver. Thus, we are concerned with an irreflexive network N having a transmitter, t, and a receiver, r, such that r is reachable from t, as illustrated by Figure 14.11(a).

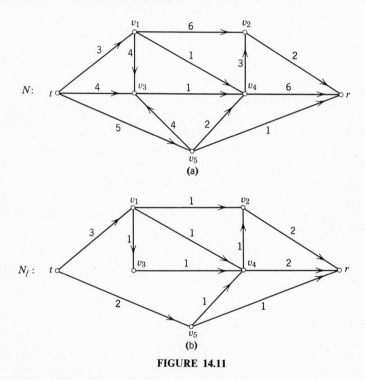

FIGURE 14.11

A *flow* f in N from t to r is an assignment of a number to each line, called its flow value, satisfying two conditions: (a) the flow value of each line does not exceed its capacity, (b) for each point other than t and r, the flow indegree equals the flow outdegree (thus units may not accumulate at intermediate points). Of course, some lines of N may have a flow value 0. Let us denote by N_f the *flow network* obtained from N when its lines take on the values specified by flow f.

In the network of Figure 14.11(a), the outdegree capacity of t is 12, and the indegree capacity of r is 9. Thus, although the lines from t are capable of carrying 12 units, no more than 9 of these units can reach r. But it is not even certain that 9 units can actually get to r, since the capacities of the intermediate lines may not be sufficiently great. By definition of a flow, it follows that in N_f the outdegree value of t and the indegree value of r are equal; this common number is called the *size of the flow*. For example, the size of the flow f whose flow network N_f is shown in Figure 14.11(b) is 5. We shall see that 5 is not the greatest size of all flows in N. A *maximum flow* in N from t to r is a flow of greatest size. In other words, the size of a maximum flow from t to r is the largest number of units that can reach r from t within N, subject to the constraints imposed by the capacities of the lines.

The principal result of this section is the "maximum flow theorem," due to Ford and Fulkerson (1957), which gives an algorithm for finding a maximum flow in a network from t ro r. We shall state this theorem and a few of its consequences. But first we require some preliminary discussion.

If S is a set of lines of N such that every path from t to r contains a line of S, then S is a *t–r cut set*.[6] In Figure 14.11(a), the set of lines adjacent from t is clearly a t–r cut set, as is the set adjacent to r. By the *capacity of a set of lines of N*, we mean the sum of the capacities of its lines. Thus, for example, the capacity of the t–r cut set of lines adjacent from t is 12. The *minimum cut capacity from t to r* is the smallest capacity among all t–r cut sets.

It is easy to see that no flow from t to r can have its size exceed the minimum cut capacity from t to r, for the flow value of each line in the t–r cut set cannot exceed its capacity. That there exists a flow from t to r whose size equals the capacity of some t–r cut set is not obvious and is the content of the "maximum flow theorem," which follows.

Theorem 14.6. In any network having a receiver r reachable from a transmitter t, the size of a maximum flow from t to r is equal to the minimum cut capacity from t to r.

The proof of this theorem is beyond the scope of this book,[7] but we illustrate it with the network N of Figure 14.11(a). As noted above, the three lines from the transmitter t constitute a t–r cut set with capacity 12. The three lines to the receiver r form one with capacity 9. But closer inspection reveals the existence of a t–r cut set with capacity 7,

[6] This is a generalization of the concept of 2-betweenness discussed in Chapter 7; indeed we might say that S is 2-between t and r.

[7] The interested reader should refer to Ford and Fulkerson (1962, pp. 11–12) or Gale (1960).

namely, $S = \{tv_1, v_3v_4, v_5v_4, v_5r\}$. It follows from Theorem 14.6 that there can be no flow from t to r with size greater than 7. And if we can find one equal to 7, its size is maximum and the t–r cut set S has minimum capacity.

The flow network N_f shown in Figure 14.12 shows that it is possible to have a flow from t to r of size 7. Note that the outdegree flow of t and the indegree flow of r are both 7. Moreover, for every other point v_i, the indegree flow equals its outdegree flow. The heavier lines of this figure, which constitute a minimum t–r cut set of the network, have flow values equal to their capacities. And, in keeping with Theorem 14.6, the size of the flow from t to r equals the capacity of this t–r cut set.

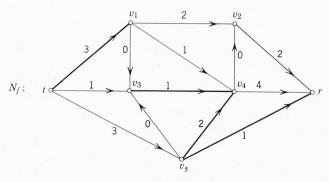

FIGURE 14.12

We have already encountered a special case of Theorem 14.6 in Chapter 9. Theorem 9.3 asserts in part that the maximum number of line-disjoint paths from u to v is the minimum number of lines whose removal results in a digraph in which v is not reachable from u. If we consider a network in which the capacity of every line is 1, then the size of a maximum flow from u to v is the maximum number of line-disjoint paths from u to v and the minimum cut capacity from u to v is the smallest number of lines whose removal makes it impossible to go from u to v. Ignoring the capacities in the network of Figure 14.11(a), we see that there are three line-disjoint paths from t to r and that the smallest number of lines in a t–r cut set is also 3.

The maximum flow theorem has interesting implications for linear programming. It also has applications that are apparently of quite a different nature. We shall see that the following set-theoretic theorem, due to Hall (1935) is related to flows.[8]

---

[8] See also, Mann and Ryser (1953).

Let $S_1, S_2, \ldots, S_m$ be a collection of subsets of a set S. A *system of distinct representatives* for the collection of subsets is a set of distinct elements $a_1, a_2, \ldots, a_n$ such that each a_i is in S_i. For example, each subset S_i could be a subgroup of the members of a club who are on a committee together. The selection of a system of distinct representatives in this setting amounts to choosing a spokesman for each committee to belong to a committee on committees, with the understanding that no individual is permitted to represent more than one committee in this supercommittee.

Theorem 14.7. Let $S_1, S_2, \ldots, S_m$ be a collection of subsets of a set S. A necessary and sufficient condition for this collection to have a system of distinct representatives is that every union of k sets of the collection must contain at least k elements, for $k = 1, 2, \ldots, m$.

The necessity of this condition is obvious. For if the union of k sets of the collection contains fewer than k elements, then even if we could use all elements in this union we would not have enough of them to represent these k sets with distinct representatives. The sufficiency is not so obvious, and will be established by constructing a network and applying the maximum flow theorem.

The network we construct is reminiscent of the digraph used in connection with the picnic problem in Chapter 12. There, in Figure 12.3, we used two kinds of points; one for families and one for sports cars. We begin here with a digraph having one point for each element a_j of S and also one point for each set S_i in the collection of subsets of S. The digraph is constructed by drawing a line from a point S_i to a point a_j whenever the set contains that element. We next introduce two new points t and r, together with a line from t to each point S_i and one from each point a_j to r. We then form a network N by assigning capacity 1 to each line; thus N is a digraph.

We interrupt the proof to give a specific illustration of this construction. Consider a set S with six elements, $a_1, a_2, \ldots, a_6$ and five subsets $S_1 = \{a_1, a_2\}$, $S_2 = \{a_1, a_2, a_3\}$, $S_3 = \{a_3\}$, $S_4 = \{a_3, a_4, a_5\}$, $S_5 = \{a_4, a_5, a_6\}$. This example is shown in Figure 14.13. It is easy to see that assigning flow values of 1 to each of the lines tS_i, $S_i a_i$, $a_i r$ for each i, $1 \leq i \leq 5$, gives a flow from t to r whose size is 5, while the lines adjacent from t form a t–r cut set with capacity 5. Note that $\{a_1, a_2, a_3, a_4, a_5\}$ is a system of distinct representatives for the sets S_i in which each set S_i is represented by the element a_i.

We now assign flow values to each line of the network so as to obtain a maximum flow from t to r. Since the capacity limitations ensure that no more than one unit flows into a point S_i, either zero or one unit

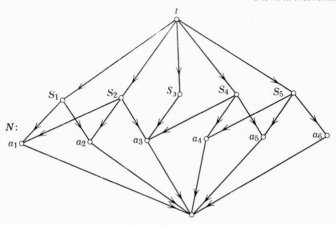

FIGURE 14.13

flows from a point S_i; and if one unit flows, it goes to the representative of S_i, say a_j. Furthermore, a_j can represent only S_i, since the flow from a_j is at most 1. Clearly, each flow gives a set of representatives for some of the subsets S_i. And a maximum flow provides a set of representatives for the greatest possible number of subsets. In the hypothesis of the theorem being proved, m is the total number of subsets S_i. Therefore, the collection of all the subsets has a system of distinct representatives if and only if the size of a maximum flow from t to r is m. Of course, it can never be greater than m, since the $t–r$ cut set consisting of the lines adjacent from t contains m lines.

We now use the maximum flow theorem to complete the proof of Theorem 14.7. For convenience, we prove its contrapositive: For a collection of subsets of S, if there is no system of distinct representatives, then there must exist a subcollection of k sets whose union contains fewer than k elements.

Suppose the collection of subsets $S_1, S_2, \ldots, S_m$ of S has no system of distinct representatives. Then the size of a maximum flow from t to r in the associated network is less than m. By the maximum flow theorem (or even by Theorem 9.3) there exists a minimal $t–r$ cut set with capacity less than m. If any line $S_i a_j$ is in a minimal cut set, then clearly it can be replaced by tS_i. Therefore, there exists a minimal cut set that consists only of lines tS_i and lines $a_j r$. Let us relabel the points of N so that this cut set consists of the lines $tS_1, tS_2, \ldots, tS_b$, and $a_1 r, a_2 r, \ldots, a_c r$. Observe that there are $b + c$ lines in this $t–r$ cut set, so that $b + c < m$, or alternatively, $c < m - b$. Since this is a cut set, all lines from the $m - b$ remaining set points, that is, from $S_{b+1}, S_{b+2}, \ldots, S_m$, go to element points $a_1, a_2, \ldots, a_c$. Since $c < m - b$, the union of these $m - b$ sets has fewer than $m - b$ elements, proving the sufficiency of Theorem 14.7.

We illustrate with the following collection of eight subsets of the set of integers from 1 to 8: $S_1 = \{3, 4, 5\}$, $S_2 = \{2, 4, 5\}$, $S_3 = \{7, 8\}$, $S_4 = \{5, 6, 7\}$, $S_5 = \{1, 2\}$, $S_6 = \{1, 3, 5\}$, $S_7 = \{1, 4\}$, $S_8 = \{2, 3\}$. The network for this collection of subsets is shown in Figure 14.14. There is a t–r cut set consisting of tS_3, tS_4, a_1r, a_2r, a_3r, a_4r and a_5r. Since its capacity is only 7, these 8 sets have no system of distinct representatives. We see from this cut set that the six subsets other than S_3 and S_4 contain in their union only the five elements a_1, a_2, a_3, a_4, a_5, illustrating Theorem 14.7.

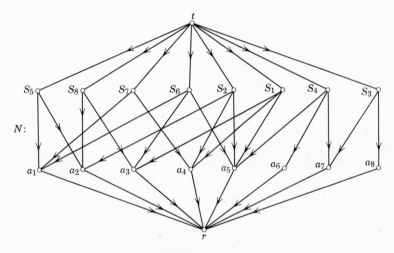

FIGURE 14.14

There is an amusing version of Theorem 14.7 that has been dubbed "The marriage problem."[9] Given a collection of boys and girls, suppose each boy knows certain of the girls. We wish to match them so that each boy can marry a girl he knows. Theorem 14.7 shows us the conditions under which this can be done. Let S be the set of girls, and let S_i be the subset of the girls with whom boy i is acquainted. We can assign each boy a wife within the laws of bigamy if and only if we can find a system of distinct representatives for the set of subsets $\{S_i\}$. By Theorem 14.7, this can be done if and only if the union of the acquaintance sets of each set of k boys contains at least k girls.

---

[9] For a discussion of this version of the problem, see Halmos and Vaughan (1950).

SUMMARY

In this final chapter, we have examined how digraph theory may be extended so as to deal with abstract systems called networks. A network N differs from a digraph D in two respects: (a) Loops are permitted in N but not in D, and (b) each line of N has an associated value. Thus a network consists of a finite relation on a set of points, together with a value system for its set of lines.

Two different kinds of value system have been considered. The first is nonnumerical and permits a distinction among different types of underlying relations. A network with a nonnumerical value system is useful in representing such empirical data as a system of interpersonal evaluations containing both positive and negative affective components. The second kind of value system is numerical and may be used to represent a great variety of empirical phenomena, including frequencies, probabilities, costs, capacities, and flows.

With each network N, there can be associated a value matrix M whose role is analogous with that of the adjacency matrix of a digraph. Here, the entry $m_{ij} = 0$ if the line $v_i v_j$ is not in N, and otherwise m_{ij} is the value of the line $v_i v_j$. Certain operations on this matrix provide effective means for yielding valuable information about its associated network.

An especially important kind of network is known as a markov chain. In this network, each point represents a state of some process, and each line x represents the conditional probability that if the process is in state fx, then its next state will be sx. Thus the value of each line of a chain is a positive number and the outdegree value of each point is exactly 1. The value matrix M of a chain is called its transition matrix. We have seen that the i, j entry of M^n is the probability of going from state v_i to state v_j in exactly n steps. Various properties of a chain are independent of the values of its lines and depend only upon the structure of the network. An important kind of chain, known as a regular chain, has the property that in some power n of its transition matrix every entry is positive. Thus, the network of a regular chain is strong. A striking feature of a regular chain is that the powers of its transition matrix approach a limit matrix in which all rows are alike.

In a cost network N, the value of each line x represents the cost of going from fx to sx via x. The i, j entry of this associated cost matrix C gives the cost value associated with the line $v_i v_j$. We have seen that it is possible to use a modified arithmetic to obtain the "powers" of C and thereby a cost-distance matrix F. Each of its entries f_{ij} gives the minimum cost along all paths from v_i to v_j and thus the cost distance from v_i to v_j. The concept of cost distance within a cost network is analogous to that of distance within a digraph, and the development of other concepts based on cost distance is straightforward. Thus, for example, we have defined a cost geodesic from u to v as a path from u to v with minimum cost length, and have presented an algorithm, analogous to Theorem 5.25, for constructing a cost-geodetic network N_g from v_i to v_j.

Finally, we discussed networks in which the value of each line x indicates its capacity, or the largest number of units that can flow from fx to sx via x. Here it is assumed that flow goes from a transmitter to a receiver of the network. The principal result of this discussion is the "maximum flow theorem" which provides a criterion for determining the greatest possible size of a flow through the network from a transmitter to a receiver. This theorem has many applications, some of which appear at first glance to be unrelated to the notion of flow. One of these concerns the set-theoretic problem of finding a criterion for a system of distinct representatives.

With this discussion, we conclude our introduction to the study of structural models. We trust that the journey has been both interesting and profitable. If we have stimulated an interest in a more rigorous treatment of the structural features of empirical phenomena, our objective has been accomplished.

EXERCISES

1. Consider each markov chain whose matrix is listed below. (a) Is it regular? absorbing? ergodic? (b) Does it have a fixed probability vector P, that is, one such that $PM = P$? (c) If so, find it. Is it unique?

$$
M_1 = \begin{bmatrix} \frac{1}{2} & 0 & \frac{1}{3} & \frac{1}{6} \\ \frac{1}{3} & 0 & \frac{1}{3} & \frac{1}{3} \\ 0 & 0 & 1 & 0 \\ 0 & \frac{1}{2} & \frac{1}{2} & 0 \end{bmatrix}
$$

$$
M_2 = \begin{bmatrix} 0 & 1 & 0 & 0 & 0 \\ 0 & 0 & 1 & 0 & 0 \\ 0 & 0 & 0 & 1 & 0 \\ 0 & 0 & 0 & 0 & 1 \\ \frac{1}{2} & \frac{1}{2} & 0 & 0 & 0 \end{bmatrix}
$$

$$M_3 = \begin{bmatrix} 0 & \frac{1}{3} & 0 & \frac{2}{3} & 0 \\ \frac{1}{3} & 0 & 0 & 0 & \frac{2}{3} \\ \frac{2}{3} & 0 & 0 & 0 & \frac{1}{3} \\ \frac{1}{3} & 0 & 0 & 0 & \frac{2}{3} \\ 0 & \frac{1}{3} & \frac{1}{2} & \frac{1}{6} & 0 \end{bmatrix}$$

$$M_4 = \begin{bmatrix} 0 & 1 & 0 & 0 \\ \frac{1}{2} & 0 & \frac{1}{2} & 0 \\ 0 & 0 & \frac{1}{2} & \frac{1}{2} \\ 1 & 0 & 0 & 0 \end{bmatrix}$$

2. The matrix M below is the matrix of a markov chain. (a) Is it a regular chain? (b) Find its fixed probability vector P. (c) Find the matrix of two-step transitions of this chain. (d) If the process starts in the first state, what is the probability that after two steps it is in this state? (e) After a large number of steps what is the approximate probability that the chain is in the first state? (f) What is the mean number of steps between two consecutive occurrences of the first state?

$$M = \begin{bmatrix} 0 & 0 & 0 & 1 \\ \frac{2}{3} & \frac{1}{3} & 0 & 0 \\ \frac{1}{3} & \frac{1}{3} & \frac{1}{3} & 0 \\ \frac{1}{6} & 0 & \frac{1}{3} & \frac{1}{2} \end{bmatrix}$$

3. A sociologist examining the economy of a country has developed a criterion whereby each individual can be placed in one of four economic classes: lower, lower middle, upper middle, or upper. He has collected information from a random sample of 500 men so that he can ascertain the class of each respondent and that of the respondent's father. His data are displayed in the table below. (a) Construct a probability matrix whose entries show the probabilities of changing class (or remaining in the same class) from one generation to the next. (b) Show that this is the matrix of a regular chain. (c) Find the fixed vector of this matrix and interpret its entries. (d) If this chain remains unchanged, what will be the approximate distribution by class eight generations hence?

Class of Respondent's Father:	Class of Respondent:			
	Lower	Lower Middle	Upper Middle	Upper
Lower	70	35	35	0
Lower Middle	20	60	60	20
Upper middle	15	30	60	15
Upper	10	10	20	40

4. Use Corollary 14.4a to find the distance matrix for the digraph of Figure 5.13 and compare the results with the distance matrix shown there.

5. Let C be the cost matrix of a network N. Show that the sequence of "modified powers" $C^{[2]}$, $C^{[4]}$, $C^{[8]}$, ... leads to the cost-distance matrix F of N by proving that F is the first matrix in this sequence which is followed by itself.

6. The network of Figure 14.15 gives the cost of shipping one ton of a certain commodity between certain cities. (a) What is the cost per ton along a geodesic from t to r? (b) Find the cost-geodetic network from t to r.

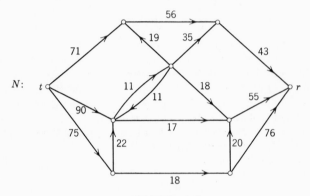

FIGURE 14.15

7. Below is the matrix of direct flight times in hours between certain cities. What is the quickest route from v_1 to v_6?

$$
\begin{bmatrix}
0 & 3 & \infty & 5 & \infty & \infty \\
3 & 0 & 5 & 2 & 4 & \infty \\
\infty & 4 & 0 & \infty & 4 & 3 \\
6 & 2 & \infty & 0 & 4 & 4 \\
\infty & 4 & 4 & 5 & 0 & 3 \\
\infty & \infty & 5 & 4 & 3 & 0
\end{bmatrix}
$$

8. Answer the following questions for the cost network of Figure 14.10. (a) What is the cost outradius? The cost inradius? (b) What is the cost outcenter? The cost incenter? (c) What is the cost diameter? (d) What is the cost outperiphery? The cost inperiphery?

9. Verify that the network N of Figure 14.11(a) has exactly two minimum $t–r$ cut sets, one of which is shown in Figure 14.12. What is the other one?

10. One of the systems of distinct representatives for the sets shown in Figure 14.13 has each set S_i represented by element a_i, $1 \leq i \leq 5$. There are seven other such systems. Find them.

11. Below are listed nine subsets of the first nine integers. Use Theorem 14.6 and determine whether this collection of sets has a system of distinct representatives. If so, find one and determine whether there are any others.

$$S_1 = \{2, 4, 5, 8\} \quad S_4 = \{4, 5, 7, 8\} \quad S_7 = \{2, 5, 7, 8\}$$
$$S_2 = \{2, 4, 5, 7\} \quad S_5 = \{2, 4, 7\} \quad S_8 = \{2, 4, 7, 8\}$$
$$S_3 = \{1, 3, 6, 8\} \quad S_6 = \{3, 4, 5, 6, 9\} \quad S_9 = \{1, 3, 6, 9\}$$

Bibliography

Abelson, R. P., & Rosenberg, M. J. Symbolic psycho-logic: a model of attitudinal cognition. *Behav. Sci.*, 1958, **3**, 1–13.

Anderson, N. H. Probability models for analyzing time changes in attitudes. In P. F. Lazarsfeld (Ed.), *Mathematical thinking in the social sciences.* New York: Free Press of Glencoe, 1954. Pp. 17–66.

Arrow, K. J. *Social choice and individual values.* New York: Wiley, 1951.

Baldwin, A. L. Personal structure analysis; a statistical method for investigating the single personality. *J. abnorm. soc. Psychol.*, 1942, **27**, 163–183.

Bavelas, A. Communication patterns in task-oriented groups. *J. accoust. Soc. Amer.*, 1950, **22**, 725–730. Reprinted in D. Cartwright & A. Zander (Eds.), *Group dynamics: research and theory.* (2nd ed.) Evanston, Ill.: Row, Peterson, 1960. Pp. 669–682.

Berge, C. *Théorie des graphes et ses applications.* Paris: Dunod, 1958. (English translation, New York: Wiley, 1962.)

Berger, J., Cohen, B. P., Snell, J. L., & Zelditch, M., Jr. *Types of formalization in small-group research.* Boston: Houghton Mifflin, 1962.

Berger, J., & Snell, J. L. On the concept of equal exchange. *Behav. Sci.*, 1957, **2**, 111–118.

Black, D. *The theory of committees and elections.* Cambridge: Cambridge Univer. Press, 1958.

Blumen, I., Kogan, M., & McCarthy, P. J. The industrial mobility of labor as a probability process. *Cornell Stud. industr. Labor Relat.*, 1955, Vol. 6.

Bush, R. R., & Mosteller, F. *Stochastic models for learning.* New York: Wiley, 1955.

Cartwright, D., & Harary, F. Structural balance: a generalization of Heider's theory. *Psychol. Rev.*, 1956, **63**, 277–293.

Cartwright, D., & Harary, F. A note on Freud's "Instincts and their vicissitudes." *Int. J. Psychoanal.*, 1959, **40**, 1–4.

Chomsky, N. *Syntactic structures.* The Hague: Mouton, 1957.

Cogan, E. J., et al. *Modern mathematics methods and models*, Vol. 2. Buffalo: Math. Assoc. Amer., 1958.

Collias, N. E. Problems and principles of animal sociology. In C. P. Stone (Ed.), *Comparative psychology.* (3rd ed.) Englewood Cliffs, N. J.: Prentice-Hall, 1951. Pp. 388–422.

Coombs, C. H. *A theory of data.* New York: Wiley, 1964.

Copi, I. M. *Symbolic logic.* New York: Macmillan, 1954.

Davis, J. A. Structural balance, mechanical solidarity, and interpersonal relations. *Amer. J. Sociol.*, 1963, **68**, 444–462.

DeSoto, C. B., & Kuethe, J. L. Perception of mathematical properties of interpersonal relationships. *Percept. mot. Skills*, 1958, **8**, 279–286.

DeSoto, C. B., & Kuethe, J. L. Subjective probabilities and interpersonal relationships. *J. abnorm. soc. Psychol.*, 1959, **59**, 290–294.

Estes, W. K. Toward a statistical theory of learning. *Psych. Rev.*, 1950, **57**, 94–107.

Feller, W. *An introduction to probability theory and its applications.* Vol. 1. (2nd ed.) New York: Wiley, 1957.

Festinger, L., Schachter, S., & Back, K. *Social pressures in informal groups.* New York: Harper, 1950.

Flament, C. *Applications of graph theory to group structure.* Englewood Cliffs, N. J.: Prentice-Hall, 1963.

Ford, L. R. Jr. & Fulkerson, D. R. A simple alogarithm for finding maximal network flows and an application to the Hitchcock problem. *Canad. J. Math.*, 1957, **9**, 210–218.

Ford, L. R., Jr., & Fulkerson, D. R. *Flows in networks.* Princeton, N.J.: Princeton Univer. Press, 1962.

French, J. R. P., Jr. A formal theory of social power. *Psychol. Rev.*, 1956, **63**, 181–194.

Fulkerson, D. L. Zero-one matrices with zero traces. *Pacific J. Math.*, 1960, **10**, 831–836.

Gale, D. A theorem on flows in networks. *Pacific J. Math.*, 1957, **7**, 1073–1082.

Gale, D. *The theory of linear economic models.* New York: McGraw-Hill, 1960.

Glanzer, M., & Glaser, R. Techniques for the study of group structure and behavior: I. Analysis of structure. *Psychol. Bull.*, 1959, **56**, 317–332.

Glanzer, M., & Glaser, R. Techniques for the study of group structure and behavior: II. Empirical studies of the effects of structure in small groups. *Psychol. Bull.*, 1961, **58**, 1–27.

Guetzkow, H. Differentiated roles in task-oriented groups. In D. Cartwright & A. Zander (Eds.), *Group dynamics: research and theory.* (2nd ed.) Evanston, Ill.: Row, Peterson, 1960. Pp. 683–704.

Hall, P. On representatives of subsets. *J. London math. Soc.*, 1935, **10**, 26–30.

Halmos, P. R., & Vaughan, H. E. The marriage problem. *Amer. J. Math.*, 1950, **72**, 214–215.

Harary, F. On the notion of balance of a signed graph. *Mich. math. J.*, 1954, **2**, 143–146.

Harary, F. On local balance and N-balance in signed graphs. *Mich. math. J.*, 1955, **3**, 37–41. (*a*)

Harary, F. The number of linear, directed, rooted, and connected graphs. *Trans. Amer. math. Soc.*, 1955, **78**, 445–463. (*b*)

Harary, F. Structural duality. *Behav. Sci.*, 1957, **2**, 255–265.

Harary, F. A criterion for unanimity in French's theory of social power. In D. Cartwright (Ed.), *Studies in social power.* Ann Arbor, Mich.: Inst. Soc. Res., 1959. Pp. 168–182. (*a*)

Harary, F. On the measurement of structural balance. *Behav. Sci.*, 1959, **4**, 316–323. (*b*)

Harary, F. Status and contrastatus. *Sociometry*, 1959, **22**, 23–43. (*c*)

Harary, F. The number of functional digraphs. *Math. Ann.*, 1959, **138**, 203–210. (*d*)

Harary, F., & Lipstein, B. The dynamics of brand loyalty: a markovian approach. *Operat. Res.*, 1962, **10**, 19–40.

Harary, F., & Richardson, M. A matrix algorithm for solutions and r-bases of a finite irreflexive relation. *Naval Res. Logistics Quart.*, 1959, **6**, 307–314.

Harris, Z. S. *Methods in structural linguistics.* Chicago: Univer. Chicago Press, 1951.

Hasse, Maria. Über die Behandlung graphentheorischer Probleme unter Verwendung der Matrizenrechnung, *Wiss. Z. Techn. Univer. Dresden*, 1961, **10**, 1313–1316.

Heider, F. Attitudes and cognitive organization. *J. Psychol.*, 1946, **21**, 107–112.

394   Bibliography

Hunter, F. *Community power structure.* Chapel Hill: Univer. North Carolina Press, 1953.

Kemeny, J. G., & Snell, J. L. *Finite markov chains.* New York: Van Nostrand, 1960.

Kemeny, J. G., & Snell, J. L. *Mathematical models in the social sciences.* New York: Ginn, 1962.

Kendall, M. G., & Smith, B. B. On the method of paired comparisons. *Biometrika,* 1940, **31,** 324–345.

König, D. *Theorie der endlichen und unendlichen Graphen.* Leipzig: Akademische Verlagsgesellshaft M. B. H., 1936. (Reprinted in 1950 by Chelsea Publishing Co., New York.)

Landau, H. G. On dominance relations and the structure of animal societies: III. The condition for a score sequence. *Bull. Math. Biophysics,* 1953, **15,** 114–148.

Lewin, K. *Field theory in social science.* New York: Harper, 1951.

Lindzey, G., & Borgatta, E. F. Sociometric measurement. In G. Lindzey (Ed.), *Handbook of social psychology.* Cambridge, Mass.: Addison-Wesley, 1954. Pp. 405–448.

Lipstein, B. The dynamics of brand loyalty and brand switching. *Proc. Fifth Annu. Conf., Advert. Res. Found.,* New York: 1959. Pp. 101–108.

Luce, R. D. Two decomposition theorems for a class of finite oriented graphs. *Amer. J. Math.,* 1952, **74,** 701–722.

Luce, R. D., Bush, R. R., & Galanter, E. (Eds.) *Handbook of mathematical psychology.* Vol. 2. New York: Wiley, 1963.

Luce, R. D., & Perry, A. D. A method of matrix analysis of group structure. *Psychometrika,* 1949, **14,** 95–116.

Luce, R. D., & Raiffa, H. *Games and decisions.* New York: Wiley, 1957.

Mandler, G., & Cowan, P. A. Learning of simple structures. *J. exp. Psychol.,* 1962, **64,** 177–183.

Mann, H. B., & Ryser, H. J. Systems of distinct representatives. *Amer. math. Mon.,* 1953, **60,** 397–401.

Marshall, A. W., & Goldhamer, H. An application of Markov processes to the study of the epidemiology of mental disease. *J. Amer. stat. Assoc.,* 1955, **50,** 99–129.

Menger, K. *Kurventheorie.* Leipzig: Teubner, 1932.

Merton, R. K. *Social theory and social structure.* New York: Free Press of Glencoe, 1957.

Moore, E. F. The shortest path through a maze. Proceedings of an international symposium on the theory of switching, Part II, The Computation Laboratory of Harvard University. *Annals,* 1959, **30,** 285–292.

Morrison, H. W. Intransitivity of paired comparison choices. Unpublished doctoral dissertation, Univer. Michigan, 1962.

Morrissette, J. O. An experimental study of the theory of structural balance. *Hum. Relat.,* 1958, **11,** 329–354.

Nadel, S. F. *The theory of social structure.* New York: Free Press of Glencoe, 1957.

Ore, O. *Theory of graphs.* Providence: Amer. math. Soc. Colloquium Publs., Vol. 38, 1962.

Parthasarathy, K. R. Enumeration of paths in digraphs. *Psychometrika,* 1964, **29,** 153–165.

Rédei, L. Ein kombinatorischer Satz. *Acta Litterarum ac Scientiarum (Sectio Scientarum Mathematicarum),* Szeged, 1934, **7,** 39–43.

Richardson, M. On weakly ordered systems. *Bull. Amer. math. Soc.,* 1946, **52,** 113–116.

Rosenberg, M. J., *et al. Attitude organization and change.* New Haven, Conn.: Yale Univer. Press, 1960.

Ross, I. C., & Harary, F. On the determination of redundancies in sociometric chains. *Psychometrika*, 1952, **17**, 195–208.

Ross, I. C., & Harary, F. A description of strengthening and weakening members of a a group. *Sociometry*, 1959, **22**, 139–147.

Sanford, N. Surface and depth in the individual personality. *Psychol. Rev.*, 1956, **63**, 349–359.

Shannon, C. E. A mathematical theory of communication. *Bell Systm. tech. J.*, 1948, **27**, 379–423; 623–656.

Silverman, D. Problem 463. *Math. Mag.*, 1962, **35**, 189.

Thompson, J. W. The importance of opposites in human relationships. *Hum. Relat.*, 1963, **16**, 161–169.

Von Neumann, J., & Morgenstern, O. *Theory of games and economic behavior*. Princeton: Princeton Univer. Press, 1944.

Weiss, R. *Processes of organization*. Ann Arbor, Mich.: Inst. Soc. Res., 1956.

Whitney, H. Congruent graphs and the connectivity of graphs. *Amer. J. Math.*, 1932, **54**, 150–168.

Zajonc, R. B. The concepts of balance, congruity, and dissonance. *Publ. Opin. Quart.*, 1960, **24**, 280–296.

Reference List of Principal Theorems

1.1 The sum of the indegrees of all the points of any digraph is equal to the sum of the outdegrees, and their common value is the number of lines.

1.2 Two digraphs D_1 and D_2 are isomorphic if and only if for any ordering of the points of D_1 there is an ordering of the points of D_2 such that their adjacency matrices are equal.

2.1 If in a digraph v is reachable from u and w is reachable from v, then $d(u, w) \leq d(u, v) + d(v, w)$.

2.4 The converse of the converse of a digraph D is D itself.

Directional duality principle: For each theorem about digraphs, there is a corresponding theorem obtained by replacing every concept by its converse concept.

2.6 A sequence from u to v contains a path from u to v.

2.7 If v is a point of a nontrivial closed sequence L, then v is in a cycle contained in L.

3.2 Let D be a digraph.
1. Every point and every line of D is contained in exactly one weak component.
2. Every point and every line lies in at least one unilateral component.
3. Every point is contained in exactly one strong component; each line is contained in at most one strong component. Furthermore, a line is in a strong component if and only if it is in a cycle.

3.3 In a digraph D, let v_1 and v_2 be in strong components S_1 and S_2, respectively. Then there is a path from v_1 to v_2 in D if and only if there is a path from S_1 to S_2 in D^*.

3.4a The condensation D^* of any digraph D has the same kind of connectedness as D.

3.6 The condensation D^* of any digraph D is acyclic.

3.8 An acyclic digraph D has at least one point of outdegree zero and at least one of indegree zero.

3.8c If every point of a digraph has positive outdegree, it contains a cycle.

3.9 The following statements are equivalent for any digraph D.
1. D is strong, that is, any two points are mutually reachable.
2. D has a complete closed sequence.
3. D^* consists of exactly one point.

3.10 For any nontrivial digraph D the following statements are equivalent.
1. D is unilateral, that is, for any two points, at least one is reachable from the other.
2. D has a complete open sequence.
3. D^* has a unique complete path.

3.11 For any digraph D the following statements are equivalent.
1. D is weak, that is, there is a semipath joining any two points.
2. D has a complete semisequence.
3. For any partition of the points of D into two subsets, there is at least one line of D joining a point of one subset with a point of the other.
4. D^s is strong.

4.2 A set S of points of a digraph D is a point basis if and only if it satisfies the following conditions:
1. Every point of D is in $R(S)$.
2. No point of S is reachable from any other.

4.3 Every acyclic digraph has a unique point basis consisting of all points of indegree 0.

4.4 Every point basis of D consists of exactly one point from each of the strong components in the point basis B^* of D^*.

4.10 If D is unilateral, then D^* has a unique source and a unique sink.

4.12 Any set of points consisting of exactly one origin from each fundamental set is a point basis, and conversely.

5.1 Let A be the adjacency matrix of a digraph D. Then in A^n the i, j entry is the number of sequences in D of length n from v_i to v_j.

5.4b A digraph is transitive if and only if it has the following structure: Every strong component S is complete symmetric, and whenever there is a path from a point of S_1 to a point of S_2, there is a line from each point of S_1 to each point of S_2.

5.18a If D is a weak digraph with connectedness matrix C and reachability matrix R, then $C = R + R' + J$.

5.19 Let $N(D) = [d_{ij}]$ be the distance matrix of a given digraph D. Then,

1. Every diagonal entry d_{ii} is 0.
2. $d_{ij} = \infty$ if $r_{ij} = 0$.
3. Otherwise, d_{ij} is the smallest power n to which A must be raised so that $a_{ij}^{(n)} > 0$, that is, so that the i, j entry of $A^n\#$ is 1.

5.21 If k is the largest positive integer entry in a given row (or column) of the distance matrix $N(D)$ of a digraph D, then every integer $0, 1, 2, \ldots, k - 1$ is also an entry in the same row (or column) of $N(D)$.

5.25 Let v_j be reachable from v_i in D. The geodetic subgraph D_g from v_i to v_j consists of all the points v_k such that $d_{ik} + d_{kj} = d_{ij}$ and all the lines $v_r v_s$ of D such that v_r and v_s are in D_g and $d_{ir} + 1 = d_{is}$.

6.3a Any two outcentral points lie in the same strong component, and by duality any two incentral points lie in the same strong component.

6.6 Let D be a strong digraph with p points, outradius r_0, and inradius r_i. Then,

$$r_0 \leq \frac{r_i + (p - 1)}{2}.$$

6.9 A set B of points is an n-basis for a digraph D if and only if it is a 1-basis for $D^{(n)}$.

6.10 Every acyclic digraph has a unique n-basis for every positive integer n.

6.12a Every acyclic digraph has a unique 1-basis.

6.13 If D has a closed sequence of odd length, it has an odd cycle.

6.14 A strong digraph has no odd cycles if and only if its points can be partitioned into two sets V_1 and V_2 such that every line has one point in each of these two sets.

6.15 Any digraph with no odd cycles has a 1-basis.

7.9 No strong digraph contains a 3, 0 line.

7.10 There are no lines in any digraph whose removal increases its category.

7.17 If D is strong, then the following statements are equivalent.

1. x is a 3, 3 line.
2. $\sim (fx \ x \ sx)_{3'}$.
3. x is not basic.

7.21 Every digraph has a line basis.

7.22 In a digraph D, x is basic if and only if it is in every line basis of D.

7.24 Every acyclic digraph has a unique line basis consisting of all its basic lines.

8.3 Let u, v, and w be distinct points of a digraph D. The point v is between u and w if and only if u and w are more strongly connected in D than in $D - v$.

8.6 There are no $1, 3$ points in any digraph. However, all other i, j types of points do occur.

8.10 Let D be a digraph in C_i. Then v is a weakening point of D if and only if no two points distinct from v are i-connected.

8.10b Every weakening point of a unilateral digraph is a transmitter or a receiver.

8.10c Any digraph contains at most two weakening points.

8.15 Let D be a digraph in C_i, where $i = 1, 2$, or 3. A point v is an $i, 0$ point if and only if it is a cut point.

8.18 Every strengthening point of a digraph D is between some pair of points.
1. If D is in C_1, then a point is strengthening if and only if it is 1-between two points.
2. If D is in C_2, then a point is strengthening if and only if it is 2- or 3-between two points.
3. If D is in C_3, then a point is strengthening if and only if it is 3- or $3'$-between two points.

9.3 If u is not adjacent to v in D, then the maximum number of point-disjoint paths from u to v in D is the minimum number of other points whose removal from D results in a digraph in which v is not reachable from u. The maximum number of line-disjoint paths from u to v is the minimum number of lines whose removal from D results in a digraph in which v is not reachable from u.

9.4 Two distinct blocks of a digraph have at most one point and no lines in common.

9.6 The following statements are equivalent for any weak digraph D with more than two points.
1. D is a block.
2. Every pair of lines lies on a semicycle.
3. Every pair of points lies on a semicycle.
4. For any three distinct points u, v, and w, there is a semipath joining u and w which contains v.
5. For any three distinct points u, v, and w, there is a semipath joining u and w which does not contain v.

9.9 The outcentral points of a strong digraph lie in a common block.

9.10 Let D be a digraph with at least three points. The following statements are equivalent.
1. D is a point invulnerable digraph.
2. For any three distinct points u, v, and w in D, there is a path from u to w not containing v.
3. For any two distinct points u and v in D, there are two point disjoint paths from u to v.

9.20 The following statements are equivalent for a strong digraph D.
1. D is a symmetric tree.
2. Every block of D is a cycle of length 2.
3. D is unipathic, and the paths joining two points are converses.
4. D is symmetric, and $q = 2p - 2$.
5. D is symmetric, and the removal of any symmetric pair of lines results in a disconnected digraph.

10.1 The following properties of a digraph D are equivalent.
1. D has no cycles.
2. Every strong component of D consists of one point.
3. D^* is isomorphic to D.
4. D and D^* have the same number of points.
5. Every sequence of D is a path.
6. It is possible to order the points of D so that its adjacency matrix is upper triangular.
7. It is possible to assign levels n_i to the points v_i in such a way that if $v_i v_j$ is in D then $n_i < n_j$.
8. D^t is a partial order.

10.5 The following statements are equivalent for a weak digraph D.
1. D is gradable.
2. The cyclic orientation index of every semicycle is one-half its length.
3. For every pair of points, the orientation index from one to the other of all semipaths joining them is the same.

10.12 A weak digraph is a tree from a point if and only if exactly one point has indegree 0 and every other point has indegree 1.

11.2 A sequence of nonnegative integers $s_1 \leq s_2 \leq \ldots \leq s_p$ is a score sequence if and only if their sum satisfies the equation:

I.
$$\sum_{i=1}^{p} s_i = \frac{p(p-1)}{2}$$

and the following inequalities hold for every positive integer $k < p$:

II.
$$\sum_{i=1}^{k} s_i \geq \frac{k(k-1)}{2}$$

11.4 In a tournament, the distance from a point with maximum score to any other point is 1 or 2.

11.6 Every tournament has a complete path.

11.9a The following statements are equivalent for any tournament T with p points.
1. T is transitive, that is, T is a complete order.
2. T is the transitive closure of a digraph consisting of a single path.
3. T is acyclic.
4. T has a unique complete path.
5. The score sequence of T is $(0, 1, 2, \ldots, p-1)$.
6. T has $\binom{p}{3} = \dfrac{p(p-1)(p-2)}{6}$ transitive triples.

11.10 The number b of transitive triples in a tournament T with score sequence $(s_1, s_2, \ldots, s_p)$ is
$$b = \sum_{i=1}^{p} \frac{s_i(s_i - 1)}{2}$$

11.10c Among all the tournaments with p points, the maximum number of cyclic triples is
$$c_{\max}(p) = \begin{cases} \dfrac{p^3 - p}{24} & \text{if } p \text{ is odd, and} \\[3mm] \dfrac{p^3 - 4p}{24} & \text{if } p \text{ is even} \end{cases}$$

11.11 If a tournament T is strong, then it contains a cycle of each length $k = 3, 4, \ldots, p$.

11.11a A tournament is strong if and only if it has a complete cycle.

11.13 Let T be a tournament with score sequence $s_1 \leq s_2 \leq \ldots \leq s_p$. Then T is strong if and only if the equation

I.
$$\sum_{i=1}^{p} s_i = \frac{p(p-1)}{2}$$

and the following inequalities hold for every positive integer $k < p$:

III.
$$\sum_{i=1}^{k} s_i > \frac{k(k-1)}{2}$$

12.1   Consider a given sequence of ordered pairs of nonnegative integers $(s_1, t_1), (s_2, t_2), \ldots, (s_p, t_p)$, where $s_1 \geq s_2 \geq \ldots \geq s_p$, $0 \leq s_i \leq p - 1$, and $0 \leq t_i \leq p - 1$. This sequence is graphical if and only if the equation

Ia.
$$\sum_{i=1}^{p} s_i = \sum_{i=1}^{p} t_i$$

and the following inequalities hold for every integer $k < p$:

IIa.
$$\sum_{i=1}^{k} s_i \leq \sum_{i=1}^{k} \min\{k-1, t_i\} + \sum_{i=k+1}^{p} \min\{k, t_i\}$$

12.2a   A functional digraph D is strong if and only if it consists of one cycle; D is strictly unilateral if and only if it consists of a cycle and a path toward a point of that cycle; D is strictly weak if and only if it contains exactly one cycle and has at least two transmitters.

12.5   A nontrivial weak digraph is an isograph if and only if it is the union of line-disjoint cycles.

12.5a   Every point of a nontrivial weak digraph D has even total degree if and only if D is the union of line-disjoint semicycles.

12.6   A weak digraph is traversable if and only if it is an isograph.

12.9   Any two suppressed digraphs of a given digraph are isomorphic.

13.2   The following statements are equivalent for any signed digraph S.
1. S is balanced.
2. For every pair of points, all semipaths joining them have the same sign.
3. The set V of points of S can be partitioned into two subsets (one of which may be empty) such that each positive line joins two points of the same subset and each negative line joins two points of different subsets.

13.3a   A signed block is balanced if and only if it is balanced at any one point. A weak signed digraph with cut points is balanced if and only if it is balanced at each of its cut points.

13.5   A signed block with more than one semicycle has a positive semicycle.

13.7   Any deletion-minimal set of lines of a signed digraph is negation-minimal, and conversely.

13.11   A signed digraph S is cycle-balanced if and only if each strong component of S is balanced.

14.1   If B and C are probability matrices, so is their product BC.

14.2   Let M be the transition matrix of a given chain. Then in M^n the i,j entry is the nth transition probability from v_i to v_j.

14.3   For a regular chain, the powers of its transition matrix M approach a limit. This limit matrix has all rows alike, and each is equal to the unique probability vector P for which $PM = P$.

14.4   Let C be the cost matrix of a network N. Let n be a positive integer such that the "modified powers" $C^{[n]} = C^{[n+1]}$. Then $c_{ij}^{[n]}$ is the cost distance from v_i to v_j, and $C^{[n]} = F$, the cost-distance matrix of N.

14.4a Consider a digraph D as a network in which every line has a value 1. The distance matrix of D is given by the cost-distance matrix F, as obtained by the method of Theorem 14.4.

14.5   Let v_j be reachable from v_i in N. The cost-geodetic network N_g from v_i to v_j consists of all points v_k in N such that $f_{ik} + f_{kj} = f_{ij}$ and all lines $v_r v_s$ of N from one of the points to another such that $f_{ir} + c_{rs} = f_{is}$.

14.6   In any network having a receiver r reachable from a transmitter t, the size of a maximum flow from t to r is equal to the minimum cut capacity from t to r.

14.7   Let $S_1, S_2, \ldots, S_m$ be a collection of subsets of a set S. A necessary and sufficient condition for this collection to have a system of distinct representatives is that every union of k sets of the collection must contain at least k elements, for $k = 1, 2, \ldots, m$.

Glossary

A point u is **adjacent to** v if the line uv is in D; u is *adjacent from* v if vu is in D.

An **alteration-minimal** set of lines of a signed digraph is one which is deletion-minimal or negation-minimal; an *alteration-minimum* set is an alteration-minimal set with the fewest lines.

A point u is **antecedent** to v if there is a path from u to v.

The *antecedent set* $Q(v)$ *of* v consists of all points of D from which v is reachable.

The *antecedent set* $Q(S)$ *of the set* S *of points* is the collection of points from which some point of S is reachable.

Balance

A *balanced signed digraph* is one in which every semicycle is positive.

A signed digraph is *balanced at* v if every semicycle containing v is positive.

The *degree of balance* β of a signed digraph is the ratio of the number of positive semicycles to the total number of semicycles.

A signed digraph is *N-balanced* if every semicycle of length N or less is positive.

A signed digraph is *cycle-balanced* if every cycle is positive.

A signed digraph is *path-balanced* if for every pair of points, all paths from one to the other have the same sign.

Bases

A *line basis* of a digraph is a minimal collection of lines which preserves reachability.

A *minimum line basis* is a line basis with the smallest possible number of lines.

A *point basis* of a digraph D is a minimal collection of points of D from which all its points are reachable.

An *n-basis* B of a digraph D is a set of points such that: (1) every point of D is reachable within distance n from a point of B; (2) no point of B is reachable from any other within distance n.

A **basic line** x is the only path from fx to sx.

Betweenness

A *line x* is *i-between two points* u and v, written $(u \ x \ v)_i$, means

for $i = 1$: u and v are 1-joined and every semipath joining them contains x;

for $i = 2$: u and v are 2-connected and every path joining them contains x;

for $i = 3$: u and v are 3-connected and every path joining them contains x;

for $i = 3'$: u and v are 3-connected and either every path from u to v contains x or every path from v to u contains x (but not both).

404

A *line* is *between two points* if it is *i*-between them, for some *i*.

A *point v* is *i-between two other points u* and *w*, written $(u\ v\ w)_i$, means

for $i = 1$: u and w are 1-joined and every semipath joining them contains v;

for $i = 2$: u and w are 2-connected and every path joining them contains v;

for $i = 3$: u and w are 3-connected and every path joining them contains v;

for $i = 3'$: u and w are 3-connected and either every path from u to w contains v or every path from w to u contains v (but not both).

A *point* is *between two points* if it is *i*-between them, for some *i*.

A **block** B of a digraph is a maximal weak subgraph having no point v such that $B - v$ is disconnected.

Boolean arithmetic on the integers 0 and 1: addition and multiplication are the same as for ordinary arithmetic except that $1 + 1 = 1$.

A **bridge** x is the only semipath joining fx and sx.

A **carrier** is a point whose outdegree and indegree are both 1.

Centrality: The *incenter* of a digraph is the set of its incentral points, that is, those points with smallest finite innumber. The *outcenter* is the set of outcentral points, that is, those with smallest finite outnumber.

Chains

A *chain* (or markov chain) is a network whose value matrix is a probability matrix.

An *ergodic* chain is a strong chain.

A chain is *regular* if some power of its transition matrix is positive.

The **complement** $\bar{D}$ **of a digraph** D is the digraph with the same set of points such that for any two points u and v, the line uv is in $\bar{D}$ if and only if it is not in D.

A **complete** path, cycle, semipath, semicycle, sequence, or semisequence contains all the points of a digraph.

Components

A *strong component* of a digraph is a maximal strong subgraph; the *strong component $S(v)$ determined by v* is the unique strong component containing v.

A *unilateral component* is a maximal unilateral subgraph.

A *weak component* is a maximal weak subgraph; the *weak component $W(v)$ determined by v* is the unique weak component containing v.

Condensation

Consider the set of points V of a digraph D and let V be partitioned into subsets $S_1, S_2, \ldots, S_n$. The *condensation of D with respect to this partition* is the digraph whose points are these n subsets (each point being labeled by the symbol used for its corresponding subset) and whose lines are determined as follows: there is a line from point S_i to point S_j in the new digraph if and only if in D there is at least one line from a point of S_i to one of S_j.

The condensation of a digraph is its condensation with respect to the partition of its points according to its strong components.

Connectedness

Points u and v are *0-connected* if they are not joined by a semipath; *1-connected* if they are joined by a semipath but not a path; *2-connected* if they are joined by a path in one direction but not in the other; and *3-connected* if they are joined by paths in both directions.

The *connectedness category* C_i of a digraph tells whether it is disconnected (C_0), strictly weak (C_1), strictly unilateral (C_2), or strong (C_3).

The **converse** D' **of a digraph** D is the digraph with the same set of points such that for any two points u and v, the line uv is in D' if and only if vu is in D. The *converse of a concept or theorem* concerning digraphs is one which results in place of the concept or theorem when the operation of converse is applied to a digraph.

Cost

The *cost distance* from u to v is the cost length of a cost geodesic from u to v.

A *cost geodesic* from u to v is a path from u to v whose cost length is minimum. .

The *cost-geodetic network* N_g from v_i to v_j is the subnetwork of N containing those points and lines of N which lie on at least one cost geodesic from v_i to v_j.

The *cost length* of a path is the sum of the costs of its lines.

A point v **n-covers** D if $R_n(v) = V$. A set S of points is an *n-cover* if $R_n(S) = V$.

A **cut point** is 1-between two other points.

A **t–r cut set** of a network N is a set S of lines such that every path from t to r contains a line of S.

The *minimum cut capacity from t to r* is the smallest capacity among all t–r cut sets.

A **cycle** consists of a nontrivial path together with a line from the terminal to the initial point of the path.

A **cyclic line** lies in a cycle.

Digraphs

A *digraph* is an irreflexive relation.

An *acyclic* digraph is one that has no cycles.

A digraph is *complete* if for every pair of points u and v, there is a line uv or a line vu.

A digraph is *equipathic* if for every pair of points u and v, all paths from u to v have the same length.

A digraph is *flexible* if it has at least three points and for any three points u, v, and w there is a path from u to v containing w.

A digraph is *functional* if every point has outdegree 1.

A digraph is *gradable* if it is acyclic and has a graded level assignment.

An *isograph* is a digraph in which for every point v, id(v) = od(v).

A strong digraph is *line invulnerable* if all its lines are 3, 3.

A strong digraph is *point invulnerable* if all its points are 3, 3.

A *symmetric* digraph is an irreflexive symmetric relation.

A digraph is *totally disconnected* if it has no lines.

A digraph is *transitive* if it contains line uw whenever it contains both uv and vw.

A digraph is *trivial* if it has just one point.

A digraph is *unipathic* if whenever v is reachable from u, there is exactly one path from u to v.

Degree

The *degree of a point* is the ordered pair [od(v), id(v)].

The *indegree* id(v) is the number of lines to v.

The *indegree value* of a point of a network is the sum of the values on all lines to the point.

The *outdegree* od(v) is the number of lines from v.

The *outdegree value* of a point of a network is the sum of the values on all lines from the point.

The *total degree* td(v) is the number of lines incident with v.

A **deletion-minimal set of lines** of a signed digraph is one whose removal leaves a balanced signed digraph, but the removal of any proper subset of it does not.

The **diameter** δ of a strong digraph is its largest outnumber.

A **disconnected digraph** is one that is not weak.

Disjoint paths

Two paths from u to v are *line-disjoint* if they have no lines in common.

Two paths from u to v are *point-disjoint* if the only points they have in common are u and v.

The **distance from u to v** is the length of a geodesic from u to v.

The *total distance* Σd_{ij} *within a digraph* D is the sum of all the finite distances $d(v_i, v_j)$ in D.

The **first point of a line** $x = uv$ is u, and is often denoted fx.

A **flow** in a network N from t to r is an assignment of a number to each line so that (1) the flow value of each line does not exceed its capacity, and (2) for each point other than t or r, the flow indegree equals the flow outdegree.

A *flow network* N_f is obtained from N when its lines take on the values specified by a flow f.

A **fundamental set** is a maximal reachable set.

A **geodesic** from u to v is a path from u to v of minimum length.

The *geodetic subgraph* D_g *from* v_i *to* v_j is the subgraph of D containing those points and lines of D which lie on at least one geodesic from v_i to v_j.

An **i, j set** S of points or lines of a digraph D has the property that D is in C_i and D–S is in C_j.

An **implication digraph** is one in which the points are interpreted as propositions and lines as implications.

A point v and a line x are **incident** if v is fx or sx.

An **isolate** is a point whose indegree and outdegree are both 0.

Two digraphs are **isomorphic** if there exists a one-to-one correspondence between their points which preserves their directed lines.

Joining: Every pair of points in a digraph are *0-joined*. Two points are *1-joined* if there is a semipath joining them; *2-joined* if at least one is reachable from the other; and *3-joined* if each is reachable from the other.

The **length** of a semipath, path, semicycle, or cycle is the number of lines in it; the length of a sequence or semisequence is the number of occurrences of lines in it.

Level assignments

An *ascending level assignment* is an assignment of integers n_i to points v_i so that if v_iv_j is in D, then $n_i < n_j$.

In a *descending level assignment*, if v_iv_j is in D, then $n_i > n_j$.

A *graded level assignment* of an acyclic digraph is one such that for each line v_iv_j, $n_j = n_i + 1$.

A *quasi-level assignment* associates with each point v_i an integer n_i so that if v_iv_j is a line of D, then $n_i \leq n_j$, with equality if and only if v_i and v_j are mutually reachable.

The **line requirement** of a digraph D is the smallest number of lines whose presence is required for the connectedness category of D not to be decreased.

The **line vulnerability** of a digraph D is the minimum number of lines in any strengthening set Y of D.

The **line surplus** of a digraph D is the maximum number of lines in any neutral set Y of D.

A **loop** x is a line of a net for which $fx = sx$.

Matrices

The *adjacency matrix* A of a digraph D is a square matrix with one row and one column for each point of D, in which the entry $a_{ij} = 1$ if the line v_iv_j is in D and $a_{ij} = 0$ if v_iv_j is not in D.

The *connectedness matrix* of a digraph has the number $n = 0, 1, 2, 3$ in its i, j location whenever points v_i and v_j are n-connected in the digraph.

In the *cost matrix* C of a network N, the diagonal entries c_{ii} are 0, $c_{ij} = \infty$ if v_iv_j is not in N, and c_{ij} is the cost of v_iv_j if v_iv_j is in N.

The *cost distance matrix* of a network N is the matrix whose entries are the cost distances between points of N.

The *distance matrix* of a digraph is the matrix whose entries are the distances $d_{ij} = d(v_i, v_j)$.

The *identity matrix* I of order n is the n by n matrix whose entries on the main diagonal are 1 and the others are 0.

A *probability matrix* is a square matrix with nonnegative entries whose row sums are all 1.

The *reachability matrix* of a digraph D is a matrix whose entries are denoted r_{ij}, where $r_{ij} = 1$ if v_j is reachable from v_i, and $r_{ij} = 0$ otherwise.

A *transition matrix* is the probability matrix of a markov chain.

A *universal matrix* J is a matrix whose entries are all 1.

A square matrix is *upper triangular* if all its nonzero entries are on or above the main diagonal.

The *value matrix* M of a network N has entry 0 if v_iv_j is not a line of N, and has the value of v_iv_j otherwise.

The **negation** of a collection of lines of a signed digraph is obtained when the sign of each line is changed.

An i, j set of points or lines is **neutral** if $i = j$.

A **net** consists of a finite set of points together with a finite set of lines, where each line is an ordered pair of points.

A **network** consists of a relation whose lines have a value assigned to them.

Number

The *associated number pair* of a point v is the ordered pair $[o(v), i(v)]$.

The *innumber* $i(v)$ is the largest distance $d(u, v)$ for all u in D.

The *outnumber* $o(v)$ is the largest distance $d(v, u)$ for all u in D.

Orders

A *complete order* is a relation that is irreflexive, asymmetric, transitive, and complete.

A *partial order* is an irreflexive, asymmetric, and transitive relation.

A *quasi-order* is a relation that is reflexive and transitive.

A point v is an **origin** if $R(v)$ is a fundamental set.

Two lines x_i and x_j are **parallel** if $fx_i = fx_j$ and $sx_i = sx_j$.

A **path from** v_1 **to** v_n is a collection of distinct points, $v_1, v_2, \ldots, v_n$, together with the lines $v_1v_2, v_2v_3 \ldots, v_{n-1}v_n$.

A path is *trivial* if it consists of a single point.

Peripherality: The *inperiphery* of a strong digraph is the set of its inperipheral points, that is, those points with greatest innumber. The *outperiphery* of a strong digraph is the set of its outperipheral points, that is, those points with greatest outnumber.

Radius: The *inradius* of a digraph is its smallest finite innumber. The *outradius* is its smallest finite outnumber.

A point v is **reachable** from a point u if there is a path from u to v.

The *reachable set $R(v)$ of a point v* is the collection of points reachable from v.

The *reachable set $R(S)$ of a set S of points* is the collection of points reachable from some point of S.

A **receiver** is a point whose outdegree is 0 and whose indegree is greater than 0.

Relations

A *relation* is a net in which no two distinct lines are parallel.

A relation is *complete* if for every pair of distinct points u and v, at least one of the ordered pairs (u, v) or (v, u) is in it.

A relation is *reflexive* if it has a loop at each point; it is *irreflexive* if no point has a loop.

A relation is *symmetric* if whenever uRv, then vRu; it is *asymmetric* if uRv precludes vRu.

A relation is *transitive* if for any three distinct points u, v, and w, whenever uRv and vRw, then uRw.

An *equivalence relation* is one that is reflexive, symmetric, and transitive.

The **score** of a point of a tournament is its outdegree.

The *score sequence* $(s_1, s_2, \ldots, s_p)$ of a tournament is the sequence of its scores ordered so that $s_1 \le s_2 \le s_3 \le \ldots \le s_p$.

The **second point of a line** $x = uv$ is v, and is often denoted sx.

A **semicycle** is obtained from a semipath on adding a line joining the terminal point and the initial point of the semipath.

A **semipath joining** v_1 **and** v_n is a collection of distinct points, $v_1, v_2, \ldots, v_n$, together with $n - 1$ lines, one from each pair v_1v_2 or v_2v_1; v_2v_3 or v_3v_2; $\ldots$; $v_{n-1}v_n$ or v_nv_{n-1}. A *strict semipath* is a semipath that is not a path.

A **semisequence** is an alternating sequence of points and lines which begins and ends with a point and has the property that each line is incident with the point before it and the point after it.

A **sequence** is an alternating sequence of points and lines which begins and ends with a point and has the property that each line is preceded by its first point and followed by its second point.

A sequence is *open* if its initial and terminal points differ; it is *closed* if its initial and terminal points are the same.

The **sign** of a semicycle, semipath, or any set of lines is the product of the signs of its lines.

A **signed digraph** is obtained from a digraph D by designating each line of D as positive or negative.

A point v is a **sink** if $Q(v) = V$.

A point v is a **source** if $R(v) = V$.

An i, j set of points or lines is **strengthening** if $i > j$.

A digraph is **strongly connected** or **strong** if every two points are mutually reachable.

Subgraphs

A *subgraph* of a digraph D is a digraph whose points and lines are points and lines of D.
The *subgraph generated by a set* Y *of lines* of D has Y as its line set and contains all points incident with a line of Y.
The *subgraph generated by a set* S *of points* of D has S as its point set and contains all lines joining two points of S.
A *spanning subgraph* of D is a subgraph with the same set of points as D.
A **suppressed digraph** of a digraph D is obtained by removing from D one suppressible point at a time until no more remain.
  A point v is *suppressible* if there are points u and w such that uv and vw are the only lines incident with v and $d(u, w) = 2$.
The **symmetrized digraph** of D is the symmetric digraph obtained from D by adding a directed line uv whenever this line is not in D but vu is in D.

A **tournament** is a nontrivial complete asymmetric digraph.

A **trajectory** is a sequence in which no line occurs more than once.

The **transitive closure of a given digraph** D is the minimal transitive digraph containing D.

A **transmitter** is a point whose indegree is 0 and whose outdegree is greater than 0.

A **tree from a point** is a nontrivial digraph with a source and no semicycles.
  A *symmetric tree* is a strong digraph with no cycle of length greater than 2.

A digraph is **unilaterally connected** or **unilateral** if for any two points, at least one is reachable from the other; it is *strictly unilateral* if it is unilateral but not strong.

A digraph is **weakly connected** or **weak** if every two points are joined by a semipath; it is *strictly weak* if it is weak but not unilateral.
An i, j set of points is **weakening** if $i < j$.

Index